540

FIBER TO FABRIC

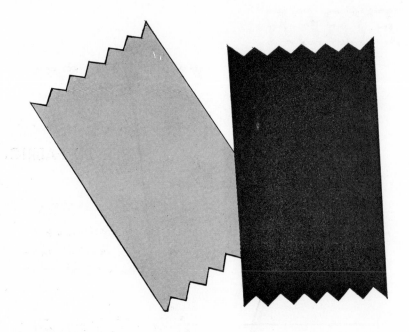

GREGG PUBLISHING DIVISION
McGraw-Hill Book Company, Inc.

NEW YORK   CHICAGO   DALLAS   CORTE MADERA, CALIF.   TORONTO   LONDON

FIBER
to FABRIC

M. David Potter
Professor of Business
San Francisco State College
San Francisco, California

Bernard P. Corbman
Head, Department of Business Technology
Bronx Community College
Bronx, New York

Third Edition

PUBLISHED BY GREGG PUBLISHING DIVISION
McGraw-Hill Book Company, Inc.
Printed in the United States of America

PREFACE

PURPOSE

The success of the first edition and the even greater widespread use of the second edition of this book have indicated the desirability of retaining in this third edition the three objectives of this text. One of these is to meet vocational needs for students expecting to enter into such business careers as retailing and to aid those already in the field. Another objective is to satisfy the needs of consumers. A third objective is to provide teachers with a basic, complete textile book that will satisfy the requirements of most teachers of a basic course in textiles. In fact, this text is easily adaptable for a methods course for teachers of textiles.

PLAN

The general plan of the former editions has also been retained with some refinements. A separate chapter is now devoted to knitting with the previous as well as new information on hosiery included in it. The material on minor fibers and minor fabric constructions is combined into one chapter.

For those who intend to enter areas of business that deal in textiles or textile products, this book provides all the basic information they may need. Its presentation does not require of the reader any prior knowledge of textiles; nor does it try to overwhelm the student with complicated technical descriptions. Rather, the information is presented in a clear, simplified manner. There is an abundance of diagrams and photographs to help make the written material even more meaningful.

For those now working with textiles or textile products, the information here is so organized as to make it possible for them to find easily whatever information they seek, whether it be properties of fibers, descriptions of fabrics, new finishes, new fibers, or the like. They need not read through a great many pages making constant cross references to find what they want.

The consumer is also given a great deal of consideration in the treatment of the general topic of textiles. He is told how to identify fibers and fabrics. The differential qualities of *all* fibers, including natural, man-made, and synthetic, are fully explained. Adequate consideration is given to the weaving and finishing of fabrics. Information is provided to assist the consumer in determining how well a particular fabric will serve his purposes through a discussion of the properties of the fibers and their blends into various fabrics. Also of particular interest to the consumer are specific facts to be considered when purchasing such items as sheets, towels, hosiery, and rugs. Consideration is also given to the care of fabrics and clothing as well as a chapter on stain removal.

TEACHABILITY

Present and future teachers of elementary textiles will find that this text presents the subject in a very teachable manner. The text is replete with visual material. Each chapter has projects and questions that provide a basis for review and further investigation. Beginning with the examination of the structure and appearance of all fibers, there follow a discussion and comparison of the important properties of these fibers. Identification of these fibers is the next logical step. Using cotton fiber as an example, consideration is given to the spinning of fiber into yarn and weaving the yarn into fabric. The discussion continues with consideration of the latest finishing processes—dyeing, printing, and so on. The text then devotes separate chapters to discussions of the twenty fibers: their production, their processing from fiber to fabric, their finishing, their blending, judging the fabrics, and glossary of fabrics. Merchandise information is provided both for motivation and as a source of pertinent consumer education information.

IMPROVEMENTS IN THIS EDITION

This third edition offers much new material. New and improved methods of finishing, such as wash-and-wear finishes for all-cotton fabrics, are discussed. New strains of cotton fiber, such as SuPima, are evaluated. The new and improved forms of Orlon and Dacron are discussed. Complete discussion of the new fibers Arnel, Creslan, Darvan, Verel, and Zefran is provided. The information includes previously unpublished data. Discussions of the advantages and disadvantages of fabrics made from blends are expanded to include the latest types of blends created with the newer fibers.

The chapter on comparative qualities of the textile fibers is appropriately expanded to consider the relative properties of all twenty fibers. The summary comparative chart is enlarged in scope and content, with the fibers listed alphabetically for greater ease in locating the desired information. The authors believe this chart to be the most complete, yet concise, textile table of its type extant.

Additional and new information on yarn manufacture and types is provided. This includes discussions on novelty, stretch, and bulk yarns with consideration of their advantages and disadvantages.

The revision contains more data on such merchandise as hosiery and rugs.

This includes more detailed descriptions of types of knitted hosiery, their gauge and denier. Also, some general information is given on the use of man-made and synthetic fibers in the manufacture of rugs, particularly with regard to the advantages and limitations of these fibers.

Aware of the importance of visualization, the authors have improved the pictorialization of the material by replacing old photographs and diagrams with more appropriate new ones, adding altogether seventy new illustrations in this third edition.

ACKNOWLEDGMENTS

Grateful acknowledgments are due the following:

C. W. Bendigo, American Cyanamid Company; Ruth Leigh, Cannon Mills, Inc.; R. W. Kennedy, Carbide and Carbon Chemicals Company; J. L. Bixby, The Chemstrand Corporation; Dr. Claudius T. Murchison, President of Cotton Textile Institute, Inc.; G. E. Ferris, Deere & Company; W. H. Radebaugh, E. I. du Pont de Nemours & Company; Dr. William E. Coughlin, Director of Textile Laboratories of Good Housekeeping Institute; Doris Kimball, *Hosiery and Underwear Review;* L. A. Beers, President of the Institute of Carpet Manufacturers of America; Harry S. Radcliffe, Secretary of the Linen Trade Association; R. C. Ball, Secretary of the National Association of Hosiery Manufacturers; Irene L. Blunt, Secretary of the National Federation of Textiles; S. Stambaugh and J. W. Dougherty, Owens-Corning Fiberglas Corporation; H. S. Ortgies, The Saran Yarns Company; W. J. Martin and D. A. Spencer, United States Department of Agriculture; J. H. Jordan and J. H. Karrh, Virginia Carolina Chemical Company; W. Jaeger, The Wool Bureau, Inc.; S. C. Carse, President of York Street Flax Spinning Company.

T. L. Taylor, Secretary of the American Angora Goat Breeders Association; J. C. Fortune, American Bemberg Corporation; S. Gates, Secretary of the American Cheviot Sheep Society, Inc.; H. A. Lindgren, Secretary of the American Romney Breeders Association; Jessie F. Ritenour, Secretary of the American Shropshire Registry Association, Inc.; Patricia Shelton and S. S. Brown, Australian News & Information Bureau; E. H. Zimmerman, American Cyanamid Company; C. Mattmann and H. R. Rex, B. F. Goodrich Chemical Company; A. F. Tesi, Celanese Corporation of America; S. Okamoto, S. Tomiyama, and Fumie Adachi, Central Raw Silk Association of Japan; A. Esplin, Secretary of the Columbia Sheep Breeders Association of America; J. R. Henderson, Secretary of the Continental Dorset Club, Inc.; C. G. Evans, Deering Milliken Research Corporation; O. R. McIntire, The Dow Chemical Company; H. C. Freeman, Jr., E. I. du Pont de Nemours & Company; G. W. Wernz, Eastman Chemical Products, Inc.; D. E. Gatter, The Irish Linen Guild; L. W. Rainard,

Joseph Bancroft & Sons Company; R. Gates, Merchandising Service; Ruth Harvey, Pepperell Manufacturing Company; R. K. Kennedy, Union Carbide Chemicals Company; C. E. Terrill, United States Department of Agriculture; and G. F. McRoberts, Whitin Machine Works.

M. David Potter
Bernard P. Corbman

CONTENTS

1 · TEXTILE FIBERS

Under the Microscope

Some knowledge of textile fibers is necessary to everyone, because textiles have such an important bearing on our daily lives. From earliest times, man has used fabrics of various types for covering, warmth, personal adornment, and even to display personal wealth. Today, fabrics are still used for these purposes. Everyone is an ultimate consumer of textile materials. You use textiles in some form even if you are not the direct purchaser. Included among consumers are merchandisers of many types, from the wholesale textile manufacturer and merchant to the retail-store sales force. Many of the industries—for example, the automobile industry—are important consumers of textiles in various forms. Other consumers are homemakers, dressmakers, interior decorators, and retail-store customers, as well as students who are studying for these and various other occupations and professions in which a knowledge of textiles is of major importance.

The merchant, particularly, and all those who work for him must be thoroughly familiar with the merchandise they are handling if they wish to be successful in the mercantile field. Only thorough knowledge will prevent the mistakes that are too often made in buying and selling.

Reasons for Studying Textiles. A study of textiles will show, for example, why certain fabrics are more durable and therefore more serviceable for specific purposes. It will explain why certain fabrics make cool wearing apparel as well as give an impression of coolness when used as decoration. The quality of cleanliness, also, may be estimated before purchasing, when that is an important factor.

Complete knowledge of textiles will facilitate an intelligent appraisal of standards and brands of merchandise and will develop the ability to distinguish quality in fabrics and, in turn, to appreciate the proper uses for the different qualities. As a result, the consumer merchant and the consumer customer will know how to buy and what to buy; and salespeople will know how to render good service to those consumers who have not had the advantage of a formal course in textiles.

In the study of textiles, the initial interest of the student will become an absorbing one when he discovers the natural fascination of fabrics and their cultural associations, particularly when factual study is supplemented by the handling of actual textile materials. The subject will seem worthwhile as you become familiar with illustrative specimens and fabrics and handle and compare the raw materials of which fabrics are made as well as the finished consumers' goods.

Sequence of Fabric Construction.   In beginning the study of textiles, you should have in your hand a sample of a *woven fabric*. Note that it is constructed by interlacing sets of yarns that run lengthwise and crosswise. It is from the interlacing, or weaving, of yarns that textile materials are made. A close examination of any one of these yarns will reveal the fibrous substance from which the yarn is made. Such yarns comprise a multitude of fibers or filaments that have been separated, made parallel, overlapped, and twisted together by various processes.

There is a logical development of raw material into finished consumers' goods. Studying textile materials in the interesting sequence of "fiber to yarn to fabric" will help you understand the construction and ultimate qualities of the fabrics with which you will become familiar. Here are the steps in the manufacture of fabrics from raw material to finished goods.

1. Fiber, which is spun (or twisted) into yarn or directly felted into fabric.
2. Yarn, which is woven or knitted or braided into fabric.
3. Fabric, which by various finishing processes becomes finished consumers' goods.

Kinds of Fibers.   The textile industry uses many different kinds of fibers as its raw materials. Some of these fibers were known and used by mankind in the earlier years of civilization, as well as in modern times. Other fibers have become important in recent years. New man-made and synthetic fibers are being produced and tested daily. Some fibers have assumed importance from time to time because of a specific quality, such as low-cost production, which is always a factor in the business world.

In this text, twenty fibers are classified into three general groups: natural, man-made, and synthetic. The first, and original, group consists of the _natural fibers,_ some produced by plants, others by animals, which have been known and used for thousands of years. protein

The second group consists of the *man-made fibers,* so called because man has taken natural materials, such as cellulose and protein (cotton linters, wood pulp, corn), and transformed their form and certain other characteristics into long and short fibers as desired.

The third group consists of *synthetic fibers*, which are so named because they do not occur in nature in any manner whatsoever. Man has taken separate chemical elements, such as carbon, oxygen, hydrogen, and others, and synthesized them into new textile fibers with many characteristics that were lacking in the natural and man-made fibers.

In this text, we have differentiated between man-made and synthetic fibers to help you understand the differences between the new fibers and the reasons for their various characteristics. But in many other publications, the two terms, man-made and synthetic, are used interchangeably. The three general groups and their sources or classification follow.

	Fibers	Sources or Classification
Natural fibers	Cotton	Cotton plant (cellulose)
	Linen	Flax plant (cellulose)
	Wool	Sheep (protein)
	Silk	Silkworm (protein)
Man-made fibers	Viscose rayon	Cotton plant (cellulose)
	Cuprammonium rayon	Cotton plant (cellulose)
	Acetate	Tree (cellulose)
	Arnel	Tree (cellulose)
	Vicara	Corn (protein)
Synthetic fibers	Nylon	Polyamide
	Dacron	Polyester
	Orlon	Acrylic
	Acrilan	Acrylic
	Dynel	Acrylic
	Creslan	Acrylic
	Verel	Acrylic
	Zefran	Nitrile-acrylic alloy
	Darvan	Dinitrile
	Saran	Vinylidene chloride
	Fiberglas	Glass

Additional animal fibers—such as camel's hair, mohair, cashmere, alpaca, llama, and vicuna—as well as certain vegetable and mineral fibers, also lend themselves to various uses in the textile industry.

Composition and Structure of Fibers. Each textile fiber has its own distinctive structural markings that, under a microscope with a magnification of at least 100, supply an absolute identification of the fiber. Certain general observations also help to identify fibers without the use of a microscope. These differences in structure determine the various characteristics of the different fibers and explain why some fibers are to be preferred to others for certain uses. The illustrations in this chapter show cross-section and longitudinal views of the various fibers as seen under a microscope.

• *Cotton.* Unlike other fibers obtained from plants, the cotton fiber is a single elongated cell. Under the microscope, it resembles a collapsed, spirally twisted tube with a rough surface. The thin cell wall of the fiber has from 200 to 400 turns of natural twist, or convolutions, to the inch. The fiber appears flat, twisted, and ribbonlike, with a wide inner canal (the lumen) and a granular effect. Chemically, the fiber contains about 90 per cent cellulose and about 6 per cent moisture; the remainder consists of natural impurities. The outer surface of the fiber is covered with a protective waxlike coating, which gives the fiber a somewhat adhesive quality.

Because of the natural twist in cotton fiber, the fibers may be spun easily into yarn. Some cotton fibers, however, look different under the microscope and do not have this natural twist. Such fibers have been subjected to the commercially important process of mercerization, causing the naturally flat, twisted cotton fiber to swell and become straight, smooth, and round. The straightness of the fiber causes light to be reflected on the smooth surface and produces a lustrous effect that is commercially valuable. The resultant fabric is called *mercerized cotton.*

• *Flax.* Under the microscope, the flax fiber shows hairlike cylindrical filaments with fine pointed ends. The filaments are cemented together at intervals

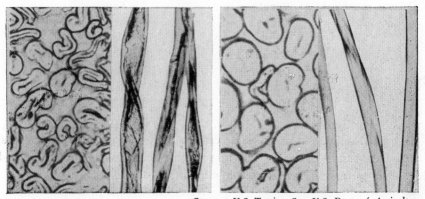

Courtesy U.S. Testing Co.; U.S. Dept. of Agriculture

Cotton   Mercerized Cotton in the form of markings, or nodes, by a gummy substance called _pectin_. The long flax filaments contain a lumen, or inner canal, which shows as a narrow line. The fiber resembles a straight, smooth bamboo stick, with its joints producing a slight natural unevenness that cannot be eliminated. Chemically, the flax fiber is composed of about 70 per cent cellulose and about 25 per cent pectin; the remainder consists of woody tissue and ash. From such fibers, linen yarns are produced that, to the naked eye, appear smooth, straight, compact, and lustrous. Linen fibers are more brittle and less flexible than cotton fibers.

• _Wool_. Wool fiber is irregular and roughly cylindrical, tapered at the end, and multicellular in structure. Under the microscope, a cross section shows three fundamental layers. The epidermis, or outer layer, consists of scales or flattened plates, ranging from 1,000 to 4,000 to an inch. These scales give the fiber its cohesive quality. They vary in type, from those having straight edges to those having marked wavy serrations. The finer, softer, warmer fibers have the more numerous straight-edged scales. The thicker, coarser, less warm fibers have the fewer, rougher scales. The better fibers with more and finer scales are duller in appearance than the poorer quality wool fibers with fewer scales.

The second layer, the cortex, is the main fiber body, which gives strength and elasticity to the fiber. The cortex consists of intermediate cells that hold the color pigment. The innermost layer is the medulla, which consists of large air-filled cells. The medulla is discernible only in coarse and medium wools and only under high magnification. It is the central canal, varying in appearance from a narrow to a broad line or from a continuous to an interrupted line. Some wool fibers that have no cortical layer are compensated with a larger proportion of medullary cells. This fact lessens the affinity for dyes, because the medulla has more

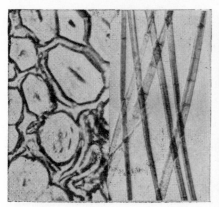 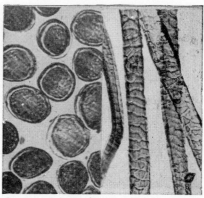

Courtesy Am. Woolen Co.; U.S. Testing Co.

Flax _Wool_

fat than has the rest of the fiber. The finer wools, having no medulla, absorb dyes more readily.

Two striking characteristics of wool fiber are its susceptibility to heat and its felting property, which is caused by the horny epidermal scales. Because of this felting property, only pressure, heat, and moisture are required to make wool fibers into the type of fabric called *felt.*

Chemically, wool is the only natural fiber that contains sulphur. It is composed of the following basic elements in these approximate proportions: carbon, 49 per cent; oxygen, 24 per cent; nitrogen, 16 per cent; hydrogen, 7 per cent; sulphur, 4 per cent. These elements combine to form a protein known as *keratin.*

• *Silk.* Raw silk fiber as it comes from the cultivated cocoon is called *bave.* Under the microscope this bave appears somewhat elliptical. It is composed of the *fibroin,* consisting of two filaments, each of which is called a *brin,* held together by *sericin,* a gummy substance that gives the bave a rather uneven surface. As the sericin is removed by hot water, the two filaments appear clearly as fine, lustrous, uniform, transparent rods.

Wild silk, or tussah silk, may be distinguished from cultivated silk by its coarse thick form, which appears flattened. Cultivated silk is a narrow fiber with no markings. Wild silk is a broader fiber with fine, wavy longitudinal lines running across its surface, giving it a dark hue under the microscope.

Chemically, the silk fibroin and sericin are composed of approximately 95 per cent protein and about 5 per cent wax, fat, salts, and ash.

• *Rayon* is a man-made fiber derived from cellulose, an inert, formless white substance found in the cell walls of all plant life. There are three varieties of rayon: viscose, cuprammonium, and nitrocellulose. Of these, the nitrocellulose

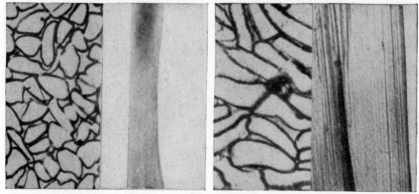

Courtesy U.S. Testing Co., U.S. Dept. of Agriculture

Silk   *Wild, or Tussah, Silk*

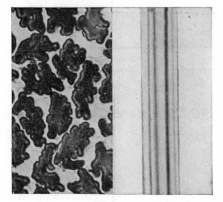
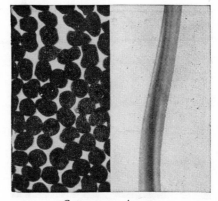

Viscose   *Cuprammonium*

variety is not manufactured to any great extent because of the high cost of the chemicals. In the history of man-made fibers, however, nitrocellulose rayon is important because it was the first to be produced. In general, rayon fiber is easily recognized under the microscope by its glasslike luster and uniform diameter. (The appearance of fine pepperlike particles on a cross-section view is an indication that the rayon has been delustered.) The rayon filaments differ according to the process used in their manufacture.

Viscose, under the microscope, shows many threadlike longitudinal lines that are spiral and somewhat glossy. A cross-section view shows a serrated edge.

Cuprammonium shows no markings. It is fine and glossy and resembles silk more closely than other fibers. The cross-section appearance is small and nearly round.

• *Acetate* is a compound of cellulose that possesses different qualities from those of viscose rayon. The fibers are fine and have line markings. They are less lustrous than viscose or cuprammonium fibers and sometimes show a central groove under the microscope. The cross-section appearance is bulbous, with indentations. The resultant fabric is called *acetate* or *cellulose acetate*.

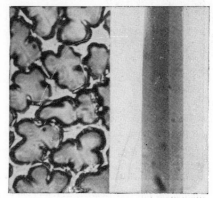

Illustrations this page courtesy U.S. Testing Co.

Acetate

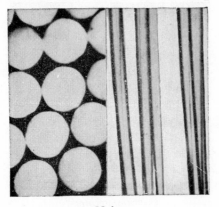

Nylon

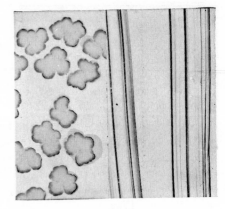

Arnel

• *Arnel* is a compound of cellulose acetate (triacetate cellulose) that possesses different qualities from those of acetate. The cross-section view is much like that of the acetate fiber, being bulbous with indentations. The longitudinal view appears straight and smooth, but it has heavy lines caused by the grooves in the surface. The fiber comes in both bright and dull forms.

• *Nylon* is a synthetic known chemically as a *polyamide*. The fibers are very fine, round, smooth, and translucent. They can be highly lustrous, semidull, or dull, depending on the amount of luster desired.

• *Dacron* is a synthetic fiber known chemically as a *polyester.* The fiber is straight, smooth, and almost perfectly round. It has a characteristic speckled appearance that is visible both in the longitudinal and cross-section views.

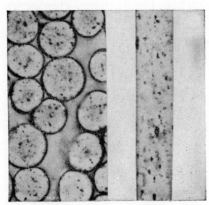

Dacron

Illustrations this page Courtesy E. I. du Pont de Nemours & Co. and Celanese Corp. of America

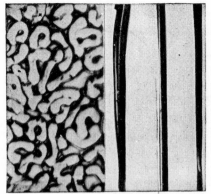
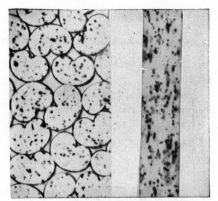

Courtesy E. I. du Pont de Nemours & Co. *Courtesy The Chemstrand Corp.*

Orlon (*staple*) *Acrilan*

• *Orlon* is a synthetic known chemically as an *acrylic*. The fiber is produced in staple (short) lengths. The cross-section shape is dog-bone. The longitudinal shape is somewhat flat and smooth. The fiber is semidull.

• *Acrilan* is another acrylic fiber. It is produced in staple form only. Its cross-section appearance is bean-shaped; its longitudinal appearance is straight and smooth. In both microscopic views it is speckled. Acrilan has a semidull, cream-colored appearance.

• *Dynel* is partly an acrylic and partly a *vinyl chloride*. It is produced in staple form only. The fibers are flat and somewhat smooth, but they are artificially crimped.

Dynel

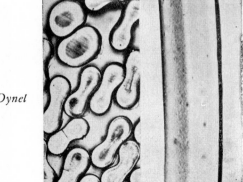

Courtesy Carbide & Carbon Chem. Co.

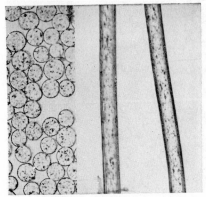

Courtesy American Cyanamid Co.

Creslan

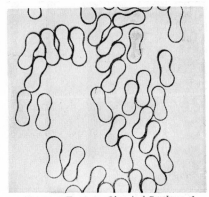

Courtesy Eastman Chemical Products, Inc.

Verel

• *Creslan* is a wholly acrylic fiber produced in staple form. Its cross-section appearance is almost round; its longitudinal appearance is straight and smooth. It has speckling similar to that of Acrilan and is also semidull.

• *Verel* is an acrylic fiber produced in staple form. The cross-section shape is dog-bone. Its microscopic appearance is similar to that of Orlon.

• *Zefran* is a *nitrile-acrylic* alloy of an *acrylonitrile copolymer*. Its cross-section shape is almost round with smooth edges. Characteristic white and black dots are scattered through it.

• *Darvan* is a *dinitrile* fiber. Its cross-section shape is flat with a slightly irregular surface with rounded edges.

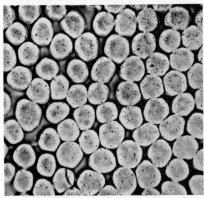

Courtesy The Dow Chemical Co.

Zefran

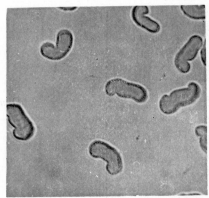

Courtesy B. F. Goodrich Co.

Darvan

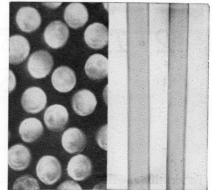

Vicara

Courtesy Virginia Carolina Chem. Corp.

• *Vicara* is a man-made fiber. It is produced from zein, a corn protein. The fiber is somewhat round and smooth. It is always cut into staple of 0.5 inch to 6 inches in length.

• *Saran* is a synthetic known chemically as a *vinylidene chloride*. The fiber is smooth, round, and translucent.

• *Fiberglas* is made of glass. The fiber is smooth, round, translucent, highly lustrous, and quite flexible. will break

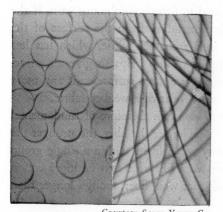

Courtesy Saran Yarns Co.

Saran

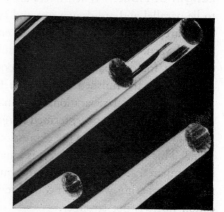

Courtesy Owens-Corning Fiberglas Corp.

Fiberglas

2 · TEXTILE FIBERS

Comparative Qualities

To identify any fiber and make a satisfactory choice of the textile desired for a particular use, you must understand the separate properties of each of the fibers. The commercial value of any fiber depends largely on the extent to which it possesses certain properties or qualities, such as tensile strength, elasticity, fineness, cohesiveness, and sufficient length—all of which facilitate the process of spinning into yarn. Fibers also must have some degree of porosity to permit the absorption of bleaching and dyeing liquids. These various properties are studied in this order.

Length	Reaction to bleaches
Luster	Reaction to heat
Strength	Effect of mildew
Elasticity	Effect of light and outdoor exposure
Heat conductivity	Reaction to alkalies and acids
Absorbency	Affinity for dyes
Cleanliness and washability	

Length of Fiber. When fibers are spun or twisted into yarn, they are made to lie parallel and are drawn out and twisted to form a continuous yarn. If the fibers are long, there will be fewer ends protruding from the surface of the twisted yarn. Fewer surface ends result in a smoother fabric, which has less attraction for dirt particles. The smooth surface also helps to give an attractive luster to the finished cloth. Short fibers cause more surface ends and more points of potential separation, thus making a relatively weaker fabric.

The length of the fiber, termed *length of staple,* is therefore of fundamental importance, giving rise to the expression, "The longer the fiber, the stronger the yarn." This statement, however, is true only when fibers within a single group are compared; for example, two or more wool fibers or two or more cotton fibers. Comparing wool with cotton reveals that wool fiber, though longer than cotton fiber, is not stronger.

Long-staple yarns within each group of fibers produce stronger, smoother, more serviceable fabrics that cost more than the less durable fabrics made from

12

*The longer fibers produce the smoother yarns; the
shorter fibers cause more surface ends.*

Combing- separating short fibers from long fibers

short-staple yarns. In wool, for example, the short-staple fiber is used in the manufacture of woolens, and the longer staple is reserved for worsteds. Worsteds are considered more serviceable. A similar distinction is found in every textile fiber. Here is the sequence of fibers when comparing length of staple.

1. Man-made and synthetic fibers are made in various lengths. The length is dependent on the ultimate use of the fiber, as well as on engineering problems in its production. The long filament is known in the textile industry as _continuous filament_ fiber and is used to produce smooth-surfaced fabrics. The short filament is called *staple,* or *spun* fiber, and is used for soft, fuzzy fabrics.

Viscose and cuprammonium rayon, acetate, Arnel, nylon, Dacron, Saran, and Fiberglas are produced in both staple and continuous filament forms. The length is dependent on the ultimate use of the fibers and on convenience of handling.

2. *Silk.* Raw silk fiber from cultivated cocoons is the longest of natural fibers. It consists of a continuous fiber that varies in length from 1,200 to 4,000 feet. It produces a smooth, lustrous fabric.   MOST elastic fiber

3. *Linen.* The flax fiber is longer than the cotton fiber and the wool fiber, ranging from 12 to 20 inches. This length accounts for the absence of lint in linen fabrics.

4. *Wool.* The length of the average woolen staple varies from 1 to 3 inches. Worsted yarns are made from staple fibers 3 to 8 inches in length.

5. The next group consists of man-made and synthetic fibers that are produced in staple form, generally ranging from ½ inch to 6 inches in length. They are frequently made into yarns resembling those of wool. They are also sometimes spun into yarns resembling those of cotton and sometimes blended to produce various effects and properties. The man-made and synthetic fibers produced in staple form only are all the acrylic fibers (Orlon, Acrilan, Dynel, Creslan, and Verel), and Zefran, Darvan, and Vicara.

6. *Cotton.* Cotton fiber is the shortest of all fibers, varying from ½ inch to

2½ inches. The bulk of the domestic cotton crop ranges from ¾ inch to 1½ inches in length.

Luster of Fibers.   Luster is produced by the reflection of light from a smooth surface. A lustrous effect in fabrics adds to their attractiveness and, in some cases, may be absolutely necessary, depending on the purpose of the fabric. On the other hand, luster may not be desired, as in napped or crepe surfaces. But an appropriate lustrous effect is a generally desired quality.

Degrees of luster are obtained in several ways. The use of long-staple yarns produces a smooth surface, which will have a natural luster. Caustic soda in the mercerizing process is a chemical method of producing luster. The satin weave and certain finishing processes also are used for this purpose.

The luster of a fiber has an important effect on its ultimate use. A fabric such as satin is expected to have a high luster and therefore should be made of a highly lustrous fiber, while a fabric such as flannel is expected to be dull and therefore should be made of a dull fiber. Here is the sequence of fibers according to luster.

1. *Rayon, acetate, Arnel, nylon, Dacron, Zefran,* and *Fiberglas.* These fibers can be produced with a very high luster, which is referred to as bright. In man-made and synthetic fibers, however, luster can be controlled to a great extent, and some of these fibers are produced in lesser degrees of luster.

2. *Silk.* The luster of silk is dependent on the amount of surrounding sericin, or gum, that is removed from the surface of the filaments. The degree of luster is generally high.

3. *Linen.* The luster of the flax fiber is apparent at all times. This characteristic is helpful in identifying the fiber.

4. *Saran.* This fiber has a soft luster.

5. *Orlon, Acrilan, Dynel, Creslan, Verel,* and *Vicara.* These fibers are always semidull. In addition, rayon, acetate, nylon, Zefran, and Darvan are also sometimes produced in semidull form. This property contributes to such uses as substituting for, and blending with, wool.

6. *Cotton.* Cotton generally does not have much natural luster. The degree of luster varies, however, with the type of cotton: the better the quality of cotton, the higher the luster.

7. *Wool.* Wool has crimp and a serrated or scaly surface. The better quality of wool has a great amount of crimp and serrations, which, in turn, reduces the amount of luster possible. A good quality of wool, therefore, does not have natural luster.

Some fibers that belong to the wool group show some degree of luster; these are the hair fibers, such as mohair, vicuña, camel's hair, alpaca, and cashmere.

Rayon, acetate, Arnel, nylon, and Darvan fibers are sometimes produced in dull form to give the resultant fabric a wool-like appearance.

Strength of Fibers. Fibers differ in their resistance to tearing apart when subjected to tension. The serviceability and durability of a fabric cannot be determined by the length of staple alone. Tensile strength is a prime necessity in fibers if the resultant fabric is to stand the strain of wear.

Here is the sequence of fibers according to tensile strength.

1. *Fiberglas.* This is by far the strongest of all the textile fibers. It is about twice as strong as cotton and about five times as strong as wool. Its use is still limited, however, because it lacks many other properties important for consumer products.

2. *Nylon.* Nylon was originally called the miracle fiber because of its great strength. Although it loses about 10 per cent of its strength when wet, it still is stronger than other fibers when wet.

3. *Dacron.* Dacron closely rivals nylon in strength. When wet, it loses only a very small percentage of its strength.

4. *Silk.* This fiber has long been known to be the strongest of the natural fibers. When the extremely small diameter of the silk fiber, which varies from .001 to .005 inch, is considered, silk is the strongest of all textile fibers. The breaking strength of raw silk is equivalent to nearly one-third of the breaking strength of the best iron wire of the same size.

5. *Linen.* The flax fiber is second in strength to silk and is especially durable. Linen gains strength when wet.

6. *Cotton.* This natural fiber has good strength. When wet, its strength may increase temporarily by as much as 30 per cent. Cotton may be permanently strengthened by mercerization.

7. *Zefran.* Although this fiber is not as strong as the average good-quality cotton, it nevertheless has satisfactory strength. It should be noted that Zefran is one of the stronger synthetic fibers.

8. *Dynel.* The acrylic fibers are closely alike in strength. In general, however, Dynel is the strongest of this group.

9. *Verel.* Verel is almost as strong as Dynel. It is the second strongest of the acrylic fibers.

10. *Creslan.* Creslan is the third strongest of the acrylic fibers.

11. *Acrilan.* Although the above three acrylic fibers do not lose any significant strength when wet, Acrilan loses up to 20 per cent of its strength when wet.

12. *Orlon.* This is the weakest of the acrylic fibers. When wet, Orlon loses about 20 to 25 per cent of its strength; however, it is about one and one-half times as strong as wool, for which it is frequently substituted.

13. *Saran.* The strength of Saran has been demonstrated by a man standing on a suspended window screen made of this fiber. Since Saran is virtually non-absorbent, it is not weakened by water.

14. *Viscose rayon.* Viscose and cuprammonium rayons are approximately equal in strength; however, since it is possible to produce some varieties of viscose rayon of greater than usual strength (known as medium- and high-tenacity rayons), viscose rayon is rated above cuprammonium. The strength of rayon fiber is conditioned by its moisture content. When wet, rayon loses from 40 to 70 per cent of its natural strength; but this strength is completely regained when the fiber is dry. Rayon, therefore, is not considered a weak fiber because it is judged by its natural strength when dry, which is one-half to one-third that of silk.

15. *Cuprammonium rayon.* The strength characteristic of cuprammonium rayon, whether wet or dry, is similar to that of ordinary viscose rayon. Cuprammonium, however, is not produced in medium- or high-tenacity forms.

16. *Darvan.* Although Darvan has a lower tensile strength than the rayons, it has better abrasion resistance. Consequently, fabrics of Darvan are quite durable.

17. *Acetate.* Acetate is a relatively weak fiber. Not only does it have a relatively low tensile strength, but it has a low abrasion resistance. Furthermore, when wet, acetate may temporarily lose up to 45 per cent of its strength.

18. *Wool.* Wool has the lowest tensile strength of the natural fibers; however, springiness and resilience actually increase its wearing strength above some of the other fibers. While wet, wool may lose temporarily as much as 25 per cent of its strength.

19. *Arnel.* The tensile strength of Arnel closely approximates that of wool. When wet, Arnel temporarily loses up to one-third of its strength. Arnel does not have good abrasion resistance.

20. *Vicara.* This is the weakest of the fibers. When wet, Vicara loses up to 50 per cent of its strength, but regains it when it dries. Although Vicara has a low tensile strength, it has good resilience, which results in fairly good abrasion resistance, somewhat like that of wool.

Elasticity of Fibers. Elasticity includes several factors. One of these is that true elasticity requires that the fiber can be elongated or stretched and, on release of the tension, will tend to return to its original length. The less stress necessary to cause the fiber to stretch, and the more nearly the fiber returns to its original length, the more elastic it is. The greater the amount of this elastic quality, the more a fiber will resist tearing. This quality of elasticity, therefore,

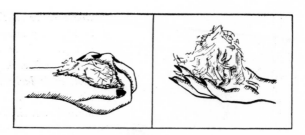

Elastic fibers produce springy yarns, and the resultant fabric is resilient and wrinkle-resistant.

contributes to the strength of a fiber and consequently to the strength of a fabric.

Another aspect of elasticity requires that the fiber can be compressed or crushed and, on release of the pressure, will tend to return to its original shape and size. When a fiber has this elastic quality, it is springy. Such fibers can be spun or twisted into springy yarns, and the resultant fabric will be resilient. This resiliency causes the fabric to be wrinkle-resistant, the resistance varying according to the degree of elasticity inherent in the fiber. Resilience also con tributes to the abrasion resistance of a fabric. Some fibers have both elastic qualities of stretchability and wrinkle resistance, but it is possible for a fiber to have none or little of either. It is also possible for a fiber not to have one qual ity, such as stretchability, but to have the other quality of wrinkle resistance.

Elasticity permits materials to drape well on the human figure. It also facilitates the spinning process, because elastic fibers do not break as easily as inelastic ones. Fibers that are naturally inelastic can be given a degree of elasticity by reducing them to short staple. Short-staple yarns contribute softness to a fabric, helping to make the fabric somewhat crease-resistant, but some strength is sacrificed. A chemical finish can be used to obtain crease resistance. This method is preferable because it does not affect the strength of the fiber. According to this broad definition of elasticity, it is difficult to establish an absolute range for the fibers. The following generalities are adequate for average consumer needs.

1. *Vicara.* Vicara can be stretched 40 per cent of its original length without breaking. It is also extremely resilient and wrinkle-resistant.

2. *Nylon.* Nylon is extremely elastic. It has an unusual ability to return to its original shape after a great deal of stretching. It does not wrinkle easily and is very resilient.

3. *Wool.* Wool is one of the most elastic fibers, certainly the most elastic of the natural fibers. It can be stretched about 30 per cent of its original length without breaking. It is known to be resilient. The better qualities do not wrinkle readily.

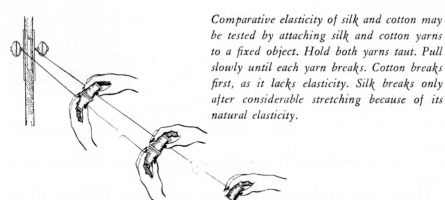

Comparative elasticity of silk and cotton may be tested by attaching silk and cotton yarns to a fixed object. Hold both yarns taut. Pull slowly until each yarn breaks. Cotton breaks first, as it lacks elasticity. Silk breaks only after considerable stretching because of its natural elasticity.

4. *Saran.* Saran can stretch up to 30 per cent of its original length before breaking. It returns to its original size slowly. It does not wrinkle easily and tends to regain its original shape.

5. *Silk.* Silk is the second most elastic of the natural fibers. With too much strain, however, it will never recover its original size. It has very good resilience.

6. *Zefran.* Zefran does not have much stretchability. It has excellent resilience. It does not wrinkle easily, and any wrinkles that may develop fall out easily.

7. *Orlon, Acrilan, Dynel, Creslan,* and *Verel.* These acrylic fibers have approximately the same elasticity. They do not have much stretchability, but they have good recovery. All the acrylic fibers are very resilient. They will not wrinkle easily, and any wrinkles that may form fall out readily.

8. *Darvan.* Darvan has an elasticity similar to that of the acrylic fibers. If not stretched too much, it recovers its original size well. It has excellent resilience.

9. *Dacron.* Dacron has even less stretchability than Darvan. The little that it may stretch is temporary, since it has good recovery to original size. Dacron has excellent resilience.

10. *Acetate.* Acetate has fair stretchability as well as fair recovery to original size. It also has fair resilience. It will wrinkle, but not as easily as rayon or cotton, and there is a tendency for the wrinkles to fall out.

11. *Rayon.* Viscose and cuprammonium rayons have approximately equal properties in this category. Their elasticity is fair. They are not very wrinkle-resistant. To overcome this, viscose fabrics can be processed to impart a good degree of wrinkle resistance. Spun rayon fabrics tend to be more naturally wrinkle-resistant because of their soft texture.

12. *Cotton.* Cotton has virtually no elasticity; therefore, fabrics made from cotton wrinkle easily. When a piece of cotton fabric is creased with the fingernail, the crease is retained; silk and wool are not so easily affected. Fingernail creasing may serve as a test, therefore, to distinguish silk and wool from cotton and linen. Cotton fabrics can be processed to be wrinkle-resistant.

13. *Linen.* Linen is the least elastic and resilient of the natural fibers. Linen fabrics wrinkle and crease easily; however, they too can be processed to improve their wrinkle resistance.

14. *Fiberglas.* Fiberglas is not elastic, but this does not imply that it is stiff. Fiberglas fabrics drape well.

Heat Conductivity of Fibers.

The quality of a fiber to conduct heat, or to act as a nonconductor of heat and therefore serve an insulative purpose, has great significance in textiles. The degree of heat conductivity determines whether fabrics are suitable for winter or for summer use.

In addition to the heat conductivity inherent in the fiber, the weaving, knitting, and finishing processes affect this quality. When a fabric is loosely constructed, for example, it has air spaces, which have an insulative property. The captive air pockets contained in a napped surface add warmth to a fabric. Keep these considerations in mind when you are concerned with the warmth or coolness of a fabric along with the following generalities about the heat conductivity of the fibers themselves.

1. *Linen.* The flax fiber is the best conductor of heat. Linen fabric is therefore most suitable for summer apparel, as it allows the heat of the body to escape easily and quickly.

2. *Cotton.* Cotton fiber is a good conductor of heat. Cotton fabrics are also suitable for summer clothing. The surface of the cloth has much to do with the degree of heat conductivity.

3. *Cuprammonium rayon.* In addition to the fact that cuprammonium rayon is inherently a good heat conductor, it also lends itself to sheer and therefore cool fabrics because the yarn can be made extremely fine in denier (diameter).

4. *Viscose rayon.* The primary reason that viscose rayon is not as cool as cuprammonium is the comparatively heavier yarn produced in its manufacture.

5. *Acetate.* Acetate is a poorer conductor of heat. Because it does not absorb much moisture, it has a tendency to feel warm and clammy on warm, humid days.

6. *Nylon.* Nylon fabrics seem to have the peculiar property of being cold in winter and warm in summer. Actually, this is dependent on whether filament or staple is used and on the construction of the fabric. The spun staple nylon has thousands of air pockets that act as an excellent insulator; therefore, the staple nylon fabrics will be warm. The warmth or coolness of the filament fabrics is dependent on the porosity of the weave and on the amount of moisture in the air and on the body, for nylon reacts to moisture in the same way as acetate does.

7. *Dacron.* Dacron is being promoted for men's summer suiting for several reasons, one of which seems to be its relative coolness for that purpose. It has outstanding wrinkle resistance and crease retention (wet or dry), good draping quality, and resistance to shrinking or stretching.

8. *Silk.* Silk is a natural protein fiber and therefore a nonconductor of heat. It may be used for winter clothing. Some people consider silk to be good as a cool summer fabric; however, the coolness of a silk garment for summer wear is directly dependent on the lightness in weight and the sheerness of the fabric: the lighter and sheerer the fabric, the cooler; the heavier the fabric, the warmer.

9. *Vicara.* This fiber is warm because it is composed of a protein. In fact, its warmth is considered to be closely comparable to wool.

10. *Wool.* Wool is very warm for two reasons: it has a scaly surface that provides air pockets for insulation, and it is composed of a protein, which is a nonconductor of heat.

11. *Zefran.* Zefran is a low conductor of heat. When it is crimped and spun into yarn, it produces a lofty yarn that has air pockets to act as insulation. Such yarns will be as warm as, or warmer than, comparable wool yarns.

12. *Darvan.* Darvan is also a low conductor of heat. Its cross section is somewhat flat and therefore can produce yarns of greater bulking power than wool or Zefran. Fabrics of Darvan can be warmer than similar fabrics of wool.

13. *Acrilan* and *Creslan.* Acrylic fibers do not have a high rate of heat conductivity. Acrilan and Creslan are in this group. When crimped, these fibers produce lightweight yarns that have many air pockets acting as additional insulation. Such yarns are as warm as, or warmer than, wool yarns of equal weight.

14. *Orlon, Dynel,* and *Verel.* These fibers are warm for two reasons: their chemical composition, which is principally acrylic, is a poor conductor; and their cross-section shapes are dog-bone or somewhat flat. As a result, these fibers have a good covering and bulking property, which provides insulation and warmth. Fabrics of these fibers are warmer than similar wool fabrics of equal weight. Another way of putting it is that fabrics of these fibers can be lighter in weight but just as warm as heavier wool fabrics.

15. *Fiberglas* and *Saran.* These fibers are unique with regard to heat conductivity. While Fiberglas filaments conduct heat, the Fiberglas staple acts as an excellent insulator because of the thousands of air pockets it traps. For this reason, Fiberglas staple batting is used for insulating refrigerators, stoves, and houses. Saran has a very low melting point. It softens at 167 degrees Fahrenheit.

Absorbency of Fibers. The quickness with which a fabric absorbs moisture and gives it up again in evaporation has an important bearing on health and comfort. Textile fibers vary in their natural absorptive capacity, but absorbency may be increased by fabric construction or by a finishing process. A loosely constructed fabric or one with a napped surface, for example, is more absorptive than a smooth-surfaced fabric.

1. *Wool.* Wool fibers absorb moisture quickly and hold a large amount, allowing it to evaporate slowly. In fact, wool can absorb up to 20 per cent of its weight in water without feeling damp, and 50 per cent of its weight in water without dripping. When wet, wool does not stick to the body and is ideal for outer wear on cold, damp days.

2. *Silk.* Silk fiber absorbs moisture readily and, like wool, can hold much water without feeling wet.

3. *Rayon.* The absorbency and drying qualities of both viscose and cuprammonium rayons are closely akin to those of silk.

4. *Vicara.* Of all the man-made and synthetic fibers that resemble and feel like wool, Vicara absorbs water more nearly like wool than any other.

5. *Linen.* Linen absorbs moisture more quickly and dries more quickly than cotton. For this reason, coupled with its strength and hygienic characteristics, it is excellent for towels and handkerchiefs.

6. *Cotton.* Cotton absorbs water rather well, but does not dry very quickly.

7. *Acetate.* Acetate does not absorb much moisture: only 14 per cent of its weight at a 95 per cent relative humidity. On warm humid days, the moisture therefore clings to the surface of acetate, and it feels uncomfortable. Acetate clings to the body and feels warm and clammy; however, it dries quickly.

8. *Arnel.* The absorbency of Arnel is slightly lower than that of acetate. It, therefore, will feel somewhat uncomfortable in hot, humid weather. On the other hand, fabrics of Arnel dry quickly.

9. *Nylon.* Nylon absorbs about half as much moisture as acetate. It also feels very clammy and uncomfortable on warm, humid days. Filament nylon garments dry very rapidly, often in one hour. Staple nylon yarn dries more slowly. Water droplets cling to the surfaces of the short pieces of nylon fiber and have difficulty evaporating from within the central portion of the yarn. Garments made of spun nylon yarn may take twenty-four hours to dry.

10. *Verel.* Although Verel is less absorbent than nylon, it is the most absorbent of the acrylic fibers.

11. *Zefran.* Zefran is slightly less absorbent than Verel. Fabrics of Zefran dry rather rapidly.

12. *Darvan.* Darvan is less absorbent than Zefran. When bulky yarns are produced, however, large amounts of water adsorb (adhere) onto the surfaces of the fibers in the air pockets.

13. *Creslan.* Although Creslan is not very absorbent, it is the second most absorbent of the acrylic fibers. Fabrics of Creslan dry quickly.

14. *Orlon.* Orlon absorbs very little moisture and dries quickly. Bulky yarns of Orlon, however, can adsorb quite a bit of water.

15. *Acrilan.* Acrilan is even less absorbent than Orlon. Fabrics of Acrilan dry quickly.

16. *Dynel.* Dynel is the least absorbent of the acrylic fibers and will dry most quickly.

17. *Dacron.* Dacron absorbs very little moisture. This makes fabrics of Dacron uncomfortable in warm, humid weather; however, Dacron fabrics dry rapidly.

18. *Saran.* Saran absorbs virtually no moisture.

19. *Fiberglas.* Fiberglas is nonabsorbent.

Cleanliness and Washability of Fibers. The consumer is interested in knowing what textiles are hygienic, how long a garment may be expected to remain clean, and whether it will require unusual care when laundering or dry cleaning is necessary. The fibers that show smooth surfaces under the microscope produce fabrics that are easy to launder; thus garments made of linen, silk, and rayon wash easily. A napped surface on any one of these materials makes it necessary to give the garment more care in washing. The fact that a fiber does not absorb much water does not imply that the fiber is unhygienic. Actually, such fibers usually do not absorb dirt particles and have relatively smooth surfaces. The water then washes the dirt off the surface, and the fiber dries quickly.

1. *Fiberglas.* A fabric made of Fiberglas filament yarn may be washed clean by either rinsing in water or even wiping with a damp cloth. Neither dirt nor water affects Fiberglas because both remain on the surface.

2. *Saran.* Saran will get slightly dirtier than Fiberglas because dirt can get imbedded into its slightly softer surface. However, it does wash easily. The water should not be too hot.

3. *Dacron.* Dacron is a smooth-surfaced fiber that does not get dirty easily. It may be laundered with a soap or a detergent. Most stains wash out readily. Heat-set garments made of Dacron do not lose their shape or permanent creases after washing. These garments also dry very quickly and do not shrink. Dacron has a tendency to *pill;* that is, to form little balls of fiber on the surface of the fabric.

4. *Nylon.* Nylon filament is also a smooth-surfaced fiber that does not get dirty easily. It may be laundered easily with a soap or a detergent. Fabrics made of nylon filament may be heat-set, so that they will retain their shape and creases or pleats after washing. Staple nylon launders easily also but takes longer to dry. Nylon staple pills very easily.

5. *Zefran.* Zefran is a relatively round, smooth-surfaced fiber that does not get dirty easily. The crimp, however, which may be given to it, does increase the degree of dirt it can attract and hold. But fabrics of Zefran wash readily and, because they can be heat-set, hold their shape well and will not shrink. Zefran may be classified along with Dacron and nylon as a wash-and-wear fiber, but Zefran does not pill.

6. *Darvan.* Because Darvan has a somewhat flat, uneven cross section, it has a slightly greater tendency to hold dirt. Fabrics of Darvan, however, wash readily, retain their creases, pleats, and shape, and will not shrink. Darvan is classified among the wash-and-wear fibers and will not pill.

7. *Orlon, Acrilan, Dynel, Creslan,* and *Verel.* All the acrylic fibers have approximately equal degrees of cleanliness. Since they are usually made into fuzzy, soft yarns, they can get dirty easily; however, fabrics of these fibers wash readily and retain their shape, creases, and pleats, and resist shrinking. They all have good wash-and-wear characteristics. Dynel is the one acrylic fiber that will not pill. The others pill to varying extents depending on the softness of the yarn.

8. *Vicara.* Vicara is a round fiber and, therefore, dirt does not cling easily. It washes very well, and does not shrink, felt, or pill. It cannot, however, be permanently shaped by heat-setting.

9. *Silk.* Silk makes a hygienic material because its smooth surface and absence of short fiber cause it to shed dust and to give up dirt readily. If handled properly, silk can be washed easily.

10. *Acetate.* Acetate is not as smooth as silk but is a clean fiber. It should be laundered with a mild soap in warm water. Acetate shrinks slightly.

11. *Rayon.* Although dirt particles may be easily removed from rayon fiber, care must be taken to avoid undue strain on the material when rayon garments are being washed. Rayon loses much of its strength when wet, but regains it entirely when dry. Rayon shrinks but may be processed so as to reduce the shrinkage to a residual amount of 2 per cent.

12. *Linen.* Because of the smooth surface of its fiber, linen gives up stains readily and affords little adhering surface for particles of dirt. Bacteria do not thrive on linen. Linen launders well; its softness is enhanced by repeated washings. Linen will shrink.

13. *Cotton.* The short cotton fiber produces a fabric with a relatively rougher surface than that of linen, silk, or rayon, and therefore soils easily. Nevertheless, cotton fabric is considered a hygienic material because it can be cleaned easily

—it withstands rough handling and boiling temperature. Cotton will shrink, but the shrinkage may be reduced to as much as 1 per cent by a preshrinking process such as Sanforizing.

14. *Wool.* The serrated surface of the outer scales of the epidermis of wool fiber attracts dust, bacteria, and dirt particles. Consequently, wool fabric requires frequent dry cleaning, or washing if the nature of the fabric permits it. Wool fabrics that have a high grease content must not be washed; they must be dry-cleaned. Wool fiber is softened by moisture and heat, and therefore the fabric shrinks easily; felting occurs when wool is washed improperly. A wool garment should not be rubbed or handled like a cotton one. Preshrinking and shrinkproofing processes are available for wool fabrics.

Reaction of Fibers to Bleaches. It is sometimes desired to bleach fabrics to get them whiter or to remove stains. Whenever a bleach is to be used, it should be put into the water and be thoroughly mixed before the garment is added. This will prevent the possibility of damaging the fabric with a bleach of too concentrated strength. With average care, *cotton* and *linen* may be safely bleached with ordinary household bleaches containing sodium hypochlorite (such as Clorox, Rose-X, and the like). Very mild solutions may also be used on *rayon, acetate, Arnel,* and *nylon.* For safer results, bleaching hydrogen peroxide may be used on fabrics of these fibers.

The safest bleach that may be used on *wool* and *silk* is hydrogen peroxide. Care should always be exercised. On the other hand, hydrogen peroxide should never be used on *Zefran* or *Darvan,* but sodium hypochlorite bleaches may be safely used.

Any ordinary bleach may be used safely on the acrylic fibers, *Orlon, Acrilan, Dynel,* and *Creslan.* However, the acrylic fiber *Verel* will discolor and therefore should not be bleached. *Dacron, Vicara, Fiberglas,* and *Saran* may also be safely bleached with sodium hypochlorite or peroxide bleaches. It should be noted that most white man-made and synthetic fibers do not usually turn gray or yellow. Sometimes the finish on the fabric may cause the discoloration. It is a good idea to wash garments first without a bleach to determine whether one is necessary.

Effect of Heat on Fibers. It is important to know what effect heat has on textile fibers, whether a fiber is inflammable, and how a fabric is to be ironed without its melting or disintegrating.

• *Cotton.* Cotton is highly resistant to degradation by heat. It scorches at about 300 degrees Fahrenheit but does not burn until the temperature is 475 degrees Fahrenheit.

• *Linen.* The reaction of linen to heat is similar to that of cotton. Because of the greater natural stiffness of linen, it should, however, be very damp when ironed; and the iron should be hotter than ordinarily used for cotton.

• *Wool.* Although wool will start to decompose at 266 degrees Fahrenheit, it does not flame. It will support combustion at 572 degrees Fahrenheit. Wool should be pressed with a steam iron, or a very damp pressing cloth should be used with an ordinary iron.

• *Silk.* Silk is less resistant to heat than wool. It will decompose at about 330 degrees Fahrenheit.

• *Rayon.* Both viscose and cuprammonium rayons burn rapidly, once the kindling point of about 350 degrees Fahrenheit is reached. A slightly cooler iron is recommended for these fibers than for cotton.

• *Acetate.* Acetate will stick to the iron at about 350 degrees Fahrenheit. At higher temperatures it will char, sputter, and flame. A cooler iron should be used for acetate than for rayon. Cigarette sparks and glowing embers falling on acetate fabrics will melt holes in the fabric on contact.

• *Arnel.* Arnel will melt at 300 degrees Fahrenheit. Heat-treated Arnel will stick at 250 degrees Fahrenheit. When ironing fabrics of Arnel, the iron must, therefore, be only moderately warm. Fabrics of Arnel will also be damaged by glowing embers.

• *Nylon.* Nylon will melt at 482 degrees Fahrenheit. It may, however, discolor or yellow at lower temperatures. It is advisable to iron nylon in the same manner as acetate. Nylon garments may be commercially heat-set to retain their shape after washing or dry cleaning without further pressing or ironing. As with acetate fabrics, cigarette sparks and glowing embers will melt holes in nylon fabrics.

• *Dacron.* Dacron melts at 480 degrees Fahrenheit. It should be ironed in the same manner as nylon. Dacron can be heat-set to hold a permanent shape or crease.

• *Orlon.* Orlon melts at about 455 degrees Fahrenheit. It has thermoplastic (heat-setting) properties similar to those of Dacron.

• *Acrilan.* Acrilan starts to shrink at 356 degrees Fahrenheit and begins to soften at 464 degrees Fahrenheit. Its color turns yellow to orange to brown on prolonged heating at elevated temperatures. Acrilan can be heat-set.

• *Dynel.* Dynel will not support combustion but will soften at about 300 degrees Fahrenheit and will melt at higher temperatures. Dynel can be heat-set to hold a permanent shape and creases.

• *Creslan.* The incipient melting point or sticking temperature of Creslan is about 450 degrees Fahrenheit as determined on a hot surface. The fiber shrinks and shrivels below this temperature, however, in common with other thermoplastic fibers, and may ignite when an open flame is applied. Cigarette sparks and glowing embers will not ignite fabrics produced from staple or cause pinholes.

• *Verel.* Verel will not support combustion. Temperatures above 300 degrees Fahrenheit, however, cause it to shrink, melt, and then harden. Fabrics of Verel can be heat-set, similar to other acrylic fibers.

• *Zefran.* The sticking temperature of Zefran is higher than that of any of the other thermoplastic fibers. It will melt at temperatures above 490 degrees Fahrenheit.

• *Darvan.* Darvan has very good resistance to degradation by heat up to 300 degrees Fahrenheit. It will stick at 340 degrees and then melt.

• *Vicara.* Vicara loses strength above 350 degrees Fahrenheit and melts at about 470 degrees Fahrenheit. It should, therefore, be ironed in the same manner as rayon or acetate.

• *Saran.* Saran is self-extinguishing. It softens at a low temperature of about 167 degrees Fahrenheit. Ironing is therefore difficult.

• *Fiberglas.* Temperatures must be extremely high to damage Fiberglas. It begins to lose some strength at 600 degrees Fahrenheit and softens at 1,500 degrees Fahrenheit. Obviously, ironing not only will not affect Fiberglas but is actually a waste of time and effort.

Effect of Mildew on Fibers. Mildew often attacks textiles, particularly where there is dampness. Mildew stains and deteriorates fabrics and leaves a musty odor. It is well to know which fibers are resistant to mildew. The following fabrics are wholly resistant to mildew: *nylon, Dacron, Orlon, Acrilan, Dynel, Verel, Zefran, Darvan, Saran,* and *Fiberglas.* If any of these fibers ever appear to get moldy, it is actually the finish on the fiber and not the fiber itself that is mildewing. Such mildew will wash off readily leaving no stains or damage.

• *Acetate* is highly resistant to mildew but may discolor.

• *Arnel* is very highly resistant to mildew.

• *Wool* and *Vicara* have good resistance to mildew but in time will succumb.

• *Silk* has good resistance to mildew but eventually will be damaged under extreme conditions of dampness and darkness.

• *Cotton, linen,* and *rayon* will definitely be attacked by mildew.

Effect of Sunlight on Fibers. Textiles are constantly exposed to the outdoors and light. Some need to be very resistant to degradation by sunlight.

• *Cotton.* Cotton loses strength in sunlight and has a tendency to yellow.

• *Linen*. Linen is much more resistant to light than cotton.

• *Wool*. Wool loses strength. Its dyeing properties, however, are improved on exposure of the fiber to sunlight.

• *Silk*. Silk will be deteriorated more quickly than cotton or wool.

• *Rayon*. Viscose and cuprammonium lose strength after long exposure.

• *Acetate*. Acetate will lose some strength but not as much as rayon.

• *Arnel*. Arnel loses some strength from exposure to sunlight but not as much as rayon.

• *Nylon*. Nylon will lose some strength after exposure over a relatively long period of time. Bright nylon is more resistant to sunlight than is the semidull or dull nylon.

• *Dacron*. Dacron also loses some strength after prolonged exposure; however, there is no discoloration. It is much more resistant behind glass than in direct sunlight.

• *Orlon*. Orlon is extremely resistant to degradation by sunlight. In fact, it is the most resistant of all the acrylic fibers to such deterioration.

• *Acrilan*. Acrilan is highly resistant to sunlight.

• *Dynel*. After prolonged exposure to sunlight, Dynel darkens somewhat and loses some strength.

• *Creslan*. Creslan is highly resistant to sunlight.

• *Verel*. Like Acrilan and Creslan, Verel is highly resistant to sunlight.

• *Zefran*. Zefran is highly resistant to sunlight.

• *Darvan*. Darvan is highly resistant to sunlight.

• *Vicara*. Vicara shows slow deterioration and loss of strength under sunlight.

• *Saran*. Saran darkens slightly. It is not deteriorated by sunlight, and as a result is used a great deal for window screens.

• *Fiberglas*. Sunlight and outdoor exposure do not affect Fiberglas.

Reaction of Fibers to Alkalies and Acids. A knowledge of the reaction of textile fibers to alkalies and acids is important, as alkalies destroy animal fibers; and acids, even in a weak solution, destroy vegetable fibers. For example, chemical tests for determining the fiber content of fabrics are made by noting the disintegration of wool and silk when exposed to a strong alkali, and a similar reaction when cotton and linen are exposed to acids. Good results in the bleaching, finishing, and dyeing processes are dependent on the reaction of the fibers to alkali or acid chemical agents. Not only is this reaction important in testing and manufacturing; it also closely touches the consumer when the care of fabrics is considered.

This reaction to alkalies and acids is most important to the consumer when fabrics are washed. As the brown soap sometimes used for household laundry is a strong alkali, it must not be used for silk or wool fabrics. Synthetic detergents, which are neutral, should be used for these protein fibers. For cotton and linen, synthetic detergents are not as effective as soap.

• *Cotton*. Cotton is destroyed by concentrated inorganic acids—such as hydrochloric, hydrofluoric, sulphuric, and nitric—and is damaged when such acids are in dilute solutions. It is not injured by alkalies even in hot, strong solutions; strong soap may be used for washing cotton.

• *Linen*. The reaction of linen to acids is similar to that of cotton. Linen is not readily damaged by alkalies, but strong soap should not be rubbed on the fabric as it will turn linen yellowish.

• *Wool*. Dilute acids do not injure wool, but concentrated acids destroy it. Wool is quickly destroyed by strong alkalies. It dissolves if completely immersed in a boiling alkali. A neutral or mild soap must be used for wool.

• *Silk*. The organic acids—acetic, tartaric, stearic, and formic—have little effect on silk. Weak inorganic acids also have little effect, but strong solutions injure silk. A dilute solution of nitric acid produces a bright yellow color in silk, and this reaction identifies silk from wool when testing.

Silk is destroyed by strong alkalies; strong soap should be avoided when washing silk. Compared with wool, silk is more resistant to alkalies but less resistant to strong acids.

• *Rayon*. Hot dilute solutions or cold concentrated solutions of strong inorganic acids, such as sulphuric, hydrochloric, hydrofluoric, and nitric, destroy rayon. The organic acids, formic and acetic, do not affect viscose or cuprammonium rayon. Rayons are not readily damaged by alkalies, but are less resistant than cotton or linen. Both viscose and cuprammonium lose tensile strength when exposed to a weak solution of a strong alkali, such as caustic soda.

• *Acetate*. Strong acids will destroy acetate. Acetate will, however, withstand solutions of organic acids as strong as 28 per cent. Acetate is easily affected by alkalies, especially if the water is very hot. Mild soaps and lukewarm water should, therefore, be used when laundering acetate.

• *Arnel*. Acids and alkalies have the same effect on Arnel that they have on acetate. Care should be taken to use mild soaps and lukewarm water when laundering fabrics of Arnel.

• *Nylon*. Nylon is affected by concentrated solutions of the strong mineral and organic acids. Alkalies, however, have virtually no effect on nylon.

• *Dacron*. Dacron has good resistance to most mineral acids, although a concentrated solution of sulphuric acid will decompose it. Dacron also has good resistance to weak and strong alkalies; however, it will be disintegrated by strong alkalies at boiling temperatures.

• *Orlon*. Orlon has good-to-excellent resistance to mineral acids and fair-to-good resistance to weak alkalies. Nor is it harmed by the organic acids.

• *Acrilan*. Acrilan has good resistance to the mineral and organic acids and fair-to-good resistance to weak alkalies.

• *Dynel*. There is little or no effect of either the acids or alkalies on Dynel.

• *Creslan*. In general, Creslan has excellent resistance to acids. Its resistance to alkalies is fair. It is best to use a mild soap when washing Creslan fabrics.

• *Verel*. Verel has excellent resistance to acids. Although it is not weakened by alkalies, it may be discolored by them.

• *Zefran*. Zefran also has excellent resistance to acids. It is resistant to weak alkalies but will be damaged by strong alkalies.

• *Darvan*. Strong acids have little effect on Darvan even at high temperatures. It has only fair resistance to weak alkalies. Ammonium hydroxide, for example, will deteriorate Darvan.

• *Vicara*. Although Vicara is protein in nature, it has great resistance to concentrated solutions of mineral acids and is very resistant to the action of alkalies.

• *Saran*. Saran has fair resistance to concentrated sulphuric acid and good resistance to others. It is unaffected by most alkalies but is affected to a limited extent by ammonium hydroxide.

• *Fiberglas*. Fiberglas is affected by hydrofluoric and hot phosphoric acids only. It is damaged by hot solutions of weak alkalies and cold solutions of strong alkalies.

Affinity of Fibers for Dyes. The readiness with which a fiber absorbs and retains dye affects the appearance and serviceability of a fabric. Affinity for dyes is usually determined by the porosity of a fiber.

• *Cotton*. While cotton does not have a natural affinity for dyes, it is usually treated to assure fastness of color. Mercerized cotton absorbs and retains dyes better than cottons not so treated.

• *Linen*. Linen fibers have a poor affinity for dyes. The hard nonporous surface of the fiber and its natural gum content (pectin) do not allow even penetration of the dyestuff. A more favorable reaction can be induced by removing the pectin by a strong bleaching process, but this may entail some sacrifice in the durability of the fabric. For this reason, unbleached linens are preferable when extreme whiteness is not a primary consideration.

• *Wool*. Wool has a very high affinity for dyes. Wool fabrics dye well and evenly.

• *Silk*. Silk has a good affinity for most dyestuffs.

• *Rayon*. Rayon also reacts favorably to dyes. The dyestuff is absorbed evenly, and the material is consequently dyed successfully.

Fiber	Composition	Structure	Length	Luster	Strength *	Elasticity	Heat Conductivity
Acetate	Cellulose acetate (synthetic)	Striated due to irregular trilobed shape	Any length	Bright, semidull, dull	17	Stretch greater than rayon. More resilient than rayon	Medium
Acrilan	Acrylic (synthetic)	Round to bean-shape, speckled	1 to 6 inches	Semidull	11	Little stretch; excellent resilience	Very low
Arnel	Cellulose triacetate (synthetic)	Irregularly shaped solid	Any length	Bright; dull	19	Stretch similar to acetate; more resilient than acetate	Medium
Cotton	Cellulose (natural)	Flat, twisted, ribbon-like, with a wide inner canal	½ to 2½ inches	Generally none. High quality has good sheen	6	Very little stretch. Wrinkles very easily but can be treated	High (Cool)
Creslan	Acrylic (synthetic)	Substantially round, speckled	1 to 6 inches	Semidull	10	Little stretch; excellent resilience	Very low
Dacron	Polyester (synthetic)	Substantially round, speckled	Any length	High	3	Practically no stretch; excellent resilience	Medium for filament. Low for staple
Darvan	Dinitrile (synthetic)	Irregular ribbon	1½ to 4½ inches	Bright, semidull, dull	16	Little stretch; excellent resilience	Low
Dynel	Acrylic (synthetic)	Irregular ribbon	1¼ to 5 inches	Semidull	8	Little stretch; excellent resilience	Very low
Fiberglas	Glass (synthetic)	Cylindrical translucent rod	Any length	High	1 (strongest)	No stretch; flexible	High for filament. Low for staple
Linen	Cellulose (natural)	Bamboolike	12 to 20 inches	High	5	Practically no stretch. Wrinkles very easily but can be treated	Higher than cotton (Cool)
Nylon	Polyamide (synthetic)	Fine, smooth, solid, round rod	Any length	Bright, semidull, dull	2	High stretch; excellent resilience	High for filament. Low for staple
Orlon	Acrylic (synthetic)	Dog-bone shape, speckled	1½ to 4 inches	Semidull	12	Little stretch; excellent resilience	Very low
Rayon, Cuprammonium	Cellulose (man-made)	Fine, smooth, solid rod	Any length	Bright, semidull, dull	14	Little stretch. Wrinkles easily but can be treated	High
Rayon, Viscose	Cellulose (man-made)	Threadlike longitudinal lines; uneven, very irregular surface	Any length	Bright, semidull, dull	15	Little stretch. Wrinkles easily but can be treated	High
Saran	Vinylidene chloride (synthetic)	Cylindrical translucent rod	Any length	Soft luster	13	Fair stretch, returns to shape slowly; good resilience	Medium (melts easily)
Silk	Protein (natural)	Smooth solid, slightly uneven diameter	1,200 to 4,000 feet	High	4	Has good stretch; very resilient	Low (Warm)
Verel	Acrylic (synthetic)	Dog-bone shape, speckled	1½ to 2½ inches	Semidull	9	Little stretch; excellent resilience	Very low
Vicara	Protein (man-made)	Cylindrical rod	1 to 6 inches	Semidull	20 (weakest)	High stretch; excellent resilience	Very low
Wool	Protein (natural)	Roughly cylindrical solid, covered with overlapping scales, crimpy	1 to 8 inches	Generally none. Poor quality has luster	18	Stretches readily, tends to return to size; very resilient	Very low (Very warm)
Zefran	Nitrile-acylic alloy (synthetic)	Almost round, dark, solid rod	1½ to 4½ inches	Bright, semidull	7	Fair stretch; resilience almost that of wool	Low

Numbers run from 1–20 (strongest to weakest); † 1–19 (most absorbent to least absorbent).

† Absorbency	Cleanliness and Washability	Reaction to Bleaches	Effect of Heat	Effect of Mildew	Effect of Light	Reaction to Alkalies	Reaction to Acids	Affinity to Dyes
7	Use mild soap, warm water; shrinks	Deteriorates; use hypochlorite or peroxide with care	Melts and burns; use cooler iron than for rayons	Highly resistant	More resistant than rayons	Weakened by strong solutions	More resistant than rayons; damaged by concentrated strong acids	Fair, but can be solution dyed
15	Retains shape; does not shrink; may pill	Resistant	Melts; reacts like nylon	Wholly resistant	Highly resistant	Fair resistance to weak alkalies	Good resistance	Good
8	Retains shape; does not shrink; dries quickly	Deteriorates; use hypochlorite or peroxide with care	Melts at higher temperature than acetate	Very highly resistant	Loses some strength	Weakened by very strong solutions	Like acetate	Fair, limited solution dyeing possible
6	Gets dirty easily; will shrink	Weakens; may be used with care	Will scorch and burn	Damaged	Loses strength; yellows	Not damaged (strengthened with caustic soda)	Easily affected	Excellent
13	Retains shape; does not shrink	Resistant	Melts at higher temperature than Arnel	Wholly resistant	Highly resistant	Fair resistance to weak alkalies	Excellent resistance	Good
17	Most stains wash out readily; dries quickly; does not shrink; retains shape	Resistant	Melts; reacts like nylon	Wholly resistant	Loses some strength over prolonged period	Good resistance to weak alkalies; fair resistance to strong alkalies	Good resistance except to sulfuric acid	Good
12	Good shape retention; must use warm water, warm iron	Resistant to hypochlorite; damaged by peroxide	Melts at fairly high (340° F) temperature	Wholly resistant	Highly resistant	Fair resistance to weak alkalies	Good resistance	Fair
16	Retains shape; does not shrink; may pill	Resistant	Will not support combustion, but will melt	Wholly resistant	Darkens somewhat; loses some strength	Highly resistant	Extremely resistant	Good; limited solution dyeing possible
19 (Least absorbent)	Dirt wipes off	Resistant	Incombustible; melts above 1,500° F	Wholly resistant	No effect	Damaged by hot solutions of weak alkalies and cold solutions of strong alkalies	Damaged by hydrofluoric, hot phosphoric, concentrated hydrochloric and sulfuric acids	None; requires special technique to apply color to surface
5	Will shrink	Weakens; use with care	Will scorch and burn	Damaged	More resistant than cotton	Not damaged (strengthened with caustic soda)	Easily affected	Fair
9	Retains shape; filament dries quickly; does not shrink	Fairly good resistance	Quickly damaged by cigarette sparks; use warm iron	Wholly resistant	Bright is more resistant than most fibers; semidull, dull, good resistance	Unaffected	Weakened	Good
14	Retains shape; does not shrink; may pill	Resistant	Melts; reacts like nylon	Wholly resistant	Extremely resistant	Fair resistance to weak alkalies	Good resistance	Good
3	May shrink; weakens when wet	Deteriorates; use hypochlorite or peroxide with care	Reacts like cotton but at lower temperature	Damaged	Loses strength over prolonged period	Weakened by strong solutions	Easily affected; like cotton	Very good
3	May shrink; weakens when wet	Deteriorates; use hypochlorite or peroxide with care	Reacts like cotton but at lower temperature	Damaged	Loses strength over prolonged period	Weakened by strong solutions	Easily affected; like cotton	Very good; can be solution dyed
18	Use warm or cold water; washes readily	Resistant	Self-extinguishing; melts at 167° F	Wholly resistant	Darkens slightly, no strength loss	Affected by ammonium hydroxide	Good resistance	Poor, generally requires solution dyeing
2	Some silk fabrics can be washed with care	Deteriorates; use peroxide with great care	Less resistant than wool; reacts similarly	Good resistance	Less resistant than cotton or wool	Destroyed by strong alkalies; damaged by weak alkalies	Somewhat affected	Excellent
10	Retains shape; shrinkage varies with type	Discolors	Will not support combustion; will become stiff and discolored	Wholly resistant	Highly resistant	Not damaged; some discoloration	Excellent resistance	Good
4	Will not pill, felt, or shrink	Resistant	Melts; should be ironed like acetate	Good resistance	Slow deterioration	Not damaged except by strong, hot solutions	Excellent resistance	Excellent
1 (Most absorbent)	Weakens when wet; will shrink, pill, felt	Deteriorates; use peroxide with care	Does not flame; will char	Good resistance	Weakens	Destroyed by strong alkalies; damaged by weak alkalies	Generally resistant except to hot sulfuric acid	Excellent
11	Retains shape; practically no shrinkage; washes easily; little pilling	Resistant to hypochlorite; damaged by peroxide	Melts at very high (490° F) temperature	Wholly resistant	Highly resistant	Resistant to weak alkalies	Excellent resistance	Very good

• *Acetate*. Acetate requires special dyes. Some colors, such as grays and blues, tend to gas-fade and turn red or purplish. Like cotton, the affinity of acetate for dyes can be increased by an alkali treatment. By special processes, the coloring pigment can be added to the acetate solution before the fiber is actually formed, making the color a permanent part of the fiber.

• *Arnel*. Arnel has good affinity for acetate dyes. Its resistance to fume fading and crocking is generally somewhat better than that of acetate, if properly dyed. Black solution-dyed Arnel has excellent fastness.

• *Nylon*. Nylon dyes fairly well when acetate dyes are used. The colors are generally fast.

• *Dacron*. Dacron can be dyed to a complete range of shades with good-to-excellent washfastness and fair-to-good lightfastness.

• *Orlon*. Orlon has good affinity for dyes in all shades. The colors have good fastness to washing and light.

• *Acrilan*. Acrilan can be dyed with acetate dyes, but the color has poor light-fastness. Wool dyes provide greater fastness and a wide range of colors.

• *Dynel*. Dynel has good affinity for dyes in a wide range of colors. The colors have excellent fastness to fumes, crocking, and washing, and also have good lightfastness. Solution dyeing is done in black, brown, and gray.

• *Creslan*. Creslan has good affinity for dyes.

• *Verel*. Verel has a varied affinity for dyes. The colors and their degrees of fastness depend on the dyes used, some of which have very good lightfastness and washfastness.

• *Zefran*. The affinity for dyes of Zefran is very good. When vat dyes are used, the colors have good-to-excellent lightfastness and excellent washfastness. Other dyes, such as acetate dyes, are not so fast.

• *Darvan*. Darvan has poor-to-fair affinity for dyes. There is difficulty in obtaining a wide range of colors, particularly dark colors. To some extent, acetate dyes are used, but they have poor fastness to light and fumes.

• *Vicara*. Vicara can be dyed with a wide variety of dyestuffs with excellent results.

• *Saran*. Saran can be dyed only by including the color before the fiber is extruded.

• *Fiberglas*. A special technique is used that causes the dye to stick to the surface of Fiberglas.

▶ TEST YOURSELF ON THIS CHAPTER

1. How may a knowledge of textiles help the consumer?
2. What is the sequence of development of fiber into fabric?
3. What practical significance has the quality of absorbency in apparel?
4. Explain how length of staple affects the quality of a fabric.
5. What quality of acetate makes it desirable for winter underwear?
6. What type of rayon would make the best-wearing coat lining? Why?
7. Why is elasticity important in textiles? How may elasticity in textile fabrics be improved?
8. What qualities of linen make it suitable for (a) towels and handkerchiefs, (b) summer suits, (c) draperies, (d) summer shoes?
9. What qualities of silk make it suitable for (a) women's dresses, (b) fishlines, (c) neckties, (d) ribbons?
10. Why is cotton used so extensively for infants' wear?
11. What qualities of rayon make it a poor fiber to use for (a) sewing thread, (b) stockings, (c) winter underwear?
12. What specific qualities have spun-rayon fabrics that are not found in filament rayons?
13. What properties may wool fabric be expected to have? How do they affect the serviceability of wool?
14. How does a napped surface affect the hygienic quality of a fabric?
15. Why does a cotton bathing suit feel cooler than a woolen one?
16. Why does a fabric of nylon filament yarn dry faster than one of nylon spun yarn?
17. What one characteristic do all the acrylic fibers have that is of great advantage to the consumer and homemaker?
18. Why is the use of Saran limited?
19. Which textiles will be damaged quickly by cigarette sparks?
20. Which textile would be considered best for curtains? Why?
21. Obtain as many samples of fabrics as you can, and cut them into small square pieces, three by three inches. Mount them on small cards. Determine the fiber content of each sample, and record your data on the card. Give all possible uses for each fabric. Give the reasons for your answers in terms of the basic qualities of the fibers.
22. Observe carefully the various contents of your home furnishings, and make a record of every item that uses any textile fibers. Add the name of the fiber used, indicating if this is a guess or the result of observation and analysis. Give reasons for each answer.

3 · TESTING FIBERS

For Identification

Textile fibers are ordinarily classified according to their substance. Cotton and linen are called vegetable fibers because they are derived from plants. Wool and silk are called animal fibers because they are derived from sheep and silkworms, respectively. Rayon, although a man-made fiber, may come under the vegetable classification because it is made from cellulose, an important ingredient of all plant life. Acetate and Arnel have their origins in cellulose. With the exception of Vicara, which is derived from corn protein, called *zein,* all the newer fibers are synthetics. These fibers have no counterpart in nature but are creations of chemists. Chemically, nylon is an amide; Dacron is a polyester fiber; Orlon, Acrilan, Dynel, Creslan, and Verel are acrylics; Zefran, a nitrile-acrylic alloy; Darvan, a dinitrile; Saran, vinylidene chloride; and Fiberglas, a form of glass

The value of classifying fibers according to substance is evident in many textile operations. Its immediate application is indicated in various physical and chemical tests for identification purposes: (1) testing by microscope, (2) the feeling test, (3) the burning test, (4) the breaking test, (5) chemical tests, (6) nontechnical tests for distinguishing linen from cotton. No single test, other than by microscope, can be depended on to give at all times immediate recognition of every fiber. Limitations will be encountered in all the tests. In practice, identification tests are used in combination. Certain tests cannot be made freely or easily in the retail store at the time of purchase. At that time, the consumer must use nontechnical tests. These are inadequate, yet they convey a certain amount of information if they have been used frequently enough to insure correct observations.

Testing by Microscope. Identification by microscope, as studied in Chapter 1, is the most reliable test that can be used to distinguish the fibers. Knowing what the fibers look like under the microscope will help you understand other identification tests. Certain manufacturing and finishing processes, such as mercerizing and delustering, affect the appearance of a fiber under the microscope. In addition, a dark-colored fabric cannot be identified under the microscope until the dyestuff is removed. The light necessary for identification cannot pass through a dark fabric. The dyestuff must be removed, or "stripped," by the use of a bleaching chemical, which is determined by the composition of the fabric. If the fabric is of vegetable substance, its color can be removed by chlorine water or by sodium hydrosulphite (3 per cent solution, boiling); if of animal substance, a ½ per cent solution of caustic soda will remove the dye.

Feeling Test. The feeling test requires skilled perception if it is to be of any value on a shopping tour. Skilled perception is acquired only after handling many different fabrics over a period of time. To understand what is meant by "to feel" a fabric, place your finger on a sample of wool. The heat generated by the finger remains in the area because wool is a nonconductor of heat. Consequently, wool fabric "feels warm to the touch." If your finger is placed on a sample composed of the vegetable fibers—that is, cotton, linen, or even rayon—the heat of the finger passes off because such fibers are conductors of heat. These fabrics, therefore, "feel cool to the touch."

- *Cotton.* Cotton is cool to the touch and feels soft and inelastic.
- *Linen.* Linen is cold and smooth and has a leathery feel.
- *Wool.* Wool is warm to the touch and feels elastic and springy.
- *Silk.* Silk feels warm, smooth, and elastic.

Limitation of Feeling Test. The man-made and synthetic fibers cannot be detected by feeling alone. For example, spun rayon can be made to look and feel like cotton, wool, or linen; spun nylon, to look and feel like cotton or linen; Vicara, to look and feel like wool or cashmere. Some of these newer fibers may even look and feel like each other in fabric form, as in the case of such acrylics as Orlon, Acrilan, Dynel, Creslan, and Verel, which have a slippery or slick feeling that the natural fibers do not have.

Burning Test. To recognize the composition of fabrics by the burning test, note three things: (1) how the yarn ignites when flame is applied, (2) condition of the burned portion, (3) odor produced by burning. If both the lengthwise and the crosswise yarns in a fabric are known to be of the same substance, the sample may be tested as a whole. Different kinds of yarn, however, are sometimes used in a fabric. When the presence of yarns of different substances is suspected, the lengthwise yarns should be separated from the crosswise yarns, and each set should be tested separately.

- *Cotton.* Cotton yarn blazes quickly when it comes in contact with the flame because the cellulose ingredient is highly inflammable. The ash is light and feathery and has a vegetable odor similar to that of burned paper; mercerized

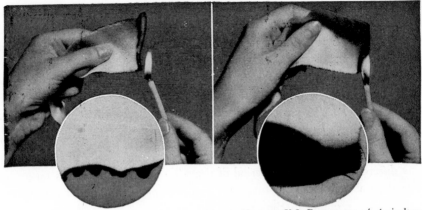

Courtesy U.S. Department of Agriculture

Pure-dye silk burns (at left) with a small flame that soon dies, leaving an ash in the form of small, brittle, shiny black balls along the edge of the fabric.
Weighted silk burns (at right) without showing a visible flame. It chars and leaves a conerent ash, a skeleton of the original fabric.

cotton produces a black ash. Because cotton is highly inflammable, do not use cotton where its proximity to flame becomes a fire hazard; for example, pot holders should be made of wool, never of cotton.

• *Linen.* Linen, when burned, produces an ash similar to cotton ash because both fabrics are of vegetable substance. Linen ash is also light and feathery and has the odor of burned paper. Linen as a fabric, however, burns somewhat more slowly than cotton because linen yarns are heavier than cotton yarns. The pace of burning, however, is not sufficiently different to aid in distinguishing linen from cotton.

• *Wool.* Wool is slow to ignite and has a characteristic small, slow, flickering flame that sizzles and curls. It can be extinguished easily, as the fabric ceases flaming when the fire is withdrawn. Wool ash is dark and crisp. It falls into an irregular shape and can be crushed easily. The ash has a strong animal odor resembling burning feathers or hair, indicating the presence of an animal substance or of a fiber obtained from an animal. The characteristic odor of burned wool is due to the sulphur ingredient.

• *Silk.* Pure silk also burns slowly and ceases flaming when the fire is withdrawn. The ash of silk appears in the form of round, crisp, shiny black beads that, like the ash of wool, can be crushed easily with the fingers. The ash gives forth an animal odor, but one that is less pronounced than that of wool, as silk does not contain sulphur.

In manufacturing, additional body is given to silk fabrics by weighting them

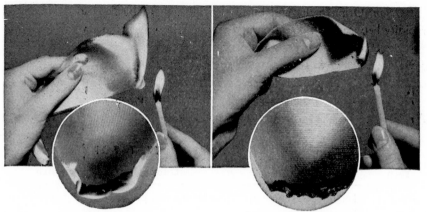

Acetate blazes (at left) as it burns. The fabric puckers, curls, and fuses into an ir-
regular black residue that hardens when cooled.
Wool burns slowly (at right) with a small flickering flame. The fabric sizzles and
curls. The ash is black, irregular, and crisp.

with metallic fillers. Weighted silk burns without showing a visible flame. The
burned part becomes incandescent; it chars and gradually smolders away, leaving a coherent ash that is a screenlike skeleton of the original fabric. The odor
of the ash of weighted silk is similar to that of pure silk.

• *Rayon.* Like cotton, rayon ignites quickly. It burns with a bright yellow
flame, sometimes more rapidly than cotton because rayon is essentially a purified
cellulose. The ash of rayon has the same odor as that of cotton and linen ash
and is similarly light and feathery.

• *Acetate.* Acetate blazes as it burns. The edge of the fabric puckers and
curls as the material fuses and melts into a hard mass. Acetate sputters and drips
like tar. The ash of acetate is hard and brittle, and is difficult to crush between
the fingers. Because of the acetic acid used in the manufacture of acetate, the
ash has an acid odor similar to that of vinegar.

• *Arnel.* Arnel is chemically similar to acetate, and its reaction to heat and
flame is similar to acetate's reaction. Arnel flames quickly and the material melts
into a hard mass. As it burns, Arnel drips like burning tar. The ash is hard and
brittle and has an acid odor like that of vinegar.

• *Nylon.* Nylon melts before burning. As it burns, it shrinks from the flame
and forms a hard round bead that cannot be crushed between the fingers. While
burning, it has a pungent odor.

• *Dacron.* Dacron melts before burning. It burns slowly, leaving a brittle
beady ash. While it burns, Dacron has a slightly sweetish odor.

• *Orlon.* Orlon melts and burns, leaving a hard black bead. It burns at a rapidity between that of cotton and acetate with an acrid odor.

• *Acrilan.* Acrilan melts and burns much like Orlon.

• *Dynel.* Dynel will not support combustion. It will shrink, harden, and become brittle, leaving a disagreeable odor.

• *Creslan.* Creslan melts and burns much like the acrylic fibers, Orlon and Acrilan.

SUMMARY OF THE BURNING TEST FOR FIBERS

Yarn	Flame	Odor	Ash
Cotton	Large yellow flame; burns quickly	Like burned paper	Light, feathery grayish ash; black ash denotes mercerized cotton
Linen	Like cotton; sometimes slower burning if yarns are heavier	Like burned paper	Like cotton; sometimes heavier if yarn is thicker
Wool	Small, slow flickering flame; sizzles and curls; ceases flaming when withdrawn from flame	Strong animal stench like burning feathers or hair	Crisp dark ash; irregular shape that can be crushed easily
Silk (pure dye)	Burns slowly; ceases flaming when withdrawn from flame	Gives off an animal odor, but less pronounced than wool	Round, crisp, shiny black beads easily crushed with fingers
Silk (weighted)	No flame; burned part becomes incandescent and chars	Same as pure silk	Screenlike skeleton of original sample
Rayon	Ignites quickly like cotton, sometimes faster	Like burned paper	Like cotton
Acetate	Flames quickly; material puckers, sputters, melts; drips like tar	Acid, like vinegar	Brittle black ash, difficult to crush between fingers
Arnel	Flames quickly; sputters, melts; flames drip like tar	Acid, like vinegar	Brittle black ash, difficult to crush between fingers; like acetate

• *Verel*. Verel generally reacts to heat and flame differently from the other acrylic fibers, as well as from most of the other fibers. It is highly flame-resistant. Verel will melt and shrink away from the flame but will not flame itself. It leaves a hard ash with an acrid odor.

• *Zefran*. Zefran flames rapidly and sputters slightly. The edge of the fabric curls as the fabric blazes. It leaves a black ash that can be crushed easily between the fingers. While it burns, Zefran has an acrid odor similar to that of burning acrylic fibers.

SUMMARY OF THE BURNING TEST FOR FIBERS

Yarn	Flame	Odor	Ash
Nylon	Melts and shrinks from flame before burning	Pungent	Hard round bead that cannot be crushed
Dacron	Melts before burning; burns slowly	Slightly sweetish	Brittle, beady ash
Orlon	Melts; burns rapidly like acetate	Acrid	Hard black bead
Acrilan	Melts; burns rapidly	Acrid	Hard black bead
Dynel	Shrinks; will not support combustion	Disagreeable	Hardens; becomes brittle
Creslan	Melts	Acrid	Hardens
Verel	Melts; shrinks from flame	Acrid	Hard black ash
Zefran	Flames; sputters slightly	Acrid	Black ash that crushes easily
Darvan	Melts and burns		Hard black bead
Vicara	Somewhat like wool	Burning chicken feathers	Small bead, easily crushed
Saran	Melts, shrinks from flame; does not support combustion		Hard bead
Fiberglas	Will not burn; melts at temperature over 1,500° F.		Melts

• *Darvan*. Darvan melts and burns, leaving a hard black bead.

• *Vicara*. Vicara burns with a small bead that can be easily crushed. The odor is like that of burning chicken feathers. In fact, being a protein fiber, Vicara reacts to flame in a manner similar to that of silk and wool.

• *Saran*. Saran does not support combustion. It will melt, shrink from the flame, and form a bead.

• *Fiberglas*. Fiberglas will not burn. If the temperature is over 1,500 degrees Fahrenheit, it will melt.

Limitation of Burning Test. As cotton, linen, and rayon show a large yellow flame, rapid burning, and a light feathery ash that gives off an odor similar to that of burned paper, the burning test is of no value in distinguishing these three fibers from one another. But this test is important in distinguishing cotton, linen, and rayon from the other fibers. Furthermore, note that many of the man-made and synthetic fibers react similarly. Both acetate and Arnel flame, sputter, and drip flaming. They burn to a brittle black ash and give off an odor of acetic acid. Nylon, Orlon, Acrilan, and Creslan melt before burning and leave a hard round bead. Dynel, Verel, and Saran do not support combustion, but they melt and leave a brittle, beady ash. These limitations or similarities provide a basic means of preliminary examination and elimination, summarized as follows.

1. Burns, forming a light feathery ash and leaving an odor of burning paper. This category would indicate cotton, linen, or rayon.
2. Burns, forming a bead with the odor of burning feathers. This category would indicate a wool, pure silk, or Vicara.
3. Burns, leaving a skeleton of ash with the odor of burning feathers. Indicates weighted silk.
4. Shrinks from flame, melts, burns, and forms a bead. This category includes acetate, Arnel, nylon, Orlon, Acrilan, and Creslan. The odor of acetic acid would provide a further breakdown in this group of acetate and Arnel.
5. Does not support combustion but will shrink, harden, and become brittle. This category includes Dynel, Verel, and Saran.
6. Incombustible but with sufficient heat will melt and shrink from flame. This is true only of Fiberglas.

Breaking Test. The breaking test is nontechnical, yet it affords a convenient means of identifying fabrics. Recognition of a yarn by the breaking test requires observation of the fiber ends when the yarn is broken apart. A piece of yarn about 12 inches long is required for this test. The yarn must be untwisted very gently to restore the natural formation of the fiber before twist was inserted by the spinning operation. Sometimes, two or more strands are combined to make up a single yarn. In such cases, the yarn must be untwisted gently until a single strand is obtained. Care must also be used when pulling a

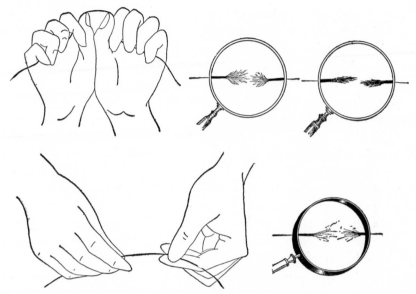

To examine the breaking pattern of cotton, linen, or rayon yarn, untwist the yarn and tear it apart. Rayon yarn will show lustrous, inelastic filaments. Cotton yarn will show brushlike ends that are short, even, and fuzzy. Linen yarn will break unevenly, showing long, pointed ends that are inelastic and lustrous.

yarn apart; otherwise, the broken fiber ends will not take their characteristic pattern.

• *Cotton.* Because cotton yarns are made from short-staple fiber, the breaking of a cotton yarn will show fiber ends that are short, even, fuzzy, and brushlike. There is a characteristic curl to the ends, caused by the natural twist of the fiber. The inelasticity of cotton yarn causes the yarn to snap when pulled apart.

• *Linen.* When it is suspected that a yarn is composed of linen fiber, a long piece of yarn is necessary for testing because long staple may be anticipated. If a break does not occur readily when the yarn is untwisted and gently pulled apart, the span must be increased to exert tension on a longer staple. Untwisting should be continued along the span, and the yarn again pulled gently. If necessary, the span should be increased again. The breaking pattern of a linen yarn shows long, straight, lustrous fiber ends that are pointed and uneven at the tips. The fiber ends never curl. They point outward with marked stiffness indicating lack of flexibility.

• *Wool.* A wool yarn has a characteristic fuzzy surface. When the yarn is pulled gently for the breaking test, it stretches easily because of its remarkable elasticity. The breaking pattern shows fiber ends that are wavy and spiral.

• *Silk*. A silk yarn stretches easily when pulled because silk ranks close to wool in elasticity. Because of its strength, the silk yarn stretches a considerable degree, breaking apart finally with a snap, but only after it has exceeded its limit of stretching. The fiber ends, when broken, appear fine and lustrous.

• *Rayon*. If tension is exerted on a dry rayon yarn, the yarn appears to be comparatively strong, though inelastic, and does not break easily. When a rayon yarn is moistened with the tongue, a slight pull breaks the yarn easily. When broken, the fiber ends create a pattern similar to that of a tree with numerous stiff branches. This effect is produced by the explosivelike bursting of the separate filaments.

Limitation of Breaking Test. One limitation of the breaking test is indicated in testing spun rayon. As spun rayon can easily simulate wool, linen, or even cotton, its breaking pattern can be similar to the characteristic pattern of wool, cotton, or linen. When the burning test is used as additional identification, the rayon yarn that resembles wool reveals the lack of animal odor that is characteristic of wool. Rayon yarn that resembles linen or cotton can be detected by exerting tension on the yarn after moistening it with the tongue. The characteristic loss of strength that rayon shows when wet is evident.

Spun rayon is only one example of the limitation of this test. It would be difficult to determine accurately whether a yarn is composed of nylon, Orlor, Dacron, or any of the other stronger synthetic fibers. These fibers are relatively strong, and the degree of tension used in trying to break these yarns by hand cannot be measured accurately. Furthermore, when broken, the ends of these yarns may look like each other, or like wool, cotton, or some other fiber, depending on whether filament, artificially crimped staple, or staple fibers were used in the manufacture of the yarn.

Chemical Tests.

In addition to the microscope, chemical tests provide positive means of identifying fibers. But chemical tests are not intended for the general consumer. Their value is demonstrated, however, by the fact that some retail stores have their own laboratories for testing fabrics.

• *To Distinguish Animal from Vegetable Fibers with an Alkali.* As strong alkalies destroy animal substances, a 5 per cent solution of lye in water (½ teaspoon of lye in a glass of water) can be used to eliminate wool and silk fibers from a sample that contains a mixture of fibers. The action of this chemical (also known as caustic soda or sodium hydroxide) is hastened by boiling the solution before the sample is immersed. The wool and silk fibers will be completely dissolved. The vegetable fibers will not be affected. Another test is necessary to identify those fibers.

• *To Distinguish Vegetable from Animal Fibers with an Acid.* As dilute acids destroy vegetable fibers, a 2 per cent solution of sulphuric acid may be used to distinguish vegetable from animal fibers. A drop of the solution is placed on a sample of the fabric, which is then placed between two blotters and pressed with a hot iron. The spotted area will become charred if the fabric is cotton, linen, or rayon.

• *To Distinguish Silk from Wool.* If the fibers in a sample are known to consist of silk and wool, and identification of each is desired, the use of concentrated hydrochloric acid (cold) will dissolve the silk and cause the wool fiber to swell.

• *To Distinguish Linen from Cotton.* Before any chemical test is made to distinguish linen from cotton, all surface dressings should be removed from the samples by boiling them for a few minutes in a solution of dilute sodium hydroxide, about ½ per cent. Then any of the following tests can be made.

Immersing cotton and linen samples in a 1 per cent solution of fuchsin in alcohol produces a rose-red color in both samples. After the samples have been washed and then immersed in ammonia, linen retains the red coloration, but cotton does not. This test is sometimes made with a 1 per cent solution of magenta, a red dyestuff. If samples of cotton and linen are immersed in an alcoholic solution of rosalic acid for a few minutes, then washed and immersed quickly in strong caustic soda and washed again, linen turns rose red, and cotton appears only slightly colored.

Cotton fibers are weakened more than linen fibers if samples are immersed in concentrated sulphuric acid for two minutes. After the samples are rinsed and immersed in weak ammonia, the cotton fibers dissolve, leaving the linen fibers unaffected. When cotton and linen samples are immersed in a solution of iodine and zinc chloride (Herzberg's stain), cotton is stained reddish purple; and linen is stained blue to purple. When samples are immersed in a caustic soda solution, cotton remains white; and linen turns yellowish.

• *To Distinguish Viscose, Cuprammonium, and Acetate.* A solution containing equal parts of concentrated sulphuric acid and iodine (crystals) may be used to distinguish each of the different fibers. When samples are immersed in this solution, a dark-blue coloration indicates viscose; a light-blue coloration indicates cuprammonium; a yellow coloration indicates acetate. Another test to distinguish acetate from rayon, when both types are known to be used in a fabric, is to immerse the sample in a 50 per cent solution of acetic acid. The acetate dissolves; rayon is not affected.

• *To Distinguish Acetate from Other Fibers.* If a sample of acetate is immersed in acetone (a chemical used in nail-polish removers), the acetate fibers are completely dissolved; other fibers, with the exception of Arnel and Dynel, are not affected.

• *To Distinguish Arnel from Other Fibers.* When a specimen of fabric or a blend of fibers is immersed at room temperature for one hour in a mixture of 90 per cent methylene chloride and 10 per cent ethanol (or methanol), Arnel and acetate will be dissolved, but other commonly used fibers will be virtually unaffected. (Dynel, however, is softened and gains weight when similarly treated.) Arnel can be differentiated from acetate by immersing a sample of fabric or fibers in benzyl alcohol at 50 degrees centigrade for one hour. Arnel is virtually unaffected, but the acetate completely dissolves.

• *To Distinguish Nylon from Other Fibers.* Nylon can be distinguished from acetate by attempting to dissolve it in acetone. Nylon will not dissolve in acetone. If the yarn or fabric is thought to contain wool and/or nylon, the fabric may be immersed in a boiling solution of sodium hydroxide. The nylon is insoluble in such a solution, but wool will dissolve. In fact, nylon's insolubility in boiling sodium hydroxide makes it easily distinguishable from most other fibers. The only common solvents in which nylon is soluble are concentrated formic acid, phenol, and cresol.

• *To Distinguish Dacron from Other Fibers.* Like acetate and nylon, Dacron is soluble in hot metacresol; however, unlike acetate, it is not soluble in acetone; and unlike nylon, it is not soluble in concentrated formic acid.

• *To Distinguish Orlon from Other Fibers.* Orlon is often blended with wool, cotton, silk, rayon, acetate, nylon, and Dacron. Even when not blended, Orlon may be mistaken for one of the other fibers. If the fiber is Orlon, it will not be affected by these common solvents: glacial acetic acid, chloroform, acetone, and 88 per cent formic acid.

• *To Distinguish Acrilan from Other Fibers.* Acrilan is insoluble in acetone, formic acid, 70 per cent sulphuric acid, and sodium hypochlorite. It will dissolve in dimethylformamide.

• *To Distinguish Dynel from Other Fibers.* Although Dynel is often used alone, it may be blended with other fibers. It is easily distinguishable, however, from other fibers by chemical tests. It is highly resistant to a wide variety of inorganic acids, bases, salts, hydrocarbons, and most organic solvents. Acetone, cyclohexanone, and dimethylformamide are solvents in varying degrees. Other cyclic ketones and certain amines cause some solvent or swelling action at high temperatures.

• *To Distinguish Creslan from Other Fibers.* Creslan may be differentiated from other fibers with which it may be blended because it will not be affected by glacial acetic acid, chloroform, acetone, or 88 per cent formic acid. But this is also true for Orlon; therefore, to determine whether the remaining fibers are Creslan or Orlon, other tests such as microscopic examination must be used.

• *To Distinguish Verel from Other Fibers.* When placed in pyridene and heated, Verel turns reddish brown but does not dissolve.

• *To Distinguish Zefran from Other Fibers.* Since Zefran has an affinity for a wider variety of dyes than is common for other fibers, it may be distinguished by a Fastucol pink-dye test. A bleached specimen dyed in a 1 per cent solution of this type of dye in a neutral bath at room temperature for three minutes will become pink, while other fibers will remain white or slightly stained.

• *To Distinguish Darvan from Other Fibers.* Darvan will dissolve in dimethylformamide at room temperature; however, Acrilan is also soluble in this solution. To differentiate between these two fibers, Calco Identification Stain #2 tints Darvan grayish pink.

• *To Distinguish Vicara from Other Fibers.* Vicara is used primarily as a blending fiber, particularly with wool, cotton, rayon, and nylon. It can be distinguished from wool by the use of caustic soda of up to 10 per cent concentration. Under these conditions, the wool will dissolve, but the Vicara will not. Hydrochloric acid will distinguish Vicara from cotton, rayon, acetate, and nylon. This acid will dissolve the latter four fibers, but it will not affect Vicara.

• *To Distinguish Saran from Other Fibers.* A 100 per cent solution of acetone will not affect Saran. At elevated temperatures, Saran will dissolve in dioxan and cyclohexanone. Saran is also soluble in ammonium hydroxide.

• *To Distinguish Fiberglas from Other Fibers.* Two specific solvents for quick identification of Fiberglas are hydrofluoric acid and hot phosphoric acid. In fact, these are the only two acids that will affect Fiberglas.

Nontechnical Tests for Distinguishing Linen from Cotton.

The identification of linen and cotton fabrics has always been of special interest to the analytical consumer. Because cotton can be made to simulate linen, additional nontechnical tests for distinguishing linen from cotton are evaluated here. Some of these tests are adequate. Others are not recommended because finishing substances commonly used in the manufacturing process interfere with the expected reaction.

• *Squeezing Test.* A simple method of distinguishing linen from cotton is the pulling of a yarn through two tightly compressed finger tips. If the yarn emerges stiff and straight, it is linen; if limp and drooping, it is cotton.

• *Curl Test.* If the end of a single filament turns in a clockwise direction when squeezed between the moistened thumb and finger, the fabric is linen. If the tip turns counterclockwise, the fabric is cotton.

• *Tearing Test.* Linen fabrics do not tear readily, but they do tend to slip apart when subjected to strain. A sample may be identified as cotton if it tears readily with a characteristic shrill sound.

• *Reaction to Oil.* If lightweight oil or glycerine is dropped on a linen fabric, a translucent area appears; if dropped on cotton, the area is opaque.

• *Ink Test.* If a drop of ink is placed on a linen fabric, the ink spreads evenly in a circular form. In contrast, a drop of ink on a cotton fabric tends to spread outward with a fading density toward the outer edge, making a slightly irregular outer rim, more oval than circular. The ink test is not considered reliable because finishing substances may interfere with this reaction.

• *Moisture Test.* A common practice is to attempt to identify linen by noting the pace of absorption when a drop of saliva is placed on the undersurface of the fabric. As linen absorbs water quickly, it is believed that this test will identify the linen fiber. But finishing substances in linen interfere with this test, and it is not recommended. Also, sheer cotton fabrics absorb a drop of saliva even more quickly than any fine linen.

▶ TEST YOURSELF ON THIS CHAPTER

1. Why is the classification of fibers according to their substance important for identification purposes?
2. List the advantages and the limitations of the burning test when it is used to differentiate cotton, linen, silk, wool, acetate, and rayon.
3. Describe three tests used to differentiate cotton and linen.
4. Describe the chemical test used to differentiate acetate and rayon.
5. Describe the breaking test as applied to cotton, linen, wool, silk.
6. Describe the differences between cotton and wool in the burning test.
7. What chemical processes would you use to distinguish the animal fibers from the vegetable fibers? to distinguish cotton from linen?
8. Why is spun rayon difficult to identify by the feeling test or the breaking test?
9. What two positive tests permit identification of rayon and acetate?
10. What are the three tests by which silk may be differentiated from rayon?
11. Compare the effect of burning on acetate and on rayon in regard to flame, odor, and ash.
12. Compare the results of the breaking test on viscose and on linen yarn.
13. Why would you choose a woolen instead of a cotton blanket to put out a flame?
14. Why could the moisture test fail to determine whether sheets were linen or cotton? What other tests would you suggest?
15. What is a sure solvent specific for Arnel?
16. What chemical tests distinguish Vicara from wool? Describe results.
17. What chemical tests distinguish Dynel from Vicara? Describe results.
18. What chemical tests differentiate nylon from other fibers? Describe results.

4 · SPINNING | Fiber to Yarn

The formation of yarn becomes possible when fibers have surfaces capable of cohesiveness. This quality is exemplified by the serrations of the wool fiber, the convolutions of the cotton fiber, and the roughness of the flax fiber. Elasticity or flexibility permits the fibers to be twisted around one another.

Primitive man discovered that a succession of fibers could be twisted into a continuous yarn. This was probably accomplished slowly and laboriously at first, but the greater strength thus produced and the many uses soon found for articles made from continuous yarns led to the invention of hand implements to aid and improve the process of twisting and spinning. Many such implements and methods are still used by the more primitive peoples in various parts of the world as well as by persons who are interested in reviving artistic handicraft. At the same time, it was necessary to invent simple methods of disentangling, separating, and arranging the fibers according to their length, other than by just using the fingers. Thus, crude methods of carding were invented to separate the fibers according to their length of staple. Uniformity of staple gives yarns a required evenness and improves the quality of the yarn.

A tangled bunch of cotton fiber is carded into orderly arrangement, drawn out, condensed to a ropelike sliver, then further condensed and twisted into yarn.

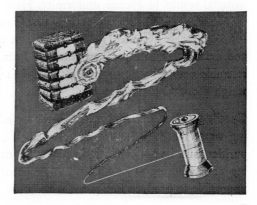

Development of Fiber into Yarn. The value and character of a yarn are determined by (1) kind and quality of fiber; (2) amount of processing necessary to produce fineness; and (3) amount of twist, which increases tensile strength in the finished yarn. The purpose of the yarn must be anticipated, as this determines the number and kind of manufacturing operations.

The development of short fibers, or staple, into yarn, when stated in terms of basic manufacturing processes, is as follows: carding, combing, drawing out, twisting, and winding. As the raw fiber passes through these processes, it is successively called *lap, sliver, roving,* and finally *yarn.* Here are the manufacturing operations in which these stages occur.

1. Lap to card sliver by the carding process
2. Card sliver to comb sliver by the combing process (if the fiber is to be combed)
3. Sliver to roving by the drawing-out process
4. Roving to yarn by the twisting process
5. Reeled on bobbins, spools, or cones by the winding process

Because the production of cotton yarn lends itself to a simple description of the manufacturing operations that make fiber into yarn, cotton fiber has been used in this chapter to illustrate the spinning process. It must be remembered, however, that all other raw fibers pass through similar spinning operations, although, of course, there are differences that will be explained in the chapters dealing with the various fibers. One such difference occurs when long strands or filaments, such as silk, are used rather than staple. In such instances, the required number of filaments are simply twisted together in a ropelike fashion as described in the paragraphs on the manufacture of silk yarns in Chapter 12.

Opening and Blending. When bales are opened at the mill, the compressed masses of raw fiber are loosened and exposed to the atmosphere. Variation in the raw material is eliminated by mixing together parts of several bales and feeding the material into the opening machines. This blending of the raw material results in greater uniformity. Hard lumps in the fibers are loosened, and the heavier impurities—such as dirt, leaves, burs, and any remaining seeds—are removed by three machines known as pickers: breaker, intermediate, and finisher. These machines clean and form the cotton into *laps,* or rolls, that resemble cotton batting; the laps are 40 inches wide and 1 inch thick, and weigh about 40 pounds each.

Carding. In the lap stage, the fibers are still in a tangled condition, containing waste material. Before this raw stock can be made into yarn, these impurities must be removed; and the fibers must be straightened. Such straightening or smoothing is necessary for all natural fibers; otherwise, it would be impossible to produce fine yarns from what is originally a tangled mass. This

initial process of arranging the fibers in a parallel fashion is known as *carding.*
The work is done on a carding machine, where the lap is unrolled and drawn
on a revolving cylinder covered with very fine hooks or wire brushes. A moving
belt, also covered with wire brushes, is on top of this cylinder. The cylinder
pulls the fibers in one direction, disentangles them, and arranges them parallel
in the form of a thin film. This film is drawn through a funnel-shaped device
that molds it into a round ropelike mass called *card sliver,* about the thickness
of a broomstick. Card sliver produces *carded yarns* or *carded cottons* serviceable
for inexpensive cotton fabrics.

Doubling. After carding, several slivers are combined. This results in a
relatively narrow lap of compactly placed staple fibers. The compactness of these
fibers permits this cotton stock to be attenuated or drawn out to a sliver of
smaller diameter without falling apart.

Combing. When the fiber is intended for fine yarns, the sliver is put through
an additional straightening called *combing.* In this operation, fine-toothed
combs continue straightening the fibers until they are arranged with such a
high degree of parallelism that the short fibers, called *noils,* are combed out
and completely separated from the longer fibers.

Courtesy Pepperell Manufacturing Co.

Cotton going through the opening machine where the fibers are loosened.

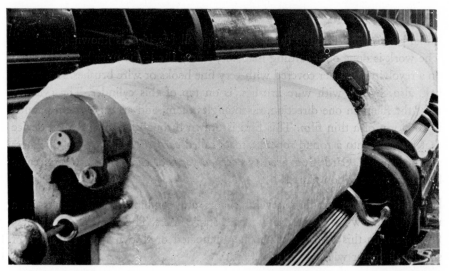

Cotton lap from the picker room where dust, leaves, twigs, and other foreign matter have been removed.

Inside of the carding machine, where the brushes clean and straighten the fiber.

Sliver leaving the carding machine, where the cotton has been further cleaned and disentangled.

Slivers are doubled to increase the density of the future cotton yarn.

Combed slivers are combined as they leave the combing machine to further increase the density and compactness of the future yarns.

Illustrations on this page Courtesy Pepperell Manufacturing Co.

On the spinning frame, the roving passes from the top through a series of rollers that draw out the cotton into a thread. The thread is twisted as it winds onto the bobbin.

The combining process forms a *comb sliver* made of the longest fibers, which, in turn, produce a smoother and more even yarn. This operation eliminates as much as 25 per cent of the original card sliver; thus almost one-fourth of the raw cotton becomes waste. The combing process, therefore, is identified with consumers' goods of better quality. Since long-staple yarns produce stronger, smoother, and more serviceable fabrics, quality cotton goods carry labels indicating that they are made from *combed yarns* or *combed cottons*.

Drawing Out. The combining of several slivers for the drawing-out process eliminates irregularities that would cause too much variation if the slivers were put through singly. The drawing frame has several pairs of rollers, each advanced set of which revolves at a progressively faster speed. This action pulls the staple lengthwise over each other, thereby producing longer and thinner slivers. After several stages of drawing out, the condensed sliver is taken to the slubber, where rollers similar to those in the drawing frame draw out the cotton further. Here the slubbing is passed to the spindles, where it is given its first twist and is then wound on bobbins.

Roving. These bobbins are placed on the roving frame, where further drawing out and twisting take place until the cotton stock is about the diameter of a pencil lead. There are two stages of roving: intermediate and fine. The operations are identical, but each machine yields a finer product than the stock it received. *Roving* is the final product of the several drawing-out operations. It is a preparatory stage for the final insertion of twist. To this point, only enough twist has been given the stock to hold the fibers together. Roving has no tensile strength; it will break apart easily with any slight pull.

In the ring spinning process, the roving (1) on bobbins, is fed between sets of drafting rolls (2) to draw the strand down to the final desired size. The spindle (3) turns the bobbin (4) at a constant speed. The front set of rolls is adjusted to deliver the yarn at a rate of speed so that the desired amount of twist is inserted as the strand moves along. The traveler (5) glides freely

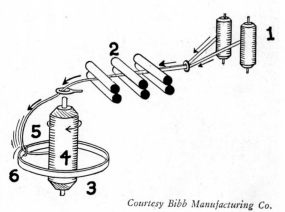

Courtesy Bibb Manufacturing Co.

around the ring (6). The tension caused by the drag of the traveler causes the yarn to wind on the bobbin at the same rate as it is delivered by the rolls.

Spinning. The roving, on bobbins, is placed in the spinning frame, where it passes through several sets of rollers running at successively higher rates of speed and is finally drawn out to *yarn* of the size desired. Spinning machines are of two kinds: ring frame and mule frame. The ring frame is a faster process, but produces a relatively coarse yarn. For very fine yarns, the mule frame is required because of its slow intermittent operation. The ring frame is more suitable for the manufacture of cotton yarns for mass production. Its hundreds of spindles, whirling thousands of revolutions a minute, and its constant spinning action provide a fast operation. The ring spinning frame completes the manufacture of yarn (1) by drawing out the roving, (2) by inserting twist, and (3) by winding the yarn on bobbins—all in one operation.

Preparation for Weaving. In the weaving operation, the lengthwise yarns that form the basic structure of the fabric are called the *warp*. The crosswise yarns are the *filling*, also referred to as the *weft* or the *woof*. The filling yarns undergo little strain in the weaving process. In preparing them for weaving, it is only necessary to spin them to the desired size and give them the amount of twist required for the type of fabric for which they will be used.

Yarns intended for the warp must pass through such operations as spooling, warping, and slashing to prepare them to withstand the strain of the weav-

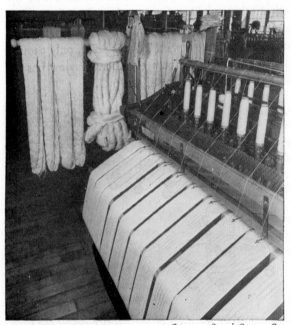

After spinning, yarn is sometimes reeled from bobbins into large skeins ready for bleaching, mercerizing, and dyeing.

Courtesy Spool Cotton Co.

Courtesy Bibb Manufacturing Co.

From spools or cones, mounted on a creel, separate yarns are wound on a warp beam.

ing process. These operations do not improve the quality of the yarn. In *spooling,* the yarn is wound on larger spools or cones, which are placed on a rack called a *creel.* From this rack, the yarns are wound on a *warp beam,* which is similar to a huge spool. An uninterrupted length of hundreds of warp yarns results, all lying parallel to one another. These yarns are unwound to be put through a starch bath called *slashing* or *sizing.* The slasher machine covers every yarn with a starch coating to prevent chafing or breaking during the weaving process. The yarns are passed over a large copper drum and are heated by steam to set the sizing. They are then wound on a final warp beam and are ready for the loom.

Amount of Twist. The amount of twist to the inch is an important factor in finished consumers' goods. It determines the appearance as well as the durability and serviceability of a fabric. Fine yarns require more twist than coarse yarns. Warp yarns are given more twist than are filling yarns. The amount of twist also depends on the type of fabric to be woven.

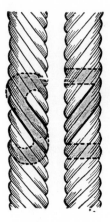

The S twist and Z twist are diagrammed here. The importance of the direction of the twist is illustrated in the diagrams of thrown silk threads shown in Chapter 12.

1. Yarns intended for soft-surfaced fabrics are given only a slack twist. They are called *soft-twisted yarns*.

2. Yarns intended for smooth-surfaced fabrics are given many twists to the inch. Such *hard-twisted yarns* contribute strength, smoothness, elasticity, and some crease resistance to fabrics.

3. Yarns intended for crepe fabrics, which have rough, pebbly, or crinkled surfaces, are given a maximum amount of twist. In this case, the direction of twist is also important and contributes crease resistance. Direction of twist may be observed by holding the yarn in a vertical position. If the spirals conform to the direction of the slope of the central part of the letter S, the yarn has an S twist; if they conform to the slope of the letter Z, the yarn has a Z twist.

Permanent crepe effects, such as chiffon, georgette, crepe de chine, canton, flat and French crepes, are produced by the use of hard-twisted yarns, some of which have left twist, others right twist. These yarns are placed alternately in the warp or in the filling, or in both. When the finished fabric is later washed or dyed, such yarns kink in different directions, producing the crepe surface.

Another satisfactory method of obtaining crepe effects during the construction of the fabric is by the use of slack warp yarns, which may or may not be wound on a separate warp beam. These yarns are held less taut than the other warp yarns and produce a permanent crinkled pattern. Seersucker and matelassé are produced in this way and prove very serviceable.

Yarn Count. In the spinning process, there is always a fixed relation between the weight of the original quantity of fiber and the length of the yarn produced from that amount of raw material. This relation indicates the thickness of the yarn. It is determined by the extent of the drawing-out process and is designated by numbers, which are called the *yarn count*.

The standard for the yarn count in cotton is 1 pound of fiber drawn out to make 840 yards of yarn; the resultant thickness or size is known as count No. 1. If the yarn is drawn out farther, so that 1 pound makes twice 840 yards, it is identified as No. 2. Thus, a No. 2 yarn will be finer than a No. 1. No. 10 denotes a still finer yarn, as it indicates that 1 pound of cotton is drawn out to ten times 840 yards. The higher the number of the yarn count, the finer the yarn in size. Yarn counts up to 20 are called coarse yarns; 20 to 60 are medium yarns; above 60 are fine yarns. Up to 20, the count rises by single numbers. Only even numbers are used between 20 and 60. Above 60, the count rises by intervals of 5 until 100, after which an interval of 10 is used. The size of mercerized cotton sewing thread used for general purposes is No. 50 or No. 60. The finest yarn ever made in the United States was No. 160, the product of 1 pound of cotton drawn out to a strand 134,000 yards long (over 76 miles). The very finest cotton yarns spun in England have been as high as No. 400. Extremely fine yarns are difficult and costly to manufacture because of the greater care required in spinning and the greater amount of twist to the inch.

The size of yarn to be used in a fabric is determined by the purpose of the fabric. Yarns of varying sizes may be used to obtain the nubbed or novelty effects and rough textures characterized by ratiné, bouclé, or éponge.

Ply Yarns. When two or more strands or yarns are twisted together, they are designated as *ply yarns*. They are termed two-ply, three-ply, and so on, according to the number used in their construction. A single yarn may be of relatively good quality; but where durability is all-important, ply yarns are preferable, assuming that the yarns have the same length of staple. Good-quality broadcloth for men's shirtings, for example, is made with ply yarns.

Yarn construction and yarn count are expressed in the following manner The term 1/30s denotes the use of a single yarn having a yarn count of 30. In the same way, 3/30s denotes the use of a three-ply yarn—that is, three strands twisted together, each having a separate yarn count of 30. A three-ply yarn, indicated by 3/30s, would be equivalent to a single yarn having a yarn count of 10. In the same way, 2/10s (containing two single strands of 10s) is equivalent in size to 1/5s.

When the number of yards in a pound of cotton is to be calculated for any given size of yarn, the yarn count is multiplied by 840 yards. For example, if the required size of a yarn is 2/10s, the fraction should be reduced to 1/5s; then the 5 is multiplied by 840; and the result is 4,200 yards.

Doubled Yarns.   Another type of yarn construction is the *doubled yarn*. This consists of two or more single strands treated as one in the weaving process; but the strands are not twisted together. The doubled yarn must not be confused with ply yarns, which are stronger because they are twisted. Doubled yarns are used for ornamental effect; they do, of course, contribute a certain amount of additional strength. Because doubled yarns have little twist, they produce luster and softness.

Novelty Yarns.   The spinning process can produce decorative effects by vary-ing the amount of twist or by twisting together yarns of different diameters, each of which may have different amounts of twist per inch. Such yarns can give fabrics almost limitless textural effects of various color combinations. Fabrics made of novelty yarns cannot generally be as durable as fabrics made of uniform yarns that have been evenly spun. A safe rule for the consumer is to remember that longer service may be expected from flat, smooth fabrics made from evenly spun yarns rather than from novelty yarns of complex character.

   • *Slub Yarns.* The consumer's desire for ornamental effects has popularized the production of yarns that are given only a small amount of drawing out. Such yarns, called slub yarns, have soft untwisted areas at frequent intervals through-out their length. They are coarse, with slight twist, having varying diameters that show irregularities typical of an incomplete spinning operation.

   If simulation of linen is desired, the use of slub yarns is easily understood. Where durability is a main consideration, their practicability is justly questioned, because a heavy yarn protruding above the level of surrounding yarns is sub-jected to friction, and the fabric soon shows signs of wear at those points after

Shantung   *Tweed*

Courtesy American Viscose Corp.

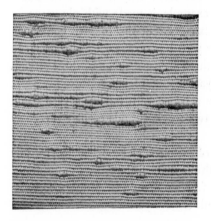

continued use. In the past, slub yarns were generally used in fabrics that possessed an especially compact construction and consequently were characterized by marked durability. Today, slub yarns do not always imply compact construction in the fabric of which they are a part. They do furnish ornamental effects, and are frequently used for that purpose in shantung and tweed.

• *Flake Yarns.* Flake yarns are variations of the slub yarns. The flake or slub effect is made by inserting soft, thick tufts of roving between binder yarns at intervals. The result is a flake yarn of varying thickness and softness, caused by the soft-effect ply held in place by the uniform binder. This type of yarn is limited to fancy-effect uses.

• *Spiral Yarns.* The general appearance of spiral yarns is that of a coarse yarn wound around a fine yarn, giving the effect of a spiral. The thicker yarn is given a slack twist and wound spirally around the fine yarn (sometimes referred to as the *core yarn*), which is given a hard twist. Other names for the

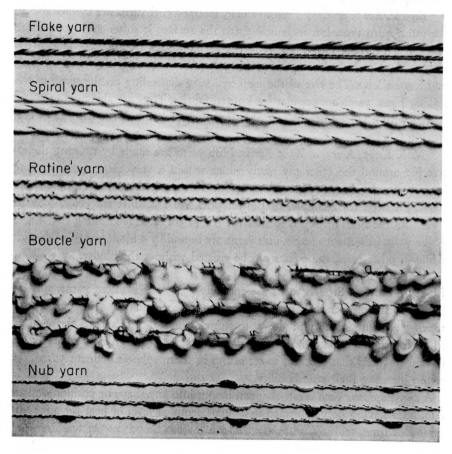

Flake yarn

Spiral yarn

Ratine' yarn

Boucle' yarn

Nub yarn

spiral yarns are *corkscrew* and *eccentric*. Spiral yarns may be made for different purposes. They may be constructed in such a way as to give the decorative spiral effect of a candy-cane pattern. Sometimes the core yarn is completely hidden by the spiraling outer yarn, as in the case of lastex where the core yarn is rubber while the outer yarn may be of cotton, nylon, or other textile.

• *Ratiné Yarns.* Ratiné yarns are a variation of the spiral yarn type, although the method of manufacture differs. The outer (effect) yarn and the core yarn are twisted in a spiral manner, but at intervals a longer loop is thrown out by the effect yarn, which kinks back on itself and is held in place by a third yarn called the binder. The binder is added in a second twisting operation going in the opposite direction of the effect yarn. The ratiné yarn's small loops on its surface give the yarn a taut, rough-surfaced effect. The technique may be applied to all major fibers and is popular for combinations of yarns made of such fibers as cotton and rayon.

• *Bouclé, Loop, or Curl Yarns.* Bouclé, loop, or curl yarns are comparable to the ratiné yarn type, but in bouclé yarns the surface is softer and has a more pronounced novelty effect. This effect is accomplished by allowing one of the plies to remain slack during the twisting operation, causing it to twist on itself and form a loop. The size of the loop will vary depending on the speed of the rollers. These yarns are popular for knitted fabrics. They are also used to create fabrics with a looped pile to resemble fur, such as karakul, for trimmings and coating fabrics.

• *Nub, Knop, Knot, or Spot Yarns.* Nub yarns are made by twisting the effect ply around the other ply many times within a very short space, causing bumps or nubs that may be spaced at intervals along the yarn. Variations are possible where, for example, two effect plies, each of different color, may be used, and the nubs arranged so that the colors are alternated along the length of the yarn. In some instances, nub yarns are bound by a binder or third thread; while in other cases, the effects can be created without the binder.

Stretch Yarns. Stretch yarns are specially processed filament yarns, such as the long, smooth, endless strands of nylon fibers. Such filament yarns have varying amounts of natural ability to stretch when pulled and to spring back to their original sizes when allowed to relax. However, when subjected to certain methods that use heat to set crimp in thermoplastic filament yarns, the crimp increases their stretchability.

A *thermoplastic yarn* is one that can be put into any shape or position desired and, after having been subjected to a predetermined level of heat for a specific period of time, will always tend to return to that shape despite washing, dry cleaning, stretching, or compressing. This principle is employed in many ways in making stretch yarns. In several methods the yarn is twisted, heat-set, and then untwisted. The kink put into the yarn by this procedure causes the yarn to act like the coil of a spring. Variations of yarn denier, the number of twists per inch, and the number of untwists give different characteristics to the fabric.

Another method is known as the *false-twist* method. Two threads are twisted together for a short distance as if they were to be made into a plied yarn and are then heat-set. These two threads are then separated and wound onto separate spools, each retaining its coiled characteristic caused by having been heat-set in a twisted or coiled position.

A permanent coiled effect is sometimes created by drawing yarn over a heated blade. When the yarn is stretched, the coils disappear but reappear when tension on the yarn is released. This method has the advantage of permitting other yarns to be twisted with the stretch yarn in the same operation.

In some methods, yarns pass onto heated gear teeth that crimp the yarn in conformity with the teeth. The resulting crimped yarns are fed into a heated stuffing box for permanent crimp retention. This produces an accordionlike action in the yarn as it is stretched and relaxed.

Stretch yarns have many advantages over untreated filament yarns. They have a soft touch and a dull appearance like that of wool rather than the sometimes undesirable sheen of some filament yarns. The resultant textural appearance of stretch yarns provides opportunity for desirable novelty effects. Fabrics or garments made of these yarns have a higher degree of absorbency and adsorbency than ordinary filament yarns, since stretch yarns provide loops and kinks to hold the moisture. This results in providing better perspiration conductivity and consequent increase in comfort to the wearer. The pockets of air caused by the coils in the yarns also act as an insulative barrier, making fabrics warmer.

Garments made of stretch yarns wash easily and dry-clean readily. They are as strong and durable as garments made of yarns of similar fibers that have not been processed into stretch yarns. In fact, the stretch characteristic is more likely to result in less strain on the yarns, fabrics, and seams of garments during the ordinary stress of putting on, wearing, and taking off. The stretchability of such garments allows them to conform to the figure and to fit better. Solution of this fitting problem is not only an advantage to the consumer but also to the manufacturer, who finds it more economical to produce fewer specific sizes, and to the retailer, who needs less space to handle fewer sizes and finds it easier to fit the consumer.

Stretch yarns are made under different trade names. Their properties vary to some extent depending on the method of manufacture and the fibers used. The best-known of these yarns are given here.

• *Agilon*. The method of manufacture of Agilon yarn is a patented process owned by the Deering, Milliken Research Trust. It is an adaptation of the method of drawing any thermoplastic yarn over a heated blade. The actual contracting and stretching characteristic of the yarn does not appear, however, until the garment made from this yarn has been washed or scoured in the finishing operation. Agilon yarn is produced in monofilament and multifilament forms. It has an additional distinguishing feature in that a filament fiber, such as nylon, can be combined with a staple fiber, such as cotton or wool, spun around it. The textural characteristics can vary, making Agilon yarn like any kind of yarn made of any kind of fiber, whether smooth or rough, soft or harsh.

Depending on the denier and processing of the yarn, Agilon can stretch up to three times its length and return to its original length on release of the tension. Unlike some other stretch yarns, Agilon yarn does not immediately snap back with an almost rubber-band action after it has been released. It recovers its original shape more slowly. This "gentle elasticity" results in less strain on the fabric and no binding, which insures increased comfort to the wearer. Garments made of Agilon yarn include men's, women's, and children's hosiery, creped fabrics for women's blouses and lingerie, and pile fabrics, such as velvets, artificial furs, and fleeces.

• *Ban-Lon*. The production of Ban-Lon yarn is licensed by Joseph Bancroft & Sons Company. The yarn is made of thermoplastic fibers that are permanently crimped by forcing them into a heated stuffing box. Ban-Lon yarn is composed of multifilament or staple fibers and has a soft hand (feel) with a dull appearance; it may impart a crepelike surface to the fabric. Ban-Lon yarn has a moderate stretch and clings to the form. It may be utilized in woven or knitted fabrics and is popular for men's socks and women's blouses and sweaters.

• *Fluflon*. The Universal Winding Company manufactures Fluflon yarn. This yarn is made on the false-twisting principle of twisting two plies of thermoplastic yarns around each other, heat-setting them, and then separating them by winding the bent or corkscrew-shaped yarns on separate spools. The final yarn may be made into singles or plied. Fluflon yarn has a high degree of elasticity. It can be stretched up to four times its original length and return to its normal size on release of the tension. The yarn has a very soft hand and a variety of uses.

• *Helanca*. This is the original stretch yarn that was introduced by the Heberlein Patent Corporation in 1947. There are now two types of this yarn:

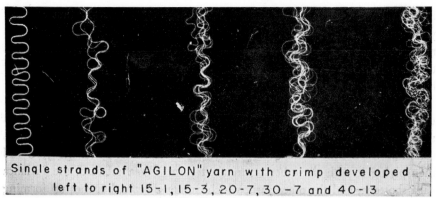

Single strands of "AGILON" yarn with crimp developed
left to right 15-1, 15-3, 20-7, 30-7 and 40-13

Agilon illustrations Courtesy Deering Milliken Research Corp.

15-Denier Monofilament stretch yarn hose.

Relaxed *Stretched*

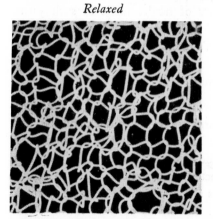

Helanca

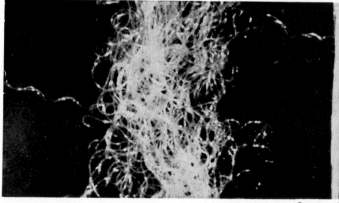

Courtesy Heberlein Patent Corp.

Relaxed *Stretched*

Helanca Hi-Test and Helanca Type SW. The former was the first of these yarns and can be stretched up to three times its original length, returning to normal size on release of the tension. Helenca Type SW is a later development that has limited stretch but excellent shape retention, imparting a crepe or bouclé texture to garments made in regular sizes.

Helanca yarn is made of nylon or Dacron by twisting, heat-setting, and then untwisting multifilament yarn to produce fine curls in the filaments. Helanca stretch yarn can be combined with other yarns that do not stretch, such as cotton or wool. This is accomplished by first stretching the Helanca yarn and then plying it with the other unstretched yarn. When released, the Helanca yarn shortens; and the other yarn, which cannot shorten, bunches up forming small loops along the surface of the thread. When pulled, the Helanca ply extends again, and the loops of the other ply straighten out. Such combinations increase the absorbency and textural effects of fabrics made of such yarns. Garments made of Helanca yarns include men's, women's, and children's hosiery, women's blouses and lingerie, men's briefs, and children's underwear. Helanca yarn can be combined with a rubber core yarn to produce firm, elastic fabrics for foundation garments and swimsuits.

Bulk Yarns. Bulk yarns come in two forms and are classified as *high-bulk* yarns and *textured* yarns. The high-bulk yarns are relatively thick and soft, and they may also have the additional characteristic of stretch. The textured yarns have the appearance and hand of yarns made of staple fiber, have the properties of filament yarns, but never have the characteristic of stretch.

• *High-Bulk Yarns.* The high-bulk yarns are always made of staple synthetic fibers, usually Orlon, Acrilan, or Dacron, but blends of these fibers can be made with other synthetic as well as natural fibers. Some high-bulk yarns are spun with a slack twist, sometimes with crimped staple, to produce a soft, thick, spongy yarn; such yarns generally do not have much natural stretch. Frequently, high-bulk yarns are made by blending stretched fibers with fibers that have been stretched and relaxed. During the dyeing operation, the stretched fibers relax; and their contraction causes the other already relaxed fibers to crimp and curl. This produces a soft, thick, but lightweight stretch yarn. Agilon and Fluflon yarns may be produced as stretch high-bulk yarns.

High-bulk yarns have the soft hand of wool or cashmere. Although they are lightweight, they are warm because the crimped fibers form air spaces within the thick yarn to provide insulation. High-bulk yarns have good water adsorbency. Garments made of high-bulk yarns wash and dry-clean readily. They may, however, pill. To avoid this, garments should be turned inside out and washed gently. Light brushing with a very soft brush will help reduce the pilling. When knitted garments made of these yarns are washed, it is best to block them, since knitted garments of slack-twisted yarns tend to sag. The durability of garments made of high-bulk yarns depends primarily on the durability of the synthetic fiber used and the amount of twist in the yarn. The more twist in the yarn, the greater the durability; however, the more twist, the less bulk in the yarn. Among the products made of high-bulk yarns are blouses and sweaters.

• *Textured Yarns.* Textured yarns are usually made of filament fibers but also can be made of staple fibers. Textured filament yarns can be made of rayon, acetate, nylon, and Dacron; textured staple yarns can be made with synthetic and natural fibers. There are variations in the technique of making textured yarns. They all involve the process of passing smooth filament yarn across high-pressure air jets that cause the individual filaments to loop up, so that a permanently textured surface of randomly situated tiny loops develops along the yarn. Different textures and effects are possible depending on the size of the loops, the closeness of the loops, the yarn size, the amount of twist in the yarn, the number of plies, and the nature of the plies. Textured yarns are dull and have the appearance and hand of staple yarns. They have bulk without weight and provide high covering power and opacity. Garments made of textured yarns launder and dry-clean readily, dry quickly, and need little or no ironing. Fabrics made of textured yarns will not pill. Textured yarns are used for shirts, blouses, and rugs. Among the trade names of textured yarns are Taslan, owned by Du Pont, and Lofted Chromspun, owned by Eastman Chemical Products, Inc.

Thread Count. The durability of a fabric depends on: (1) the kind and quality of the fiber, (2) the tensile strength of the yarn, (3) the amount of twist in the yarn, (4) the use of ply yarns as compared with singles, and (5) compactness of construction. Compactness is one of the most significant factors when considering the durability of a fabric. It is determined by the closeness of the yarns after the fabric is woven. A closely woven fabric has a larger quantity of yarns than a loosely woven one and is therefore more serviceable. A garment made from such a fabric shrinks less in washing, slips less at the seams, and is more apt to keep its shape.

A fabric of compact construction has a high thread count. *Thread count,* also known as *cloth count,* is determined by counting the number of warp yarns and filling yarns in a square inch of fabric. These yarns are commonly referred to as *ends* and *picks,* terms that are synonymous with *warp* and *filling,* respectively. To ascertain the thread count, it is necessary to have a pick glass, sometimes called a thread counter, which is a magnifying glass mounted on a small stand with a square opening in its base. Through this opening, warp and filling yarns are magnified and counted. If the square opening is a ¼-inch size, the number of yarns counted in the quarter inch, when multiplied by 4, gives the number of yarns in 1 inch of the fabric. Some pick glasses have a ½-inch square opening; others have a full square inch. The largest size minimizes the possibility of error in computation.

Thread count should not be confused with yarn count. Yarn count measures the degree of fineness in yarns; thread count measures the number of warp and filling yarns in a square inch of fabric. While these counts are separate devices of measurement, there is a direct relationship between them. If coarse sheeting with a low thread count is to be constructed, thick or coarse yarns will be used. These give the fabric greater resistance to hard wear.

• *Typical Thread Counts.* Thread counts range from as low as 20 threads to the inch, used in tobacco cloth, to as high as 350 threads to the inch, found in typewriter-ribbon fabrics. An example of thread count used as a standard is illustrated by the Summary of Types of Muslin and Percale Sheets in Chapter 9. With some finished goods, such as sheeting, thread count is sometimes given as a single number, which is the addition of warp and filling. A total thread count of 140 threads to the square inch, for example, means that each sheet must have 74 warp yarns and 66 filling yarns to the square inch. The first number indicates the warp; the second is the filling. Thus a 74 × 66 is described as a 140.

• *Balanced Construction.* A fabric is said to be well balanced if the number of warp yarns and filling yarns are almost equal. For example, a piece of muslin with a thread count of 64 × 60 is considered well balanced. A piece of gauze with a thread count of 28 × 24 is also well balanced. In contrast, a broadcloth with a count of 100 × 60 has poor balance. Although good balance of warp and filling produces a fabric with good wearing qualities, a balanced construction is not always obtainable with certain staple fabrics. Broadcloth shirting, for example, uses approximately twice as many warp yarns as filling yarns. The nature of its construction, therefore, makes it impossible for it to be well balanced according to thread count; yet it is a durable fabric if its thread count is high.

Sometimes, a fabric may have good balance in its thread count, but it may be altogether unsatisfactory because of weakness in either warp or filling yarns. The factor of tensile strength of both sets of yarns must, therefore, always be taken into consideration when a fabric is being judged. Both yarn count and thread count determine the suitability and value of finished goods. A safe rule to remember is that a high-count fabric even with poor balance will give better wear than a low-count fabric with good balance.

▶ TEST YOURSELF ON THIS CHAPTER

1. How are fibers made into yarns?
2. Describe the carding process and what it does to the cotton fibers.
3. Explain why a fabric woven from slub yarns may not wear well.
4. Why would it be difficult to make fabric directly from roving?
5. What is meant by yarn count? Why is it important?
6. Why is thread count especially important?
7. In what way do differences in the raw material affect the formation of yarn?
8. Compare the carding and the combing processes.
9. Explain the processes involved in the manufacture of yarn. Use a rough diagram to illustrate your explanation.
10. What are the qualities that determine the value of the yarn?
11. Explain the meaning of 1/60s, 4/20s, 3/30s.
12. Explain the difference between ply yarns and doubled yarns.
13. How is variation in yarns obtained in the spinning process?
14. How does twist in a yarn affect the finished fabric?
15. For what kind of fabrics are yarns given a very slack twist in spinning?
16. What are the different types of novelty yarns?
17. What are the purposes and characteristics of these novelty yarns?
18. What are the properties of stretch yarns? Give some common trade names for stretch yarns.
19. How do the properties of bulk yarns differ from those of stretch yarns?
20. What is the difference between high-bulk yarns and textured yarns?

5 · WEAVING | Yarn to Fabric

The second stage of development of fiber into fabric is the weaving process. Although there are other methods of cloth construction, that of weaving, or interlacing, yarns has foremost place. The interlacing, or weaving, process probably became known to primitive man before spinning. At first, materials available for weaving were used in their natural state, just as they grew. As time passed, spinning slowly developed because man discovered that the raw materials could be changed somewhat and improved before they were woven. Primitive man may have observed the interlaced grasses and twigs in the nests of birds, and thus discovered how he could make protective clothing for himself, baskets and nets, and thatchlike huts and fences. Or he may have seen rushes naturally interlacing as they grew. In the course of time, rude looms were made, which were crudely simple and hand operated. Yet the modern power loom used in the textile industry today contains essentially the same parts and performs the same operations as the simplest hand-operated loom.

Essential Weaving Operations. On the modern loom, the warp yarns are wound on a cylinder called the *warp beam,* which is at the back of the loom. The warp extends to another cylinder called the *cloth beam* at the front of the loom, on which the fabric is rolled as it is constructed. Supported on the loom frame between these two cylinders, the warp yarns are ready to be interlaced by the filling yarns, producing the woven fabric.

In any type of weaving, four operations are fundamental. They are performed in sequence and are constantly repeated. If these operations are carefully noted, the more varied and advanced constructions of fabric will be readily understood. The essential parts of the loom are: warp beam, cloth beam, harness or heddle frame, shuttle, and reed. These parts perform the following operations.

Shedding—raising warp yarns by means of the harness or heddle frame.
Picking—inserting filling yarns by means of the shuttle.
Battening—pushing filling yarns firmly in place by means of the reed.
Taking up and letting off—winding the finished fabric on the cloth beam and releasing more of the warp from the warp beam.

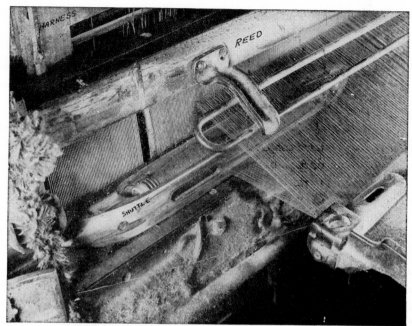

Courtesy American Woolen Co.

This loom in operation shows how the harness and heddles (in the upper left) are lifting and lowering units of warp yarns to form the shed through which the shuttle is passing. The reed automatically moves forward to batten each newly woven yarn.

• *Shedding.* On a primitive loom, the weaver had to raise each alternate warp yarn with his finger or with a stick to insert the filling yarns into the warp. Weaving was therefore a very slow process. The raising of the warp yarns formed an opening, or shed, through which the filling yarn was inserted. This first weaving operation therefore became known as *shedding.*

On the modern loom, simple and intricate shedding operations are performed automatically by the heddle frame. This is a rectangular frame to which a series of wires, called heddles, are attached. As the warp yarns come from the warp beam, they must pass through openings in the heddles. Each opening may be compared to the eye of a needle. The operation of drawing each warp yarn through its appropriate heddle is known as *drawing in.*

The bobbin of filling yarn lies inside the shuttle, and the yarn is pulled through a small opening in the side as the shuttle moves swiftly across the loom.

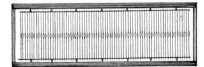

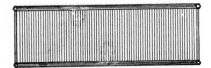

Warp yarns pass through the eyes of the heddles (shown in center) and are raised or lowered as one unit.

The warp yarns are evenly separated and held parallel as they pass between the teeth of the reed.

In the simplest weave construction, the heddle frame raises or lowers certain groups of alternate warp yarns so that the filling yarns alternate in passing under one group of warp yarns and over another. The heddle frame is better known as the *harness,* and that term is used hereafter in referring to the number of harnesses used for the different types of weaves.

• *Picking.* As the harnesses raise the heddles, which raise the warp yarns, the filling yarn is inserted through the shed by a small carrier device called a *shuttle.* The shuttle contains a bobbin of filling yarn, which emerges through a hole in the side as the shuttle moves across the loom. One passage of the shuttle from one side of the loom to the other is known as a *pick.*

• *Battening.* All warp yarns pass through the heddle eyelets and through openings in another frame that resembles a comb and is called a *reed.* With each picking operation, the reed pushes automatically, or battens, each filling yarn against the portion of the fabric that has already been formed. This third essential weaving operation is therefore called *battening.* It gives the fabric a firm compact construction.

In the drawing-in process, each warp yarn must be drawn through its assigned heddle. This is determined by the construction design on the white card, which can be seen in this picture on the top of the machine. The warp units are then drawn through the reed.

Courtesy National Association of Wool Manufacturers

• *Taking Up and Letting Off.* With each shedding, picking, and battening operation, the newly constructed fabric must be wound on the cloth beam. This process is known as *taking up.* At the same time, the warp yarns must be released from the warp beam; this is referred to as *letting off.*

Classification of Weaves. The manner in which groups of warp yarns are raised by the harnesses to permit the insertion of the filling yarn determines the pattern of the weave, and in large measure the kind of fabric produced. Weave patterns can create varying degrees of durability in fabrics, adding to their usefulness and also to their appearance. In a simple weave construction, consisting of the filling going under one warp and over the next, two harnesses are needed: one to lift the odd-numbered warp yarns, and a second to lift the even-numbered warp yarns. For advanced weaves, more than two harnesses are required, and as many as forty for figured weaves.

The three basic weaves in common use for the majority of fabrics are plain, twill, and satin, with respective variations. Important constructions are also obtained from the following weaves: pile, double cloth, gauze, swivel, lappet, dobby, and Jacquard.

Construction of Cloth Designs. In the textile industry, a pattern of the weave to be used in the construction of a fabric is designed on cross-sectioned paper. A draft of the design of the weave is indispensable when setting up a loom for a particular weave or color effect, as it indicates the particular harness and heddle through which each warp yarn is to be drawn. Textile designers use such graph paper to plot out fabric weave designs. The horizontal squares represent the filling yarns; the vertical squares represent the warp. The student may obtain a working knowledge of weaves by reproducing such designs on graph paper and then carrying out the actual weaving operations on a miniature loom made of stiff cardboard or a cigar box.

Plain Weave. The plain weave is sometimes referred to as the tabby, homespun, or taffeta weave. It is the simplest type of construction and is consequently inexpensive to produce. On the loom, the plain weave requires only two harnesses. Each filling yarn goes alternately under and over the warp yarns across the width of the fabric. On its return, the yarn alternates the pattern of interlacing. If the yarns are close together, the plain weave has a high thread count, and the fabric is therefore firm and will wear well.

As the manufacture of the plain weave is relatively inexpensive, it is used extensively for cotton fabrics and for fabrics that are to be decorated with printed designs, because the surface that it produces is receptive to a direct print. The appearance of the plain weave may be varied by differences in the closeness of the

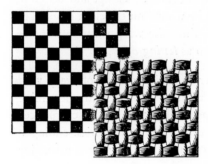

The construction design for the plain weave resembles the familiar checkerboard. The way in which filling yarns pass under and over alternate warp yarns is shown at the right. When fabric is closely constructed in the plain weave, there is no distinct pattern.

weave, by different thicknesses of yarn, or by the use of contrasting colors in the warp and filling. The last method gives the effect of a design. In addition, two variations of the plain weave afford simple decorative effects; namely, the basket weave and the ribbed, or corded, weave.

Fabrics in Plain Weave. In cotton: batiste, broadcloth, bunting, calico, cambric, challis, chambray, cheesecloth, chintz, crash, crepe, crinoline, cretonne, duck or canvas, flannelette, gingham, Indianhead, lawn, longcloth, muslin, madras, nainsook, oilcloth, organdy, osnaburg, outing flannel, percale, percaline, ratiné, seersucker, scrim, sheeting, tarlatan, voile.

In linen: airplane cloth, art linen, cambric, crash, dress linen, handkerchief linen, sheeting, theatrical gauze.

In wool: albatross, blanket cloth, challis, flannel, homespun, nun's veiling, tweed.

In silk, rayon, or other filament yarns: canton crepe, chiffon, China silk, flat crepe, georgette, habutai, mousseline de soie, radium, shirting silks, taffeta, voile, crepe de chine.

• *Basket Weave.* The variation of the plain weave known as the *basket weave* uses doubled yarns to produce the design that resembles the familiar pattern of a basket. Two or more filling yarns with little or no twist are interlaced with a corresponding number of warp yarns. They are woven in a pattern of 2×2, 3×3, or 4×4, instead of 1×1, which is the plain weave.

The weave used in the popular oxford shirting varies slightly from the regular basket weave in that it has a 2×1 construction; but the size of the single yarn—a coarser yarn used as the filling—is approximately equivalent in size to the two separate warp yarns. As the coarser yarn has no twist, the fabric is of soft texture and has a degree of luster.

Many variations of the yarn construction of the basket weave are possible. For example, there may be a 3×2 or a 5×3, and so on. The size or thickness of the combined warp yarns will, however, always equal the size or thickness of the corresponding filling yarns. This provides a certain degree of balance and pattern to the fabric.

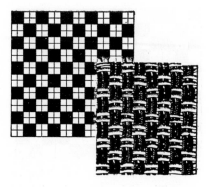

The basket weave is a variation of the plain weave. Two (instead of one) filling yarns pass under and over two (instead of one) warp yarns. This weaving method results in a simple, attractive pattern, so named because baskets have long been woven in this manner.

The basket weave produces an attractive loosely woven fabric that stretches easily and hangs well. It is therefore suitable for drapery and covering fabrics, such as monk's cloth. Due to the characteristic looseness of construction and the low tensile strength of yarns that have little or no twist, this weave is not considered desirable for clothing purposes where the factor of durability is a primary consideration.

Fabrics in Basket Weave. In cotton: monk's cloth, hardanger cloth, oxford shirting or suiting, panama cloth.

In wool, silk, rayon, or other filament yarns: shepherd's check or plaid.

• *Ribbed Effects.* Ribbed, or corded, effects are further variations of the plain weave. The rib may be produced in the warp or in the filling by alternating fine yarns with coarse yarns, or single yarns with doubled yarns. Ribbed effects are popular, but the consumer should remember that sometimes inferior yarns are used in their manufacture, especially when the yarns that make the rib are

This picture of monk's cloth shows how the interweaving of two filling yarns with two warp yarns constructs a loosely woven fabric with an attractive basket-weave pattern.

The design for oxford cloth shows how a large filling yarn having no twist is woven under and over two single, twisted warp yarns.

The left drawing shows a ribbed or corded effect running in the direction of the warp. The right shows the ribbed effect running in the direction of the filling.

hidden in the thickness of the cloth. As these yarns do not show on either side of the fabric, sometimes extremely short-staple yarns or yarns with insufficient twist are used. A ribbed fabric will not be durable if the ribs are too pronounced, because the coarse yarns that produce the rib tend to pull away from adjacent fine yarns. Also, in ribbed effects, an entire yarn is exposed to friction, thus lessening the durability of the fabric.

Fabrics in Ribbed Effects. Filling-ribbed fabrics include: poplin and broadcloth in cotton; bengaline, faille, taffeta, and ottoman in silk, rayon, and other filament fibers. Warp-ribbed fabrics, usually referred to as *waled* or *corded*, include Bedford cord, piqué, and dimity.

Twill Weave. A distinct design in the form of diagonals is characteristic of the second basic weave, called the *twill*. Changes in the direction of the diagonal lines produce variations, such as the herringbone, corkscrew, entwining, and fancy twills. Increased ornamentation may be obtained by varying the diagonal, but the chief values of the twill weave are its strength, firmness, and drapability. The yarns are usually closely battened, making an especially durable fabric. Twill weaves are therefore commonly used in men's suit and coat fabrics and for work clothes, where strong texture is essential.

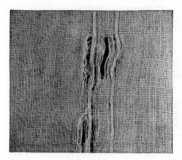

When too coarse a yarn is combined with fine yarns for a ribbed effect, the fine yarns adjacent to the rib soon break when subjected to strain or to heavy wear.

Courtesy U.S. Department of Agriculture

This drawing shows a three-shaft twill; that is, two warp yarns are interlaced with one filling yarn to form the diagonal.

The basic diagonal of the twill weave is shown in all these drawings. The direction of the diagonal and the number of harnesses used produce different surface designs. The drawings at the left show left-hand twills; those at the right are right-hand twills.

These variations of the twill weave show broken twills (herringbone) in the first two drawings; a gabardine in the third; and a corkscrew twill in the fourth.

In the twill weave, the filling yarn interlaces more than one warp yarn, but never more than four, as strength would be sacrificed by so doing. On each successive line, or pick, the filling yarn moves the design one step to the right or to the left, thus forming the diagonal. Whichever the direction of the diagonal on the face of the fabric, the design runs in the opposite direction on the reverse side.

Twill weaves are named according to the number of harnesses required to make the design. A three- or four-harness twill is a frequently used term. The words "shaft" or "leaf" are sometimes substituted for "harness," hence the term *three-shaft* or *four-shaft twill.*

Twill weaves are also classified as *even* or *uneven* according to the number of warp and filling yarns that are visible on the face of the fabric. The even twill, for example, shows an equal number of warp and filling yarns in the recurring design, such as two over and two under. This pattern makes what is called a four-shaft twill, and it requires four harnesses.

The common herringbone twill.

The characteristic diagonal of the twill weave can be seen in this sample of a twill fabric.

Courtesy National Association of Wool Manufacturers

Most twill weaves are uneven. An uneven twill may show more warp than filling yarns in the recurring design; this is called a *warp-face twill*. If more filling yarns than warp yarns show on the face, the weave is called a *filling-face twill*. An example of an uneven twill is three and one, or three up and one down, indicating the manner in which the harnesses are lifted and lowered. The result is a warp-face twill.

Fabrics in Twill Weave. Wool fabrics are usually right-hand twills, as the diagonal lines run from the upper right-hand corner toward the lower left. Wool twill-weave fabrics are: broadcloth, cashmere, cheviot, covert, flannel, gabardine, mackinaw, melton, pilot cloth, serge, tweed, whipcord, worsted cheviot.

Silk fabrics are also right-hand twills. They include foulard, merveilleux, silk serge, and surah.

Cotton fabrics are usually left-hand twills, as the diagonal lines run from the upper left to the lower right corner. They include canton flannel, covert cloth, coutil, denim, drill, gabardine, hickory shirting or hickory stripe, jean, khaki, middle twill, outing flannel, silesia, ticking, venetian cloth, whipcord.

The twill weave is not used much in the production of linen, as linen yarns make a naturally strong fabric. It may be found in linen ticking, twill toweling, and towel drills.

Satin and Sateen Weaves.

In basic construction, the satin weave is similar to the twill weave. But the diagonal of the satin weave is not visible because it is purposely interrupted. A continuous diagonal would interfere with the luster and smoothness that are desired in the satin weave.

The satin weave employs a minimum of five harnesses because a smaller number would simply result in forming a twill weave. The use of five harnesses produces a five-shaft construction; that is, the filling yarn passes over one warp yarn and under four warp yarns. The yarn advances more than one warp yarn on each pick, thus interrupting the diagonal. When more harnesses are used, more filling yarns are interlaced by the warp yarn. The number may run as high as eleven, making what is termed a twelve-shaft construction because one filling yarn interlaces every twelfth warp yarn.

No surface design is visible on satin fabric because the yarns that are to be thrown to the surface are greater in number and finer in count than the yarns that form the undersurface of the fabric.

• *Floating Yarns.* Because the interlacing yarn passes over more yarns than it passes under, long yarns, called *floats,* are exposed on the surface of the fabric. Since these floats lie compactly on the surface with very little interruption from the yarns going at right angles to them, reflection of light on the floats gives satin fabric its characteristic luster, which is the primary object of the satin weave. When the floats are in the warp, the satin weave produces a warp-faced fabric, and the luster appears in the direction of the warp. When

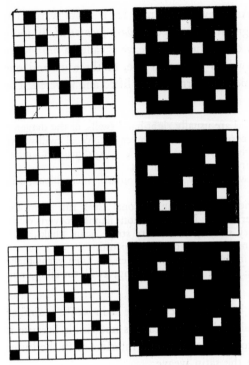

Diagramatic comparisons of satin and sateen constructions.
Top left: *five-shaft sateen*
Top right: *five-shaft satin*
Center left: *eight-shaft sateen*
Center right: *eight-shaft satin*
Lower left: *twelve-shaft sateen*
Lower right: *twelve-shaft satin*

the manner of interlacing is reversed so that the filling yarns are thrown to the surface, a filling-faced fabric is produced, and the luster appears in the direction of the filling. This variation is sometimes referred to as the *sateen weave*. (Sateen is also the name given to a cotton fabric that has floating yarns in either warp or filling.)

The long floats found in the satin weave might be called a disadvantage as they represent a minimum of interlacings, and therefore a potential weakness in the fabric. The longer the float, the greater the chance that the surface of the

These drawings show long floats typical of sateen and satin weaves. The right diagram, with the floats in the filling direction, is a five-shaft sateen construction. The left diagram, with the floats in the warp direction, is an eight-shaft satin construction.

Satin and sateen weaves.

fabric will snag, roughen, and show signs of wear. But the long float gives satin fabric its desired luster and smoothness. The luster makes the fabric suitable for dressy wear; and the smoothness for use as lining.

Satin-weave fabrics drape well because the weave is heavier than the twill weave, which, in turn, is heavier than the plain weave. More harnesses are employed in the satin weave, thus compressing a greater amount of fine yarn into a given space of cloth. The quality of drapability makes satin fabrics preferable for evening dresses.

Fabrics in Satin Weave. In silk or rayon: slipper satin, merveilleux, damask, duchesse, double-faced satin, satin-faced crepe.
In cotton: damask, sateen, ticking, venetian cloth.
In linen: single and double damask.

Designing a Satin Construction. When making a design for a satin construction, the interlacings on successive lines must be separated by a proper interval to avoid forming the contiguous diagonal. When the proper interval for any shaft construction is selected, the design will not repeat itself until the number of successive picks that make up the desired shaft have been interlaced. In a five-shaft construction, for example, the design begins to repeat on the sixth line; in an eight-shaft, on the ninth line; in a twelve-shaft, on the thirteenth line.

Designing a Sateen Construction. An eight-shaft sateen construction illustrates here the rules that must be followed to select a suitable interval.

1. Arrange in pairs the numbers that will add up to the desired shaft number. For an eight-shaft sateen, the shaft number is 8. The pairs are: 1 and 7, 2 and 6, 3 and 5, 4 and 4.

2. Eliminate the pair that contains the number 1 and the number below the shaft number, which is 7 in this case. A contiguous diagonal would result if these intervals were used, producing the conventional twill weave.

3. Next, eliminate the pairs that have a common divisor and those that are

In this eight-shaft sateen construction, each of the horizontal lines of blocks represents a filling yarn or pick. The blocks covered by letters are the points at which the filling yarns interlace the warp yarns on each successive pick. In the eight-shaft satin, the filling is carried across the back, creating the float in the warp. The basic idea of the warp-faced satin can be seen when this diagram is turned sidewise.

divisible into the shaft number. This step eliminates 2 and 6, 4 and 4. The pair 3 and 5 remains. These numbers are the only intervals that can be used in an eight-shaft construction. If any of the eliminated numbers were used as an interval, the fabric would show no interlacing whatever for one or more warp yarns; in fact, there would be no fabric, as it would fall apart.

Now that the only possible interlacings have been worked out, the design can be constructed. (See the accompanying drawing.) For convenience, here the interlacing begins in the lower left square, at *A*. The horizontal rows of squares represent filling yarns—that is, the successive picks on the loom. The vertical rows represent the warp yarns.

The interval to be used for this particular design could be 3 or 5; in this case, 5 has been selected. As this is to be an eight-shaft construction, the interlacing on the first pick will be 7 squares (warp yarns) apart at *B* and *C*.

To find the warp yarn that will interlace on the second pick, count 5 to the right, beginning with the square above the interlacing that is already started at *A*; thus, the interlacing occurs at *D*. Adjacent interlacing on the same line will be 7 squares apart, at *E*.

To find the warp yarn that will interlace on the third pick, start with the square above *D*. Count 5 to the right, and interlacing *G* is plotted. Adjacent interlacings will be 7 squares apart.

On the fourth pick, interlacing *I* is found by counting 5 to the right of the square above *F; J* is found by counting 5 to the right of the square above *G* (or 7 squares from *I*).

This same procedure determines the interlacing points on successive picks, additional interlacings always being 7 squares apart.

On the ninth pick, the design starts to repeat, which proves the accuracy of the construction of an eight-shaft weave.

Where it is not possible to plot subsequent interlacing by continuing to count to the right, because of the small area of the design, interlacings on successive picks can be determined by counting 3 to the left instead of 5 to the right. If the interval 3 had been used to count to the right, 5 would have been used to count to the left.

Fabrics in Sateen Weave. In cotton: damask, sateen, ticking.
In linen: single and double damask.

Pile Weave.

The pile weave is a fancy weave that also includes a plain or a twill construction. In contrast to the three basic weaves that produce a flat surface on a fabric, the pile weave introduces a decorative third dimension, creating an effect of depth. Its construction is especially desirable when softness, warmth, and absorbency are desired. Pile-weave fabrics are also durable if the

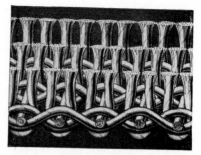

This drawing shows the pile weave as it looks after the wires that have raised the filling yarns have been withdrawn.

Cut pile, shown in this drawing, can be produced by using wires equipped with razorlike ends that cut the loops as the wires are withdrawn.

proper yarns and adequate compact construction are used. In the manufacture of rugs, for example, a strong, tightly twisted staple with compact construction in the base cloth will withstand long wear.

The pile is produced by weaving an additional warp yarn or filling yarn into the basic structure. The additional yarn is drawn away from the surface of the fabric by thick wires, which form loops at regular intervals. These loops may be cut or closely sheared, or left uncut if a loop surface is desired, as in Brussels carpet.

When the pile is produced by an extra warp yarn, the result is a warp-pile fabric, of which terry, carpet, and plush are examples. Fabrics are classified as plush when the pile is more than ⅛-inch high. When the pile is produced by an extra filling yarn, the result is a filling-pile fabric, of which velveteen and corduroy are examples.

In certain cut-pile fabrics, the wires used to form the loops are equipped with razorlike ends, so that the loops are cut when the wires are withdrawn, thus producing the cut pile exemplified by broadloom carpet. Cut-pile fabrics are produced economically by constructing double-cloth fabrics, as explained in the following section, then cutting the two cloths apart.

Pile effects can also be created by using varying tension in the warp yarns. In the manufacture of rugs, such as chenille, Wilton, velvet, and tapestry, various processes are used for pile effects, including hand knotting.

Fabrics in Pile Weave. In cotton: chenille, corduroy, duvetyn, frieze, plush, terry (turkish toweling), velour, velveteen.
   In wool: frieze, plush, velour, rugs of all kinds.
   In silk, rayon, and other filament yarns: chenille, frieze, fur fabrics, plush, transparent velvet, velour, velvets of all kinds.
   Linen is seldom made in the pile weave.

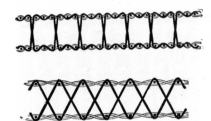

The double-cloth weave can be produced by either of the two methods shown here: the V method in the upper drawing, and the W method in the lower. Cutting the yarn that holds the two cloths together makes two separate cut-pile fabrics.

Double-Cloth Weave.

In the double-cloth weave, two fabrics are woven on the loom at the same time, one on top of the other. The fabric may have a plain weave on one side and a twill weave on the other. Each of the fabrics requires its separate sets of warp and filling yarns. They are combined by interlacing some of the warp or filling yarns or by means of a complete fifth set of stitching yarns. The surfaces of such fabrics may show different patterns or color on each side by varying the yarns as to color and size. A true double-cloth weave is never a pasted construction.

Because the double-cloth weave produces two pieces of fabric combined into one, fabrics so woven are commonly regarded as strong and warm. Warmth, however, is due primarily to the insulative properties inherent in a fiber; bulk and thickness alone do not give warmth. Also, strength cannot be judged by mere thickness or weight. It cannot be assumed that a double-cloth weave will have the qualities of warmth and strength; on the contrary, the fabric may be heavy, bulky, and needlessly expensive. Sometimes, this method of construction is chosen to use a cheaper material on the reverse side of the fabric, thus reducing the cost of a heavy fabric.

Fabrics in Double-Cloth Weave. In cotton: double-faced blankets, bathrobe blankets.

In wool: polo cloth, steamer rugs, overcoatings.

In silk and other filament yarns: upholstery fabrics of all kinds.

Gauze Weave.

The gauze weave must not be confused with the weave used in manufacturing gauze bandages or cheesecloth; these materials are made with the plain weave. The gauze-weave construction produces a fabric very light in weight and with an open-mesh effect. Curtain materials and some cotton dress goods are woven with this weave. Such lightweight fabrics have a strength that could not be provided by the plain weave. In the gauze weave, strength is gained by the manner in which the yarns are intertwisted: each filling yarn is encircled by two warp yarns twisted about each other.

The gauze weave is sometimes referred to as the *leno weave* because it is made on a leno loom, but the true leno weave is merely a variation of the gauze

The gauze weave is shown at the left, the leno weave at the right. Note how the filling yarns in the gauze weave are encircled by two warp yarns twisting around each other, a construction that gives strength although the mesh is open. In the leno weave, the second of each of two warp yarns merely passes around the first yarn.

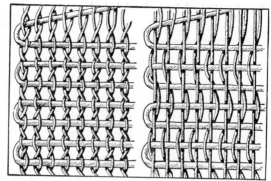

Courtesy U.S. Department of Agriculture

weave. On the leno loom, the action of one warp yarn is similar to the action of the warp in the plain weave. A second warp yarn passes around the first warp simultaneously and alternately over and under the filling yarn. The leno is sometimes used in combination with the plain weave to produce a stripe or figure on a plain background. Generally, the term "leno" is used synonymously with "gauze."

Fabrics in Gauze Weave. In cotton: grenadine, marquisette, mosquito netting, rice net, mesh shirtings.

In silk, rayon, and other filament yarns: bolting cloth, curtain madras, grenadine, marquisette.

Swivel Weave.
The swivel weave is the method by which decorative effects, such as dots, circles, or other figures, are interwoven on the surface of a fabric while it is being constructed on the loom. The weaving of the design requires an extra filling yarn and additional small shuttles. A separate shed is made for these shuttles. While the fabric is being constructed, the row of small shuttles drops across the width of the loom, and each shuttle interweaves its separate design with a circular motion on a small area of the warp. A long thread is carried on the undersurface of the fabric from one design to the next. Different colors may be used in each of the designs because each figure is woven by its own shuttle containing its own miniature bobbin.

The decoration produced by the swivel weave is not considered durable, because the swivel yarns are cut when the fabric is completed and cannot be securely fastened. The cut ends roughen the undersurface of the fabric and may pull out if it is handled carelessly in laundering.

Fabrics in Swivel Weave: dotted swiss, grenadine, curtain madras.

Lappet Weave.
The lappet weave is also used to superimpose a small design on the surface of a fabric while it is being woven. In the lappet weave, the de-

sign is stitched into the fabric by needles that operate at right angles to the construction. Thus, the lappet weave is very similar to embroidery.

The lappet design is made with one continuous additional warp yarn carried on the back of the fabric from one design to the next. Only one color is possible. The floating threads on the back are cut away when the fabric is completed, but the ends are fastened securely and will not pull out easily.

Fabric in the Lappet Weave. Dotted swiss produced by the lappet weave is superior to swivel-weave dotted swiss.

Dobby Weave. The dobby weave is a patterned weave used to construct designs that cannot be produced by the plain, twill, or satin weaves. The designs are simple, limited in size, and usually geometric in form. They are found in shirtings and tie fabrics. The dobby weave is created on a plain loom by means of a mechanical attachment, called a *dobby* or *cam,* which raises or lowers as many as twenty-four to forty harnesses containing the series of warp yarns that form the pattern. Although a large number of harnesses is used in this construction, the design is always small and does not make use of long floats. The most familiar type of dobby weave is bird's-eye, the small diamond pattern that has an eye in its center.

Fabrics in Dobby Weave. In cotton: bird's-eye, huckaback.
In linen: cretonne, huckaback, mummy cloth.
In wool: granite cloth.

Jacquard Weave. In any of the weaves that have been described, the number of harnesses determines the construction. For example, two harnesses are required for the plain weave, three or more for the twill, and five to twelve for the satin weave. As many as forty can be manipulated by the special attachment of the dobby. The dobby designs are not intricate, however. They are limited to straight lines, edges, steps, or small circular lines.

For curves, swirls, and large-sized figures, it was necessary to devise a different mechanism that would allow an unlimited range of intricate designs. This need is met by the Jacquard attachment, named after its inventor, Joseph Marie Jacquard, a Frenchman. The Jacquard mechanism controls thousands of heddles, which lift one or more warp yarns independently of others without the use of harnesses. Its action is similar to that of the player piano, where each note is governed by a hole on the music roll and is sounded when the hole passes over a certain opening.

The Jacquard design is first worked out on squared paper. Cards are then perforated to correspond with the design; they are laced together and placed on the Jacquard attachment. The moving cards pass over a battery of needles

Here is a close-up of Jacquard cards laced together as they appear on the mechanism at the top of the loom. As the cards move, needles behind the cards drop through the perforations and lift strings, which, in turn, lift heddles.

Courtesy Mohawk Carpet Mills, Inc.

mounted on top of the loom. Each needle controls a string, which when released picks up the heddle to which it is tied. The perforations on the cards allow the needles to drop through, and lift certain strings, which, in turn, lift single heddles independently of others. The preparation of a Jacquard weave is the most expensive part of its construction. Setting up the loom may take several weeks or months; but once set, the pattern to be produced can be used and reused for different materials. This is the most expensive form of weaving, and it is chiefly used for linen and for upholstery materials.

Floats are inevitable in the Jacquard weave because of the elaborate designs. As in the satin weave, long floats may affect the wearing quality of the fabric; also, long cotton yarns exposed to friction cause lint. Compact construction of the fabric, however, offsets the tendency to friction and wear. The consumer should select the better-quality fabrics when purchasing those having the

This Jacquard loom in operation shows the laced cards at the top of the loom. The long slanting strings control the heddles immediately below the cards. The heddles raise and lower the warp yarns in accordance with the pattern punched on the cards above, the filling yarn making the design as the shuttle passes across the loom.

Courtesy St. Mary's Woolen Manufacturing Co.

Jacquard weave, especially when purchasing linen damask because table linens receive hard wear and repeated washings.

Fabrics in Jacquard Weave. In cotton: matelassé, damask, tapestry.
In linen: single and double damask.
In wool: tapestry.
In silk, rayon, and other filament yarns: brocade, brocatelle, damask, and tapestry.

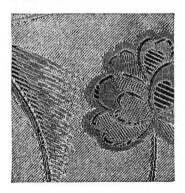

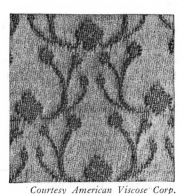

Courtesy American Viscose Corp.

*Damask produced by the
Jacquard.*

*Brocade produced by the
Jacquard.*

Distinguishing Warp and Filling. Persons who handle fabrics must be able to identify the warp and the filling yarns, because the direction of the warp determines the way in which the fabric should be cut when a garment is made from it. In a new piece of yard goods, the direction of the warp is easily distinguished. The length of the fabric indicates the warp yarns. Also, if a piece of the fabric shows part of the selvage, which is the firm edge of the cloth, then the yarns parallel to the selvage are warp yarns. The opposite yarns are the filling yarns. When a sample of fabric contains no selvage, the warp and filling may be identified by observation of the weave.

1. In plain weaves, a greater number of yarns running in one direction indicates the warp.
2. In twill weaves, the filling yarns run in the direction of the diagonal, which may be toward the right or toward the left.
3. In satin weaves, the floating yarns are the warp yarns.

When the name of the fabric is known, its characteristic features aid in distinguishing the warp and filling. For example, the ribs of dimity and of piqué run in the direction of the warp; the ribs of rep, faille, bengaline, and poplin in the direction of the filling. When colored stripes show in such fabrics as chambray, madras shirtings, and in some dress goods, the direction in which the stripe runs usually indicates the warp.

When the warp and the filling cannot be identified by the foregoing aids, the sets of yarns may be examined for the following characteristics.

1. Exerting tension on a sample by holding it in both hands and pulling, at the same time pressing with the thumbs and forefingers, will show which set of yarns is stronger. The stronger set will be the warp, because warp yarns have to withstand the tension of the heddles in the weaving process. The filling

SUMMARY OF BASIC WEAVES

Weave	Characteristics	Advantages	Limitations
Plain	No distinct design unless yarns have contrasting colors	Maximum yardage; easily produced; inexpensive; strong; adaptable for direct printing and other finishing processes	Sleazy fabric if thread count is low
a. Basket	Basket pattern	Attractive; inexpensive	Not durable for apparel
b. Ribbed	Corded effects	Ornamental	Not serviceable if of inferior construction
Twill	Distinct diagonal design	Strong, firm texture; increased drapability; interesting designs	Requires care to keep clean
Satin	Luster; interrupted diagonal design discernible with magnifying glass	Beauty contributed by luster; smoothness; maximum drapability	Excessively long floats may snag and roughen fabric

yarn, which emerges from the bobbin of the shuttle as it crosses the fabric, is under little tension.

2. When one set contains yarns of varying sizes, this set is usually the warp. Filling yarns are usually of the same size.
3. The set of yarns that can be more easily stretched is the filling.
4. Yarns of inferior quality are commonly used as filling in inexpensive fabrics. When both sets of yarns are carefully compared, the inferior yarn is usually the filling.
5. When a yarn has a hard twist, as in serges and overcoatings, it is generally the warp yarn.
6. Yarns with slack twist usually are the filling yarns. Yarns with little twist are used as filling when a soft, lustrous effect is desired.
7. If one set consists of thicker yarns, this indicates the filling, as the bulk produced by large-sized yarns dispenses with the need for a great amount of twist.
8. If ply yarns are used they probably indicate the warp.
9. In a napped fabric, the warp runs in the direction of the napping, because the fabric has been run through the machine in the direction of its length.
10. In light cotton or silk fabrics, a marked evenness between the yarns indicates the warp. This evenness is the result of the mechanical movement of the reed

as it battens the filling yarns when the cloth is being constructed. In patterned weaves, such as a herringbone twill, the impact of the battening operation leaves small reed marks that distinguish filling from warp yarns.

▶ TEST YOURSELF ON THIS CHAPTER

1. Explain why lappet ornamentation is permanent and swivel is not.
2. Why are harnesses not required in the Jacquard weave?
3. Construct designs for variation of the plain and the twill weaves.
4. Construct a design for producing a ribbed effect in the warp.
5. Describe the basic operations of the weaving process, naming specific parts of the loom.
6. Compare the pile weave and its uses with the double-cloth weave and its uses.
7. Differentiate between plain weave, ribbed weave, basket weave, and twill.
8. Compare the advantages and disadvantages of the twill and satin weaves.
9. Which of the three basic weaves is: (*a*) The most durable? Why? (*b*) The most beautiful? Why? (*c*) The most inexpensive to produce? Why?
10. What weave would you prefer in a skirt, a suit, curtains? Why?
11. Is it of any advantage to the consumer to know the basic differences between the three foundation weaves? Why?
12. Why was the Jacquard weave revolutionary in the weaving industry?
13. Contrary to common belief, why does the gauze weave embody strength?
14. Differentiate between damask and a fabric made by the dobby weave.
15. To the cards on which you mounted small samples of fabrics and identified them as to fiber content and use, add the names of the fabrics' weaves.
16. Wind a piece of yarn or string around a square piece of cardboard, about 4 by 4 inches, so that on each side of the cardboard there are parallel yarns in close rows. These are similar to the warp yarns on a loom. Thread another piece of yarn of a contrasting color in a large needle. Insert it through the parallel rows to produce the weave pattern of the three foundation weaves.

6 · FINISHING

Appearance and Serviceability

Newly constructed fabric as it comes from the loom does not represent finished consumers' goods. It must pass through various finishing processes that make it suitable for many different purposes. Finishing enhances the appearance of the fabric and also may add to its serviceability and durability, thus increasing its value. Familiarity with finishing processes enables the consumer to recognize and judge quality in fabrics. The untrained purchaser is influenced too readily by quantity rather than by quality. He is likely to choose the large, the bulky, the heavy. As manufacturers and retailers conduct their businesses to meet existing demand, textile fabrics are finished to a large extent to satisfy this type of purchaser. This explains why many fabrics are "oversized" and others are weighted. If fabric is not properly constructed and if finishing processes are used to conceal inferior construction or to simulate superior quality, the durability of the finished product is questionable.

This does not mean that all finishing is intended to deceive the consumer, for no type of finish should be labeled as spurious until the purpose of the fabric has been considered. A sustained demand for a particular kind of finished fabric usually explains its continued production.

Converting Gray Goods. Finishing processes have assumed such great importance in the textile industry that this phase of textile manufacturing is undertaken by a highly specialized group of middlemen called *converters*. Conversion of *gray goods,* or goods *in the gray,* includes the various types of finishing processes as well as subsequent dyeing and printing.

The converter contracts for a volume purchase of gray goods and converts this unfinished product into finished consumers' goods in accordance with either solicited demand, based on orders taken by his selling force, or with anticipated demand, which is an estimate of the immediate market.

The term *gray goods* does not imply that the fabric is gray in color. It is another form of the term *greige goods,* originally applied only to unfinished silk fabrics, but now used to denote any untreated or unfinished fabric as it comes from the loom.

Kinds of Finishing Processes.

Finishing may take many forms, for it must be adapted to the kind of fiber and yarn used in the fabric and, most important of all, to its intended purpose. One type of gray goods may emerge from a certain finishing process in a form suitable for curtains, while the identical gray goods put through other finishing processes can be used for dress material.

Even the factor of thread count, so important in the evaluation of a fabric, can be changed by the kind and amount of finishing. Cotton can be given the soft finish required for such fabrics as batiste, nainsook, and lawn, the napped finish required for flannelette and duvetyn, the hard stiffened finish typical of cambric and linene, or the lustrous effect of chintz.

The most common finishing processes are listed here. The list does not represent a sequence, nor are all the processes applicable to all kinds of gray goods. Some fabrics must be put through more than one process. Some of the first-named operations are essential preparatory processing for other final finishes, since each fabric is given its own characteristic finishes.

Singeing or gassing	Beetling
Bleaching	Napping
Mercerizing	Gigging
Shrinking	Shearing
Fulling and other wool-shrinking processes	Crepe and crinkled effects
Tentering	Crease resistance
Crabbing	Water repellency
Decating (or decatizing)	Flameproofing
Sizing or dressing	Mothproofing
Weighting	Mildewproofing
Calendering	Milium processing
Schreinerizing	Slip resistance
Moiréing	Antiseptic finishes
Ciréing	Drip-dry finishes
	Embossing

Singeing or Gassing.

If a fabric is to have a smooth finish, singeing is one of the first essential preparatory processes. It burns off lint and threads, as well as all fuzz and fiber ends, leaving an even surface before the fabric passes through the mercerizing process or any printing operation.

Singeing is accomplished by passing gray goods rapidly over rows of gas flames or electrically heated plates at a speed of 100 to 250 yards a minute. After singeing, in the case of cotton fabrics, the cloth is given a bath and is then steeped for several hours in large boiling vats, called *kiers,* which contain caustic soda, soda ash, and lime. Thorough circulation of these cleansing agents prepares the fabric for the subsequent bleaching operation.

All kinds of fabrics made of short-staple yarns are singed. Singeing may also be done in the yarn stage; for example, lisle yarn, made of highly twisted fine cotton staple, is always singed to obtain its characteristic smooth surface.

Bleaching. If cloth is to be finished white or is to be given surface ornamentation, all natural color must be removed by bleaching. This is also necessary if discoloration or stains have occurred during the previous manufacturing process. Bleaching can be done in the yarn stage as well as in the constructed fabric. The kind of chemicals to be used depends on whether the fabric or the yarn is composed of vegetable or of animal fibers. When cloth has been bleached for finishing, it is called *bleached goods*.

Cotton or linen fabrics may be bleached by washing only, with subsequent exposure to the sun. Some of the finest Irish linens are bleached in this manner. The slowness of the method eliminates possible overbleaching, which causes deterioration in fabrics. Chemicals bleach fabrics more quickly but require the utmost care, as too much penetration of the bleaching agent weakens or even decomposes the fibers.

As the use of any strong bleaching agent eventually causes weakness in a fabric, the consumer should select unbleached goods when extreme whiteness is not essential. As fully bleached white goods are preferred however, additional bleaching is necessary as part of the laundering job. Otherwise, white goods eventually take on an unattractive yellowish tinge. If colored goods are selected when possible—for example, in men's underwear—no bleaching is required in laundering, and the garments consequently last longer.

• *Bleaching Cotton and Linen.* Oxidizing agents, such as chlorinated lime or hypochloric acid, are used for bleaching cotton and linen, the vegetable fibers. A similar bleach can be obtained by diluting a concentrated solution of sodium hypochlorite, which is better known to the consumer by such trade names as Clorox, Rose-X, Dazzle, and the like. Chlorine is an oxidizing agent that bleaches coloring matter in vegetable fibers; but because it is a strong chemical, it also weakens the fabric. To prevent any serious damage from such bleaches to the fabric, the bleach should be used with care. Approximately one tablespoon of bleach to a gallon of water is usually sufficient to be effective. It is best to first add the bleach to the water and then place the garment in the water so that the bleach will be properly diluted and distributed evenly to all of the fabric.

Commercial bleaching of cotton and linen fabrics is essentially the same in principle. Gray goods are passed through chlorinated lime or hypochloric acid. The material is then put through a mangle and placed in bleaching bins, where it remains from two to twelve hours, depending on the strength of the bleaching agent and the material. To neutralize the action of the bleach, a mild solution of sulphuric acid is used afterward. The fabric is then rinsed in clear water and dried. The least injurious chemical bleach used on cotton is hydrogen peroxide. The fabric is also thoroughly rinsed after being treated with this bleach.

Sunlight also may be used to bleach cotton and linen. It is used extensively in Ireland to bleach linen. The gray goods are spread out on the grass and are gradually bleached by the sun. This process is known as *grass bleaching*. The longer the linen remains in the sunlight, the whiter it gets; however, it correspondingly weakens.

• *Bleaching Wool and Silk*. For silk and wool, strong oxidizers cannot be used as they injure animal fibers. White silk and white wool fabrics do not remain white long because exposure to light and air brings back the natural discolorations. In bleaching silk or wool, deoxidizers or reducing agents, such as sulphurous acids or fumes of burning sulphur, are required. The safest bleach is a mild solution of hydrogen peroxide.

• *Bleaching Rayon*. A very mild solution (milder than for cotton or linen) of sodium hypochlorite or hydrogen peroxide may be used to bleach rayon. For safest results, the water should be warm rather than hot; and the fabric should then be thoroughly rinsed in warm water.

• *Bleaching Acetate*. A characteristic of white acetate is that it remains white; therefore, bleaching should not be necessary. However, if some finish is used to coat the fabric, and the fabric then seems to yellow, a very dilute solution of sodium hypochlorite or hydrogen peroxide may be used with care.

• *Bleaching Arnel*. Arnel has excellent white retention. However, if a blend fabric containing Arnel fiber is to be bleached because the other fiber or fibers have yellowed, a mild solution of sodium hypochlorite or hydrogen peroxide may be used with care.

• *Bleaching Nylon*. Nylon has good white retention, but under certain circumstances it may become yellowish or grayish. A very mild solution of sodium hypochlorite is recommended for such conditions.

• *Bleaching Dacron*. Dacron may be bleached by a variety of oxidizing agents. For home use, sodium hypochlorite is recommended.

• *Bleaching Orlon, Acrilan, Dynel, Creslan, and Verel*. These fibers are wholly or partly acrylic. Their reactions to bleaches are very similar, except for Verel. The most effective and safest bleach for the others is sodium hypochlorite. Verel, however, tends to discolor; and bleaching should be avoided.

• *Bleaching Zefran*. Although Zefran may be safely bleached with a solution of sodium hypochlorite, it will be damaged by hydrogen peroxide.

• *Bleaching Darvan*. Darvan will also be damaged by hydrogen peroxide and should therefore be bleached with a solution of sodium hypochlorite.

• *Bleaching Saran*. Saran has good resistance to such bleaches as sodium hypochlorite or hydrogen peroxide.

• *Bleaching Fiberglas*. Fiberglas never needs to be bleached. It always retains its whiteness.

Mercerizing. Mercerizing is an important preparatory process for cotton fabric. It is also used in the finishing of linen. The fabric is singed before mercerizing, but mercerizing may precede or follow bleaching. Mercerizing changes the chemical composition of the fiber, strengthening its cellular lines by causing it to swell in diameter and to contract in length; the gain in strength may be as much as 20 per cent. *Mercerizing* is the simplest chemical method of producing luster in cotton and linen. In addition to increased strength and luster, this process gives fabrics greater absorbency for dyes. Mercerization can also be done in the yarn stage.

Highly mercerized fine cotton yarns can make cotton broadcloth shirting look like silk, and cause cotton damask to be mistaken for linen. When lisle yarn or high-count yarn is mercerized, a silklike luster results that causes the material to be erroneously called "silk lisle."

Gray goods are mercerized by immersion in a specially prepared solution of caustic soda for about ten minutes under conditions of moderate uniform heat and tension. The caustic soda is washed out, and the yarn or fabric is put through a heated acid bath to neutralize the caustic soda. It is then rinsed in clear water and dried. The combined action of the caustic soda, heat, and tension changes and strengthens the fiber cells, thus improving and strengthening the fabric or yarn.

Durene Finish. This is a standardized process of mercerizing that utilizes a fine quality of cotton yarn. Manufacturers who maintain standards established by the Durene Association of America are allowed to label their product "Durene Yarns." These yarns are made of fine long-staple combed cotton and are always of two-ply construction.

Cotton yarn, highly magnified, as it appears before gassing and mercerization. Note the dullness of the yarn and the fuzz on its surface.

Cotton yarn, highly magnified, as it appears after gassing and mercerization. Note the smooth, lustrous appearance and absence of fuzz.

Shrinking. When fibers are spun into yarn, they are under constant tension during the weaving process. Their physical condition is changed, but not permanently fixed: the fibers tend to revert to their natural state, causing shrinkage. The yarns are made to assume a final condition by shrinking the fabric in a preparatory finishing process that minimizes subsequent shrinkage, such as immersion in cold water, followed by hot water, steaming, or a chemical treatment. Any such method permits the manufacturer to label his product as preshrunk. But even when textile fabrics are preshrunk, they are liable to further shrinkage when washed. The amount of additional shrinkage that may occur after washing is sometimes stated on the label.

To realize maximum preshrinkage in finishing, the fabric must be given a preshrinking operation in which no tension is exerted while the fabric is damp. General adoption of such preshrinking methods for all fabrics is not feasible. Additional expense is incurred, and in some cases prized qualities inherent in certain fabrics are sacrificed.

In general, the factors that control shrinkage are the stability of the fiber and the construction of the fabric. Construction is based on the type of weave, the amount of twist in the yarn, the thread count, and the yarn count. The final finishing process also affects shrinkage; for example, a water-repellent quality in a fabric offers resistance to subsequent shrinkage.

If the label on a fabric mentions shrinkage, the fabric must conform to rulings on shrinkage issued by the Federal Trade Commission. One important provision states that if a product is to be labeled preshrunk or shrunk, the label must specifically indicate how much additional shrinkage is to be expected. Formerly, a manufacturer's label reading "fully shrunk" or "will not shrink" or "shrink-proof" did not guarantee that substantially more shrinkage would not take place with continued laundering.

A machine known as a *launderometer* is used to make washing tests in testing laboratories. A similar, though larger, machine is used for determining shrinkage. Measured distances are marked in indelible ink or with fine threads on unwashed samples of the fabric. The samples are then placed in glass jars containing a washing solution. The jars are sealed and rotated in a tank filled with water that is maintained at a constant temperature. After an interval, the samples are removed, dried, and pressed. Any change in the measurements marked on the samples determines the amount of shrinkage.

Compressive Shrinkage. Compressive shrinkage is a patented, standardized method that has succeeded in reducing shrinkage in cotton and linens to a practical minimum. The fabric is deliberately shortened in both width and length, resulting in a tighter and closer weave and, consequently, in a higher thread count. Fabrics shrunk by this method are frequently identified as "Sanforized." This term is a registered trade-mark and indicates that the fabric has a residual shrinkage of not more than 1 per cent, and that tests have been made to insure that it conforms to this standard. The process is carried out on a machine about 65 feet long as follows:

1. Normal shrinkage is determined by subjecting a test sample of the fabric to ordinary washing conditions, using the United States Government wash test.
2. Careful measurements before and after the wash test indicate how much the fabric shrinks in length and width.
3. The compressive-shrinkage machine is set to shrink the fabric to the exact dimensions that the wash test indicated.
4. The fabric is dampened with pure water and live steam, which soften it in preparation for the adjustments to be made in length and width.
5. The width is adjusted by a stretching action, in which the fabric is gripped along its selvages.
6. The fabric is then held firmly against a heavy wool blanket which is under controlled tension.
7. As the tension of the blanket is relaxed to the desired measurements, the fabric shrinks uniformly in length.
8. The fabric is then carried around a heated drum while drying, and the surface finish is restored.
9. A sample is tested again to make certain that additional shrinkage will not exceed 1 per cent.

Perma-sizing. This is a shrinkproofing process developed for, and applied to, knitted cotton goods, which has proved to be effective.

Rigmel Shrinking. Rigmel shrinking is a patented method of mechanical shrinking, somewhat similar to compressive shrinkage. A cotton fabric is put through a standard wash test to determine the precise shrinkage in inches per yard and is subsequently shrunk to planned dimensions that permit anticipation of residual shrinkage.

Sanforsetting. Rayon fabrics may be preshrunk by a process known as *Sanforsetting.* It will be noted that this term has a resemblance to the term used for preshrinking cotton up to 1 per cent. The process is owned by the same company, Cluett, Peabody & Co., Inc. This process is somewhat similar to the Sanforizing technique. There is, however, a residual shrinkage of not more than 2 per cent.

Cylinder Method. This method for shrinking wool uses two perforated cylinders, which steam the fabric as it is rolled off one cylinder and rewound on the other. The steamed fabric is then wound loosely around a wood roller, where it dries and cools slowly and naturally.

London Shrinking. London shrinking is a cold-water process of preshrinking wool fabrics. Lengths of wool fabric are retained between wet blankets for about twenty hours. The moisture of the blankets penetrates into the fibers of the cloth. The cloth is then dried slowly and subsequently subjected to a hydraulic pressure of about 3,500 pounds. Cold-water shrinking originated in London. It is considered one of the best methods.

Chlorination Process. This is a chemical method of treating wool so that the fabric will be shrink proof. The wool fabric is treated with a dilute solution of calcium or sodium hypochlorite. Some of the scales of the fibers are removed, causing fusion of the outer and inner part of the fibers. As a result, shrinkage decreases. When this protective scaly covering is removed, however, the felting quality is lessened, and the durability of the fabric is affected. But luster and affinity for dyes are increased. Steaming or fulling does not have this result. Chlorinated wool is chiefly used in woolen underwear, socks, and sweaters. Among the trade names for this process are Harriset, Hypol, Kelpie, Kroy, Sanforlan, Schollerizing, and Protonizing.

Resin Treatment. This is also a chemical shrinking process. The wool fabric is treated with an organic resin. The treatment has no harmful effect on the properties or handle of the fabric. There may be a residual shrinkage of not more than 2 per cent. Some trade names for this process are Lanaset, Pacifixed, and Resloom.

Fulling. The process of fulling, an important operation in the finishing of wool fabrics, actually operates as a preshrinking process for wool. The fibers are cleaned, scoured, and condensed by a combination of moisture, heat, soap, and pressure. Sometimes, chemicals are added to increase the adhesion of the fibers. The condensing is a natural result of the felting property of wool fiber—shrinkage takes place because the fibers are drawn together. As a result, the fabric has a fuller, more compact body.

Tentering. As a fabric passes through various finishing processes, it becomes irregular in width. To restore its proper width, the cloth is stretched in some parts and shrunk in others. This process, called *tentering*, is done on a machine that grips the fabric along the selvages with movable clips in chain form, so that it can be jerked along its length. The fabric is fastened on the tentering machine while it is moist, and steam is sprayed from underneath to aid in the stretching and shrinking. Before the fabric leaves the machine, it is dried by heating devices. The tiny holes or marks of the clips are sometimes noticeable in the selvages of yard goods.

In properly finished fabrics, the filling threads are at right angles to the warp. If the angle varies, the fabric is described as "on the bias." Tentering helps to straighten the warp and filling threads and to smooth the fabric.

Crabbing. In finishing wool fabrics, a stretching process called *crabbing* passes the cloth over rollers into hot water or steam. The fabric is then put into cold water, after which it is pressed. This process is similar to tentering, as the fabric is stretched or loosened where necessary and finally set at the width at which the warp and filling yarns are in proper relation to each other. Consequently, there is no hidden strain on any portion of the fabric. Crabbing also prevents the formation of creases or other forms of uneven shrinkage in subsequent finishing operations.

Decating (or Decatizing). *Decating* is a finishing process that may be applied to wool fabrics to set the nap and develop the luster. In wet decating, the material is tightly wound on a perforated iron roller and immersed in a trough of hot water which is circulated through the fabric. In dry decating, steam is

Courtesy Pepperell Manufacturing Co.

On the tenter frame, the cloth is held to the correct width and given a final drying in a hot chamber.

used instead of hot water. Decating may be applied to rayon and other man-made and synthetic fabrics to improve the hand, color, and luster of the fabric, or to overcome uneven or blotchy dyeing.

Sizing or Dressing. Cotton and linen can be given stiffness, smoothness, weight, and strength by immersion in a solution of starch. This process is commonly known as *sizing*. A small amount of starch in consumers' goods, especially in cotton fabrics, helps to retain freshness while they are on the dealers' shelves. Cotton fabrics that are usually sized are organdy, lawn, voile, and buckram. Some sizing is acceptable, but the consumer should refrain from purchasing fabrics that have too much sizing because it may conceal inferior construction. Sizing fills in the openings in the constructed cloth, creating an appearance of greater compactness; thus, a low thread count is not immediately discernible at the time of purchase. If a fabric loses body after one or more washings, it has been oversized.

Excessive sizing can be detected by rubbing the fabric between the hands. This causes the sizing to come off in the form of a fine powder. An absolute test can be made by touching the fabric with a drop of weak iodine; if starch is present, a blue color appears. Other substances used for dressing fabrics are flour, dextrine, glue, shellac, fats, wax, and paraffin. The starches give weight; glue gives stiffness; fats give softness; wax and paraffin produce luster. Starch, baked brown before using, is known as *dextrine,* or *British gum;* in this form, it gives a soft dressing to a fabric.

Cotton fabric is sometimes sized with clay chalk, barium sulphate, calcium sulphate, or magnesium sulphate to make it especially heavy and close in texture. Some sizings make cotton fabrics susceptible to mildew, but this tendency can be offset by the addition of zinc chloride to the sizing bath.

• *Glazing.* A stiff polished or glazed surface can be obtained by the application of starch, glue, mucilage, or shellac. The process makes a fabric resistant to dust and spots and minimizes shrinkage. This finish is found principally on chintz. Vita-glaze is a typical trade-mark for this process.

• *Permanent Sizing.* Permanent sizing effects can now be achieved without the use of starch. A chemical process changes the cellular structure of the fiber. By this method, sheer and medium-weight cottons are given stiffness, which sometimes lasts throughout the life of the fabric. These processes are known by specific trade names. They vary in method, in the chemicals used, and in the degree of permanency of the final finish. All have the property of making the fabric smoother, and it soils less easily because dirt tends to slide off rather than to cling. As a result, fabrics with permanent sizing usually require less laundering and therefore last longer. Some of these permanent finishes are:

Ankord. Ankord, a starchless finish given to cotton and rayon gray goods, increases tensile strength, improves luster, and reduces shrinkage.

Bellmanizing. In the Bellmanizing process, permanent crispness can be given to sheer cottons by sealing the fibers chemically with resinous compounds. The fibers undergo basic structural changes; they become round, stiff, and firm, and thus resistant to untwisting, fraying, and creasing. The chemical compounds do not dissolve in laundering. No starch is used in the process or required in subsequent washing. The Bellmanizing process is effective on sheer cottons, such as batistes, lawn, voiles, and organdies.

Clearight. This is a starchless process that imparts lasting crispness. Clearight is generally used on sheer fabrics.

Saylerizing. Saylerizing is a starchless finish similar to Bellmanizing. It gives permanent crispness to medium-weight as well as to sheer cottons.

Sheercroft. Sheercroft is a starchless finish that imparts crispness and increases luster, giving cotton a linenlike appearance.

Stabilized. The Stabilized process gives a finish like sizing. It also adds body to spun rayon and to cotton, but the finish is not permanent.

Staze-Right. This finish gives luster and crispness to organdies and marquisettes and is resistant to washing and dry cleaning.

Basco. This starchless finish increases strength and gives permanent luster and a linenlike appearance to fabrics.

Trubenizing. Trubenizing is a patented process that prevents wilting in collars and cuffs. Fabric made of acetate yarns is used to interline the collars and cuffs.

which are then immersed in acetone and pressed with a hot iron; the result is a permanent stiffness that does not require starching. This process also gives rise to the term *fused* collars and cuffs.

Weighting. Fabrics are sometimes weighted to give them additional body. When cotton fabric is weighted with any of the various sizing agents, it is heavier and appears to be closely constructed. Its poor construction becomes apparent after washing, however. The consumer should learn to judge such fabrics for their quality, not for their apparent weight.

Weighted silk fabrics have become acceptable in the textile industry. The weight and body of the fabric are increased by immersing it in a solution containing metallic salts. The salts permeate the yarns and become a permanent part of the fabric but cannot be detected by handling. If excessive metallic salts are used in the weighting, they eventually weaken the fabric. The Federal Trade Commission has issued specific regulations with respect to kinds of weighting and their proper labeling.

Only low-grade wool fabrics are weighted. As much as 40 per cent additional weight can be obtained by felting extremely short wool fibers into the fabric. These fibers, called *flocks*, are obtained when wool fabrics are washed, brushed, and sheared. An excessive amount of flocks can be detected by brushing and shaking the fabric vigorously. Careful examination of the selvage will also reveal flock particles. Treating wool fabric with magnesium chloride causes an excessive water content, referred to as "watered stock."

Cotton may be weighted by one of two processes. A flat cotton fabric, such as sheeting, can be heavily starched, and the construction will look and feel very compact. Rubbing the fabric between the hands will cause the dry starch to fall out. The second method is a flocking procedure that is used on napped cottons. These flocks, as with wool, are forced into the fabric under air pressure. They can be detected in the same manner as with wool.

Calendering. *Calendering* is essentially an ironing process. It presses out folds or creases in the fabric by passing it around a series of heavy, highly polished steam-heated rollers that move at different rates of speed and have varying degrees of heat. Calendering flattens the fabric, removing inequality of surface. It imparts smoothness and luster, but not permanently. For highly lustrous effects, the fabric is sized before it is run through the calendering machine. The smoothness and the luster are determined by the degrees of heat and the amount of pressure, as well as by the amount of sizing if any is used.

The calendering process varies according to the type of finish desired. For a light calendering effect, the fabric is passed between cylinders without heat. The pressure alone removes wrinkles and imparts smoothness.

Close-up of the calender showing the cloth passing over heavy rolls, where it is smoothed and pressed.

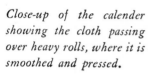

Courtesy Pepperell Manufacturing Co.

Wool fabrics are sometimes calendered or polished. The process adds a soft luster. Typical of such fabrics are wool broadcloth and sheen gabardine.

Schreinerizing. *Schreinerizing* is an inexpensive method for imparting luster to low-priced cottons. Steel rollers, finely engraved with lines and exerting a pressure of 4,500 pounds, impress on the fabric diagonal ridges ranging from 125 to 600 to the inch. Reflection of light from these ridges gives the fabric a lustrous effect somewhat similar to that produced by mercerization. But the luster produced by schreinerizing is not permanent, because the imprinted ridges disappear with repeated launderings. This finish is suitable, however, for lingerie fabrics and for linings and sateens, as the slightly rough surface produced by the diagonal ridges reduces the tendency of fabrics to cling. If the fabric has been mercerized, the additional schreinerizing produces a luster simulating that of silk.

Moiréing. By attaching engraved rollers to the calendering machine, the attractive, lustrous wavy design known as *moiré* can be produced. The best moiré results are obtained on fabrics that have rib effects in the filling. Fine lines are imprinted on the raised filling yarns by hydraulic engraved rollers exerting over 100,000 pounds pressure to the square inch. The luster is produced by the divergent reflection of light on the lines of the design.

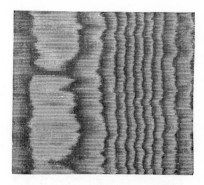

The best moiré results are obtained by imprinting the pattern on ribbed fabrics. Luster is produced by divergent reflections of light on the lines of the design.

Courtesy American Viscose Corp.

A moiré pattern on a rayon fabric is more lasting than the same pattern on a similar silk fabric, because the natural elasticity of silk does not permit the permanent retention of an embossed design. On acetate, moiré is definitely permanent, because acetate fabrics have a melting reaction when subjected to the heat of the moiréing process, thus absorbing and hardening the pattern as the cloth cools. A similar condition can be obtained with nylon because of its tendency to melt and to hold a shape.

An entirely different method of moiréing cotton is obtained by treating the fabric with a chemical and then embossing the cloth. The moiré is permanent provided the fabric is cared for properly. It should be washed with a mild soap in lukewarm water and never should be bleached.

Ciréing. The *ciré* process may be applied to silk and rayon, usually satins and taffetas. Wax or a similar compound is applied to the fabric, followed by hot calendering. The result is a supergloss almost metallic in appearance.

Beetling. *Beetling* is a common finishing process for linen. The yarns are flattened by the impact of wooden mallets. This hammering actually closes the weave and gives the cloth a firm, flattened, lustrous appearance. All table linen is put through this process, but dress linens are never beetled.

Beetling differs from calendering. The smoothness and gloss obtained by the calendering process are the result of horizontal pressing and are not permanent, whereas in beetling the action performed is a vertical impact that permanently flattens the yarns.

Cotton fabrics can be made to simulate linen by beetling, as the process gives cotton the firm feel and lustrous appearance of linen.

Napping. A napped fabric should not be confused with a pile-weave fabric. In the pile weave, the thickness is a true third dimension produced by loops from an extra warp or filling yarn. In the napped fabrics, the thickness is only a surface fuzziness that is the result of a brushing process. When a fabric is to be napped, the yarns intended for the construction of the cloth are given only a slack twist in the spinning process.

The fuzzy finish produced by napping makes a soft fabric, which provides warmth because of the insulative air cells in the nap. The thicker the nap, the more air cells, and the warmer the fabric. In men's suitings, where long wear is desired, a napped surface acts as a protection against objectionable luster. The fact that stains can be removed easily from a napped surface is an additional advantage. On the other hand, napping may also serve to cover up a sleazy construction as well as weaving imperfections. It is generally considered that excessive napping tends to weaken the fabric, especially where a heavy nap has been produced.

Single napping signifies that both sides of a cloth have been napped in one direction; *double napping* signifies that both surfaces have been napped in opposite directions, which produces greater surface density, increased firmness, and greater warmth. Flannelette, wool flannel, suede cloth, and duvetyn exemplify napped fabrics. Cotton and spun rayon fabrics are napped when a soft, fuzzy surface is desired.

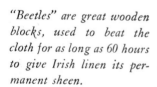

"Beetles" are great wooden blocks, used to beat the cloth for as long as 60 hours to give Irish linen its permanent sheen.

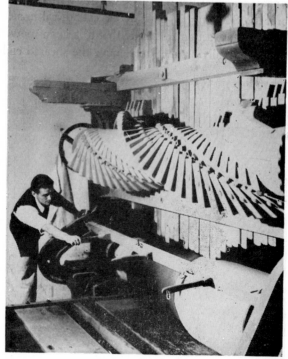

The teasel, a dried flower head with stiff, hooked bracts, is used to produce the fuzzy surface on napped fabrics.

Vegetable burs called *teasels* are used for napping finer grades of wool fabrics. Long cylindrical rollers containing closely set wires, which act like brushes, also perform the teaseling operation. As the brushes slide over the revolving fabric, they pull the top fibers and raise the protruding ends above the surface of the cloth in the form of a fleecelike nap. If a heavy nap is desired, teaseling is repeated several times.

• *Gigging*. Wool fabrics may be napped, or they may be subjected to a raising process called *gigging*. The fabric is first saturated with water. When the fibers of a moist wool fabric are raised, they tend to curl and shrink. When brushed in one direction, a smooth and lustrous appearance results.

Shearing. Pile-weave fabrics and fabrics that have been napped are usually sheared to give an attractive smooth surface to the cloth. Shearing levels all surface irregularities caused by the plucking action of the teasels in the napping process. Shearing is done by a cylindrical machine having rotating spiral blades whose action resembles that of a lawn mower. After shearing, the fabric is automatically brushed to remove the sheared ends of the yarns.

A rotating spiral blade shears surface irregularities from napped and pile fabrics. A brush (shown in lower part) removes the sheared ends.

Courtesy National Associated Wool Industries

Crepe and Crinkled Effects. The permanent types of crepe effects are obtained by the use of hard-twisted yarns in the weaving process, as described in Chapter 5. Crepe surfaces can also be produced by certain finishing processes, but the results are not so satisfactory. One finishing method imprints a crinkled effect by means of engraved rollers, similar to that produced when the thumbnail is drawn across tissue paper. The finish disappears with repeated washings, however.

In another finishing method, caustic soda is impressed on the fabric in the form of figures or stripes. The fabric is then washed. The part imprinted with the soda shrinks, and the other part puckers. A similar effect is obtained by using strips of wax in place of the caustic soda. Plissé crepes are produced by these methods. The degree of permanency of these crepe effects can be detected by pressing the thumb heavily on a portion of the fabric and stretching it sidewise at the same time. The ease with which the pressed portion will be smoothed, leaving no or little ripple on its surface, will indicate the relative permanency of the crepe.

A chemical method gives a crepe effect to silk by treating the fabric with concentrated sulphuric acid for a few minutes, followed by rinsing and neutralization with a weak alkali. There is a decrease in luster and a slight loss in strength. This method calls for careful manipulation, because too long an exposure in the acid injures the silk.

A permanent crinkle may be obtained on a fabric that will melt, such as nylon. The fabric is put through a hot roller on which there are raised figurations. The contact of the fabric against the raised hot surfaces causes it to melt and pucker at those points.

Crepe fabrics tend to stretch and shrink when subjected to any wetting operation.

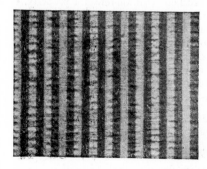

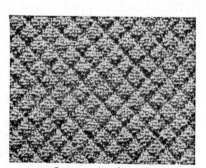

Courtesy American Viscose Corp.

In seersucker, a crinkled effect is obtained by the use of slack warp yarns.

In matelassé, a crinkled effect is produced by the Jacquard.

Crease Resistance. Both silk and wool enjoy a quality of elasticity that makes them resistant to wrinkling, creasing, or crushing. The vegetable fibers do not have such inherent elasticity. Slacks made of cotton, linen, or long-staple rayon, for example, are not so serviceable as wool slacks because the vegetable fibers crush easily. A crease-resistant finish for these fabrics is therefore desirable. Such a finish may be obtained in several ways.

The use of short-staple yarn, particularly in linen and rayon, produces a quality of softness in the fabric that makes it crease-resistant to some degree, but durability is sacrificed. The soft surface of a napped fabric also gives crease resistance. Fabrics with crepe surfaces possess a real crease-resistant quality, the degree being determined by the process used to produce the crepe surface.

Chemical methods are also used to give cotton and linen fabrics varying degrees of elasticity by impregnating the yarns with synthetic resins and gums. Phenol formaldehyde, urea formaldehyde, and acrylic resins are most commonly used. These produce an elasticity that does not disappear with dry cleaning and washing if the fabric is handled with care. There are several patented processes on the market today.

Anticrease Finish. In the anticrease process, a solution of formaldehyde resins is baked into the cloth, penetrating the fibers and resulting in a softened flexible fabric. Fabrics so treated are not absolutely crease-resistant, but they resist crushing, recover easily, and tend to shrink less in laundering. Because of the added weight of the resin, drapability is increased. This finish may be used on cotton, linen, rayon, and acetate fabrics.

Perma-Pressed. A wrinkle-resistant process applied to cotton fabrics.

Unidure. This finish is applied to spun rayons to avoid excessive wrinkles. Wrinkles that do occur will hang out. Unidure adds body to the fabric and improves the brightness and fastness of color. It also reduces shrinkage and stretch and is not affected by dampness and wilting weather.

Wat-A-Set. This is a wrinkle-resistant finish for cotton fabrics.

Wrinkl-Shed. This process gives cottons an excellent wrinkle-resistant property. It is difficult to wrinkle such cotton fabrics, and any wrinkles will hang out overnight. The finish does not come out and actually gives the fabric longer life.

Vitalized Finish. The Vitalized finish, also known by its English trade name *Tebilized,* is a patented crease-resistant process similar to the Anticrease finish. It gives additional "vitality," or elasticity, by the use of synthetic resins. It is applicable to both cotton and linen cloth. Fabrics so treated are heavier and shrink less. Washing or dry cleaning does not affect the finish.

Water Repellency. There is only one method of making a fabric permanently waterproof: by coating the surface of the cloth with rubber or with plasticized synthetic resins treated with solvents. The application of either of these solutions, repeated if desired with separate dryings, and subsequent vulcanizing or baking, closes the pores of the fabric, making it permanently impervious to water. But such waterproofing has the disadvantage of giving excess weight to the fabric and eliminating porosity, so important for health and comfort. When rubber solvent is used, cracks eventually appear in the surface coating.

Consumers prefer garments that have been made repellent to water rather than absolutely waterproof. The fabrics are sprayed or brushed with resins, waxes, metallic soaps, or linseed oil, which impregnate the fibers and fill in the spaces between the yarns, giving the fabric a water-repellent quality. Water-repellent fabrics must not be confused with waterproof fabrics. A water-repellent treatment does not affect the natural characteristics of a fabric, including its porosity. These protective coatings tend to disappear when exposed to friction and wear. A water-repellent quality, however, can always be restored to a fabric.

Silk can be made waterproof by treatment with oil, both sides of the cloth being coated with linseed oil varnish. This method changes the original appearance of the fabric: it produces a smooth hard surface and a quality of translucency. Oiled silk is popular for shower curtains and light raincoats.

Wool fabric has a natural water repellency that makes this fiber suitable for raincoats that are used in a light rain. Napped surfaces and fabrics with high thread count have natural water repellency. When fine, highly twisted yarns are constructed into fabrics having a high thread count, the garment is sometimes windproof as well as water-repellent.

Any fabric can be made water-repellent by spraying it with a solution of paraffin in benzine. A fine coating of paraffin is produced on the cloth. This finish is not permanent.

Some patented processes that have water-repellent features are: Cravenetting, Zelan, Aradex, Impregnole, Koroseal, Neva-Wet, Aquasec, Bandri, Hydrovised, Rainfoe, Repel-o-tex, Sayles Storm King, Wat-A-Tite

Cravenetting. The fabric to be made moisture-repellent is placed in a solution of aluminum stearate, pressed until dry, and then passed through a tallow soap solution. The aluminum stearate is precipitated on the fabric. With continued wear, fabrics so treated may lose some of their rainproof quality, as dry cleaning and high temperature tend to decompose the aluminum stearate coating. The finish is applied to wool fabrics.

Zelan. The E. I. du Pont de Nemours & Company has patented the Zelan process, which gives a water-repellent finish to cotton, linen, and viscose rayon. This finish can be applied only under carefully controlled conditions to the unfinished cloth at a finishing plant. To be effective, the Zelan finish must be applied after mercerization, but before any other finishing agent—such as soap, salt, oil, gum, or starch—is used. The treatment contains no rubber, wax, or insoluble soap. It does not coat the fabric but permeates and becomes a part of the fiber without impairing the natural porosity of the fabric. It is regarded as a permanent finish because its water-repellent quality endures repeated washings as well as dry cleanings. Other advantages that may be claimed for fabrics treated with Zelan are that stains and spots can be sponged off with a damp cloth, and that the fabrics resist perspiration and wrinkling, manifesting a softness of texture that improves appearance.

Aradex. The Aradex treatment, which is somewhat similar to the Zelan finish, uses a chemical emulsion that imparts qualities of water repellency, spot and stain resistance, and improved crease resistance. In contrast, the Aradex finish is not permanent, since it is affected by laundering and dry cleaning; but the finish can be restored after cleaning. Aradex does not coat the cloth and thus permits the normal circulation of air. The appearance and feel of the fabric are not impaired.

Impregnole. In the Impregnole process, a fatty emulsion is used that contains paraffin hydrocarbons and aluminum salts. This process makes cotton and wool fabrics water-repellent as well as resistant to spots, stains, perspiration, and wrinkles. One immersion is sufficient, and the emulsion is easily applied. Washing and dry cleaning remove this water-repellent quality, but the finish can be restored.

Koroseal. The Koroseal process can be applied to any finished fabric except acetate. It makes fabrics impervious to water, wind, moths, and mildew, and resistant to acid, grease, sunlight, perspiration, and stains. Koroseal fabrics do not contain any rubber or oil; consequently, they will not deteriorate by cracking, sticking, or peeling and therefore serve a multitude of uses. The coating applied to the surface of the fabric is plasticized white powder, polyvinyl chloride, which is obtained by compressing two gases—acetylene from coal and limestone, and hydrogen chloride from salt. The result is a tough, stretchable plastic coating having unusual properties.

Flameproofing.
Only mineral, asbestos, glass, or metal substances are really fireproof. Textile fabrics cannot be made absolutely fireproof, but they can be chemically treated to retard inflammability. Fabrics so treated may be regarded as flameproof, which means that they will not flame or burn actively. *Flameproofing* is a practical form of fire protection where a fire-resistant quality is desirable, as in fabrics used for awnings, mattresses, work clothes, or draperies.

The objection to most fire-retardant compounds is that the fabric so treated loses this quality in washing or in dry cleaning. Also, such compounds sometimes affect the feel of a fabric, causing it to lose softness and flexibility. Where the fire-retardant quality is lost in washing or in dry cleaning, it can be restored by reprocessing with a commercial fire-retardant compound. Some of the trade-marked names that indicate a fire-retardant quality are Du Pont, Fire-Retardant, Saniflame, Neva-Flame. These are applicable to all fabrics except acetate. Permaproof 300 has been described as the first finish that permits cloth to be laundered repeatedly without losing its fire-retardant properties.

Among the most effective flameproofing compounds is one that uses ammonium sulphamate. It makes a fabric fire-resistant without imparting a harsh quality. The fabric must be reprocessed after washing, but this is not necessary after dry cleaning, as the ammonium sulphamate finish is fast to dry-cleaning solvents.

Textile fabrics may be given a fire-resistant quality by a simple home method of immersing them in a solution of 70 per cent borax and 30 per cent boric acid. If the fabric to be treated is already water-repellent, soap should be added to the solution so that an even wetness and absorbency will be obtained. This method does not alter the appearance of the fabric, but the treatment must be repeated after every washing.

Mothproofing. Wool fabrics are sometimes mothproofed as one of the finishing operations to the cloth by impregnating the yarns with a chemical. Of all these preparations, tests seem to indicate that the most effective are Mitin F F, Eulan C N, and Lanoc C N. These are fast to other finishing processes as well as dry cleaning, but are only moderately fast to washing.

Simple home methods of moth-damage prevention comprise daily brushing of apparel after wearing, frequent exposure to sunlight, and dry cleaning before placing the garments in airtight storage and cold storage at a maximum temperature of 40 degrees Fahrenheit. For additional protection, various commercial compounds are available for use in the home. Among these are naphthalene and paradichlorobenzene (moth balls, flakes, and cakes). These do not act as a repellent, as is commonly thought. They will actually kill the moth, eggs, and larvae, provided the closet, chest, or package containing the wool fabrics is airtight. The atmosphere must be thoroughly saturated for these substances to be effective. The container should be hung above the clothes so that the vapor will flow down over them.

Many sprays are also available. Some of these—such as Atomoth, Berlou, Boconize, Larvex, and Ya-De—contain either a fluoride or silicofluoride. These are very stable to exposure to light and air and are not removed by dry cleaning. They are, however, water-soluble and also may give rise to white markings when the fabric is rubbed. They also may cause a harshening of the fabric's hand. Products containing carbon tetrachloride, such as Moth Gas, are also effective but are inflammable. Others containing arsenic, such as Per Mo, are poisonous to humans as well as to moth larvae.

Products containing DDT in concentrations of at least 5 per cent kill moth grubs quickly. These sprays are sold under such proprietary names as Black Flag, Gulf Trak, and SLA. However, DDT has the disadvantage of dry-cleaning and washing out.

Mildewproofing. The use of sizing in finishing makes a fabric susceptible to mildew if it is later exposed to moisture and warmth.

To prevent mildew, inorganic salts—such as magnesium chloride, calcium chloride, and zinc chloride—are used as warp sizing. Washing, however, tends to remove the mildewproof quality. Among recent developments has been the use of turpentine and formaldehyde as preventives. One compound that is not easily washed out is a 1–2000 solution of phenyl mercuric acetate in water. This is one of the most effective mildewproofing agents.

Shower curtains or other cotton fabrics may be mildewproofed at home by soaking the material in very soapy water, then, without rinsing, dipping it into a solution of copper sulphate. Antiseptics, such as boric acid and carbolic acid, also prevent rapid growth of the mildew fungus.

Milium.   Milium treatment adds a coating of metallic particles on one side of a fabric to give remarkable warmth-retentive properties. Any fabric to be used as a lining can be coated with this resinated metal (usually aluminum) spray, which adds less than an ounce to the weight of the lining and does not interfere with the porosity or pliability of the fabric. The metal prevents body heat from radiating outward through the garment by reflecting the heat back toward the wearer. Tests using a wind velocity of 15 miles an hour have shown that a wool outer fabric with a milium satin lining is approximately equal in warmth to an untreated satin lining plus an 8½-ounce wool interlining with the same outer fabric.

Slip Resistance.   In fabrics that have a low thread count, the warp yarns sometimes slip along the filling yarns. Unusual wear or strain on some part of a fabric may cause the same action, known as *slipping*. It is not frequent with rough-surfaced fabrics made of hard-twisted yarns. Permanent firmness can be given to fabrics by immersing them in synthetic resins, then stretching and drying them under tension. The deposit of resin at the points of interlacing in the weave prevents the yarns from slipping. This treatment is advantageous for smooth-surfaced rayons, as the smoothness of the synthetic yarn causes it to slip and fray. Fabrics labeled "slip-resistant" should be examined closely for thread count, as the resinous coating may be used to create an effect of compact construction.

Slippage at the seams may be the result of low thread count as well as poor construction of the fabric.

Courtesy U.S. Department of Agriculture

Antiseptic Finishes. Chemical antiseptic finishes impart a self-sterilizing quality to a fabric. The appearance and the feel of the fabric are unchanged, and no chemical odor remains. Dry cleaning does not impair the finish. Sanitized, Hygienized, Sani-Age, and Vita-Fresh are trade-marked names exemplifying these finishes.

Drip-Dry Finishes. Several processes utilizing chemical resins have been developed for treating cotton fabrics so that garments made of fabrics with drip-dry finishes will dry smooth and need little or no ironing after washing. In addition to this advantage, such fabrics have the usual properties of moisture absorption, soft hand, and neat appearance of untreated cotton fabrics. Drip-dry finishes have been used primarily on broadcloth and oxford shirting. *only Cotton*

Each company has its own trade name for its drip-dry finish, and its effectiveness depends on the particular process. Among the most widely advertised finishes are AMC—Bradford, Arrow Wash-and-wear 100% Cotton, Dri-Smooth, Manhattan Mansmooth, and Van Heusen Vantage All Cotton.

Garments made of fabrics treated with drip-dry finishes usually may be commercially laundered. The primary advantage, however, is that such garments launder easily at home and need no ironing. This tends to increase their wear since home laundering is less harsh. In some cases, it is advisable to use a mild soap. Generally, bleaches may be safely used. Do not wring such garments or spin-dry them in a washing machine or in a dryer. Rinse them well, hang them on wooden or plastic hangers, buttoned and straightened out, and allow them to drip-dry. Metal hangers may cause rust stains.

Not all drip-dry finishes produce the same results. Some garments tend to pucker at the seams when they dry; some require quick, light ironing with a cool iron. Since the care of drip-dry finished garments varies with the particular finish, read the instructions on the garment tag to determine which is best suited to your needs. In any event, follow the care instructions for most satisfactory results.

Note that drip-dry finishes are applied only to all-cotton fabrics. There are other fabrics (studied in later chapters) that are referred to as drip-dry or wash-and-wear. These are constructed entirely of thermoplastic man-made or synthetic fibers or of such fibers in blends with natural fibers. The extent to which garments made of such fabrics will drip-dry and have shape retention is dependent on the inherent properties of the fibers and on the proportion of thermoplastic fibers in the fabric—not on the finish.

Embossing. The process of producing raised figures or designs in relief on surfaces of fabrics by passing the cloth between heated engraved rollers is known as *embossing*. The process can be applied to fabrics made of all types of fibers with the exception of wool. This finish is permanent when applied to fabrics made of thermoplastic fibers. It is not permanent when applied to untreated fabrics made of natural fibers or man-made fibers that are not thermoplastic; however, if these fabrics are treated with certain chemical resins, the embossing is considered to be permanent. To preserve the embossed finish of such fabrics, they should be washed in lukewarm water with a mild soap, never be bleached, and be ironed on the wrong side while damp.

When plain-woven fabrics treated with these chemical resins are embossed, they can resemble fabrics that are generally more expensive. The decorative effects also enhance the beauty of the cloth. Various trade names, such as Picolay and Clokay, have been given to particular fabrics of this type. There have also been trade names, such as Everglaze, which apply to a group of fabrics similarly treated to produce a variety of effects.

▶ TEST YOURSELF ON THIS CHAPTER

1. Describe one important preparatory finishing process for smooth-surfaced fabrics.
2. Name six finishing processes for producing luster.
3. In each pair of the following finishes, which type is preferable and why? (*a*) waterproof or water-repellent; (*b*) fireproof or flame-resistant?
4. What is the purpose of weighting? Why would it be unwise to buy a heavily weighted silk garment?
5. Explain two finishing methods by which a crinkled effect is achieved.
6. What is the result of beetling? How does it compare with schreinerizing?
7. How is starch used in finishing fabrics?
8. Explain the following processes: singeing, mercerizing, calendering.
9. How may a finishing process deceive the consumer?
10. Discuss shrinkage, telling (*a*) why it occurs, (*b*) whether it can be prevented entirely, (*c*) methods preferable for cotton, (*d*) methods preferable for wool.
11. Discuss the advantages of napping. Name the disadvantages, if any.
12. What fabrics are naturally crease-resistant? How can this quality be produced in other fabrics?
13. What method of bleaching is preferable? Is there any advantage in buying unbleached fabrics?
14. Why are finishing processes necessary?
15. Explain tentering and crabbing.
16. Visit the yard-goods department of a large retail store. Obtain the name of the finishers of ten different fabrics by noting the labels. Describe the fabrics, appearance, and finish characteristics.
17. What is meant by a drip-dry or wash-and-wear garment?
18. How effective is the drip-dry finish?
19. How are fabrics embossed?
20. Under what circumstances will embossing on fabrics be permanent?

7 · DYEING | Finishing with Color

As the textile fibers have been examined and tested for their differential qualities and as the spinning and weaving processes have been explained, the qualities of durability and serviceability have been constantly stressed. When the yarn is woven into fabric, the interesting and intricate designs of weaves begin to add beauty of appearance as well as serviceability. The various finishing processes suggest additional means of enhancing the appearance of the newly formed fabric. It remains for the dyeing and printing processes to provide lasting beauty and delight to the eye. Both these processes add color to fabrics, and color delights by stimulating or soothing. Dyeing and printing differ in the method by which color is applied to fabric. In the dyeing process, fiber, yarn, or fabric is immersed in a solution of dyestuff and is thus saturated with the dye. In printing (described in the following chapter), a pattern or a design is imprinted on the fabric in one or more colors by using dyes in paste form.

Selection of Dye. To select the proper dye for a fiber, it is necessary to know which dyes have an affinity for the vegetable, animal, man-made, or synthetic fibers. In general, the dyes used for cotton and linen may be used for viscose and cuprammonium rayons; but it was necessary to produce a special class of dyes for acetate. When a dye colors fabric directly with one simple operation of immersion, without the aid of an affixing agent, the dye is said to be a direct dye for that fiber. Direct dyes are the easiest to produce, the simplest to apply, and the cheapest in their initial cost as well as in application. They are the most fugitive, however; that is, they are not fast to washing or to light. The term *bleeding* describes dyes that run in washing. When dye rubs off a fabric exposed to the friction of wear, it is termed *crocking*.

Requirements for colorfastness differ. Fastness to *light* is important in draperies, for example, as they must stand strong light daily but do not need to be washed frequently. Fastness to *washing* is important in dress fabrics and household linens because they must undergo frequent washings. Therefore, both the kind of fiber to be dyed and the intended use for the fabric enter into the selection of the dye.

Mordants. A dye that has an affinity for one type of fiber may not adhere to other types of fibers. But it is possible to dye finished fabric containing a mixture of fibers by using a mordant in the dye bath. Salts of metals and tannic acid are typical examples of such chemical agents. The mordant adheres to the fiber for which the dye has no affinity, and the dye adheres to the mordant. Such dyes are called *mordant* or *adjective* dyes.

Natural Dyes. Primitive man obtained dyes from flowers, nuts, berries, and other forms of vegetable and plant life, as well as from mineral and animal sources. These sources have provided such "natural dyes" throughout civilization. They are no longer used in quantity by the dyeing industry, but they are still used in Oriental countries to a certain extent for rug dyeing and in many parts of the world for native handicraft.

The principal vegetable dyes are: fustic, sumac, catechu or cutch, madder, henna, saffron, logwood, indigo, and alizarin. Animal dyes, such as cochineal, squid sepia, lac, and Tyrian purple, are obtained from species of fish and small insects. Minerals provide such dyes as Prussian blue, chrome yellow, and iron buff.

Artificial Dyes. Although artificial dyes were first derived from coal tar in 1856, they were not developed in the United States to any great extent until World War I, when the supply of imported synthetic dyes was cut off. Since then, the United States has built up a dye industry that is unsurpassed. Innumerable dye compounds made from coal tar have now supplanted natural dyes. These artificial or synthetic dyes are constantly being improved as to beauty of color and colorfastness. Lasting beauty of color is an important factor in consumers' finished goods. Durability of color depends on: (1) selection of the proper dye for the fiber to be dyed; (2) selection of the method of dyeing the fiber, yarn, or fabric.

Classification of Synthetic Dyes. The synthetic dyes are classified as (1) acid, (2) basic or alkali, (3) neutral or substantive. The acid dyes are used chiefly for wool, and the basic dyes chiefly for silk. The substantive dyes are a new class especially adapted for cotton, linen, and rayons. For this reason, they are called direct cotton dyes. They are also known by the specific names that describe their method of application: direct or salt dyes, developed dyes, sulphur dyes, vat dyes, and naphthol or azoic dyes.

• *Acid Dyes.* In the textile industry, acid dyes are known as *commercial colors.* They are used as direct dyes for wool and Vicara; they are also used when delicate tints are required for silk. Acid dyes also may be used on Orlon, Acrilan, Dynel, and Creslan. They can be applied with some difficulty to nylon.

Acid dyes are inexpensive and fairly fast to light, but they are not fast to washing. Acetic acid or sulphuric acid, and sometimes Glauber's salt (sodium sulphate), is used in the dye bath.

Wool may be given increased fastness to both light and washing by boiling the fabric in a chromate solution after the first dye bath. This is called after-chroming. A special group of acid dyes known as *chrome dyes* is used.

• *Basic Dyes.* Basic dyes are direct dyes and have been used chiefly for silk because they give brilliant, full colors. They can also be used with a mordant for cotton, linen, acetate, nylon, Orlon, Acrilan, Dynel, Creslan, and Verel. Basic dyes are not fast to light, washing, perspiration, or atmospheric influences; they tend to bleed or crock. These dyes are frequently used as an aftertreatment for fabrics that have been previously dyed with acid colors.

• *Direct or Salt Dyes.* Direct dyes for cotton and linen, and viscose and cuprammonium rayons are known as *direct cotton dyes* because they achieve very bright, full colors for that fabric. They are sometimes used for reclaimed wool and for inferior grades of wool. When so used, a small amount of acid must be used. Direct dyes may also be used for nylon, Dynel, and Creslan. A limited range of direct-dye colors is also possible for Acrilan.

Because sodium chloride (household salt) is included in the dye solution, direct cotton dyes are also known as *salt dyes*. The salt helps to drive the color into the fabric by lessening the solubility of the dye in water. The process is one of simple immersion and absorption rather than one requiring affixing chemical agents or compounds. When direct dyes are used for cotton fabrics, they do not need to be bleached, except when a half bleach is necessary to prepare the fabric for light shades.

Direct dyes are not fast to washing. An aftertreatment with potassium bichromate or formaldehyde gives an additional degree of fastness in washing. A similar treatment with copper sulphate increases fastness to light. More expensive operations, such as are used in developed, sulphur, vat, and naphthol or azoic dyes, produce additional degrees of colorfastness.

• *Developed Dyes.* Developed dyes are used for cotton, linen, rayon, acetate, Arnel, Dacron, Acrilan, and Darvan. The color is developed by additional treatments, which also make the dye fast to washing. But developed dyes are not fast to light. As these dyes do not bleed, they are called *tub-fast colors,* and are used for women's apparel that must withstand frequent washings.

Developed dyes cost more because of extra operations. After the fabric has been immersed in a suitable dye bath and rinsed, it is dipped in a cold acid solution of sodium nitrite; this process is known as *diazotizing*. The original dye is transformed into an active chemical, which is combined with a developer (beta naphthol) in another cold bath. This third treatment develops a new color that is insoluble in water and therefore fast to washing. Developed dyes are also fast to acids and alkalies.

• *Sulphur Dyes.* Sulphur dyes are used for cotton, linen, and viscose rayon. These dyes are fast to washing, light, and perspiration, but have one weakness: excessive chlorine bleaching will strip the color. They are more expensive than direct dyes because unusual care is required in extra operations.

Sulphur is insoluble in water, but it is made soluble with the aid of sodium sulphide and soda ash. The dyeing is done at high temperature and with a large quantity of salt, which helps to drive the color into the fabric. After immersion in the dye bath, followed by rinsing, the fabric is oxidized to the desired shade by exposure to the air or, chemically, by the use of potassium bichromate and acetic acid. The oxidizing process must be carefully controlled because penetration of the dye is retarded by premature oxidation. Also, oxidation changes sulphur to sulphuric acid, which may be harmful to the fabric. Excess chemicals and excess dye must be completely removed by thorough washing. Sulphur dyes penetrate more thoroughly than any other dye because of the high temperature and the alkalinity of the dye bath. They are excellent for khaki and for the heavy piece goods used in work clothes. Sulphur dyes produce dull colors, such as navy, brown, and black. They are used for blacks more than any other dye. If stored for a great length of time, fabrics become tender.

• *Vat Dyes.* Vat dyes are the fastest dyes for cotton, linen, and rayon. They also may be applied to nylon, Dacron, Orlon, Acrilan, Dynel, Creslan, Zefran, and Vicara with the use of a mordant. Vat dyes are not only resistant to light and to acids and alkalies, but they are equally resistant to the strong oxidizing bleaches used in commercial laundries. In this respect, vat dyes excel sulphur dyes, which are not fast to chlorine washing. In reds and pinks, however, absolute colorfastness is sacrificed for brilliancy of dye. Consequently, a label stating that a garment is vat-dyed is not a guarantee that the fabric is absolutely fast to washing if it is of brilliant color. The name "Indanthrene" on labels indicates that a special type of dye has been used that is particularly fast to light and to washing. This type was among the first of the synthetic vat dyes.

The old-fashioned method of fermenting and steeping indigo in a vat gave vat dyes their name. They are prepared today on the same principle, but they are chemically purer and the process is shorter. Vat dyes are expensive because of the initial cost as well as the method of application. They are insoluble pigments; but they are made soluble in water by the use of a strong reducing agent, such as hydrosulphite dissolved in the alkali, sodium hydroxide. The fabric is immersed in this solution. Subsequent exposure to air or immersion in an oxidizing bath (bichromate) restores the dye to its insoluble form as a part of the fiber.

• *Naphthol or Azoic Dyes.* Naphthol or azoic dyes are as satisfactory as vat dyes in their fastness to washing and to strong bleaching agents, but not in fastness to light. When a bright red that will be fast to washing and to light is desired for cotton or rayon, a naphthol red dye is used. Azoic dyes also may be used for acetate, Arnel, nylon, Acrilan, Dacron, and Vicara.

The method of applying these dyes is somewhat similar to that of developed dyes, as it involves diazotizing. The fabric is first immersed in naphthol, which impregnates the fibers; it is then dipped into the diazotized color bath. The dyeing is followed by thorough soaping and rinsing. Naphthol or azoic dyes are sometimes referred to as *ice dyes* because ice is frequently used to bring the the dyes to a low temperature.

• *AZO Dyes.* AZO dyes, which are sulphonic acid dyes, account for almost half the total production of dyes. In the use of AZO dyes, the fiber may be treated with a chroming solution that deepens the color and produces a greater fastness on the fiber.

• *Acetate Dyes.* When acetate was first made, it could not be colored with dyes that were available at that time. Special acetate dyes were produced after experimentation. These dyes do not have affinity for any of the natural fibers or rayon. They will dye nylon, Dacron, Acrilan, Dynel, Creslan, and Verel, but the final shade of the color will not be the same as the acetate shade. Acetate dyes may be used on all man-made and synthetic fibers with varying degrees of success.

Two groups of acetate dyes are now used: (1) those that dye directly, and (2) those that require diazotizing and affixing agents in developing the color. Some of the earliest acetate dyes are known as S.R.A. dyes. This name was derived from "sulphoricinoleic," the acid required to make the dyes soluble in water.

Selection of Method of Dyeing. Textiles may be dyed at any stage of their development from fiber into fabric by the following methods:

Stock dyeing, in the fiber stage
Yarn dyeing, after the fiber has been spun into yarn
Piece dyeing, after the yarn has been constructed into fabric
Cross-dyeing, a combination of either stock dyeing or yarn dyeing, with subsequent piece dyeing
Solution pigmenting or dyeing, before the man-made or synthetic fiber is extruded through the spinneret

Stock Dyeing. In stock dyeing, the fibers are immersed in a dye bath, and the dyestuff is allowed to penetrate them. This method is considered most desirable because maximum penetration may be expected when material is in this form. A dye that penetrates to the center of a fiber will resist rubbing; therefore, stock-dyed fabrics are likely to be colorfast. Yarns spun from dyed fibers are uniformly colored. If there is any irregularity of color, it is evened up in the subsequent carding, drawing-out, and spinning operations. Dyed fibers are more difficult to spin than undyed ones, however, because a degree of flexibility is lost in the dyeing process.

Woolens are often stock-dyed. The completeness of this method is reflected in the expression, "dyed in the wool," which is used to attribute the quality of thoroughness. Stock dyeing produces mixture effects and color blends, of which oxford suitings and tweed homespuns are examples.

Yarn Dyeing. When dyeing is done after the fiber has been spun into yarn, the fabric is described as *yarn-dyed*. This method is also sometimes referred to as *skein dyeing;* the yarn is on spools or is in the form of skeins when immersed in the dye bath. The dyestuff has a chance to penetrate to the core of the

Courtesy Pepperell Manufacturing Co.

Cotton-staple stock dyed in a kettle containing 1,000 pounds of fiber.

Plaids are constructed of yarns dyed in the yarn stage.

Courtesy National Association of Wool Manufacturers

yarn, similar to the penetration of the fiber in stock dyeing. Yarn-dyed fabrics are usually deeper and richer in color, and tend to be more colorfast than when the fabric is dyed after it is woven. When yarns have been dyed separately, interesting color effects can be introduced into the weaving process by combining yarns of different colors. In such fabrics, the warp yarn is usually one color; and the filling, another color. Combinations of different-colored yarns are checked gingham, striped percale, shepherd's check, plaid, chambray, seersucker, and heather mixtures.

Courtesy Bibb Manufacturing Co.

In package dyeing (a form of yarn dyeing), bobbins or cones of yarn on a single large rack (at left in picture) are immersed at one time in a huge vat.

Piece Dyeing. When cloth is dyed after it is woven, the process is called *piece dyeing,* sometimes *dip dyeing.* In piece-dyed fabrics, the dye does not penetrate and envelop the fibers or yarns as in stock dyeing or yarn dyeing. But this method is advantageous to the manufacturer because it permits him to keep his production close to changing fashion demands. When fabric is to be piece-dyed, it is woven "in the gray," and can be subsequently dyed to supply any current seasonal color. This method is also economical because less dyestuff is required. It is commonly used for the less expensive fabrics.

Piece dyeing is limited to the production of solid colors, but two-color effects may be obtained by constructing the fabric of fibers or yarns that have been specially treated so as to take a deeper color or to absorb no color at all. From the point of view of the consumer, piece dyeing is the least desirable process, because complete penetration does not take place and the fabric may fade. When light spots show at frequent intervals, this is an indication that the fabric was piece-dyed; in this case, only the surface of the yarns took the dye. The consumer can generally detect piece dyeing by raveling and untwisting a single yarn, and examining the innermost part to see whether the dye has penetrated. Piece dyeing is used for a wide variety of fabrics: linens, silk crepes, and sheer cottons, such as organdy and voile.

Cross-Dyeing. Cross-dyeing is a combination of stock dyeing or of yarn dyeing with subsequent piece dyeing. Cross-dyeing produces varied effects. For

Piece dyeing in a modern stainless-steel dye vat.

Courtesy St. Mary's Woolen Manufacturing Co.

instance, either the warp or the filling yarns may be stock-dyed or yarn-dyed, one set of yarns being left undyed. The fabric is piece-dyed after weaving; thus, color is given to the undyed yarn in a second dye bath, and the yarns that were originally stock-dyed or yarn-dyed acquire some additional coloring, which blends with the piece-dyed portion of the fabric.

If yarns of vegetable fibers have been combined with yarns of animal fibers in a fabric that is to be piece-dyed, two separate dye baths must be used. The fabric is dipped into both solutions, each of which affects the fiber for which it has an affinity. This provides colorful effects.

A mordant can be included in a single dye bath to cause the dye to adhere to the fiber for which it does not have an affinity. Thus, the more expensive method of cross dyeing, requiring two dye baths, need not be used.

Still another method of cross-dyeing is to immerse a fabric composed of two different types of fibers into one dye bath containing two different dyes, one specific for each of the fibers. For example, a fabric composed of viscose rayon and acetate yarns may be cross-dyed in this manner. When the fabric is removed from the dye bath, the viscose rayon yarns will be one color, and the acetate yarns will be another color.

Solution Pigmenting or Dyeing. In producing man-made or synthetic fibers, a great deal of time and money can be saved if the dye is added to the solution before it is extruded through the spinnerets into filaments. This method also gives a greater degree of colorfastness. A process called *solution pigmenting* or dyeing has been used with varying degrees of success for man-made and synthetic fibers ranging from rayon through Saran and Fiberglas. Some effective results have been obtained.

Two outstanding examples of the solution-pigmenting process for acetate fiber are Chromspun and Celaperm. The former is the trade name for the process developed by the Tennessee Eastman Company; the latter is the trade name for a similar process developed by the Celanese Corporation of America. These solution-pigmenting processes were developed to overcome two problems in dyeing acetate yarns and fabrics: inability to absorb dyes well and evenly, and the tendency to fade, particularly gas-fade. Chromspun and Celaperm insure uniform color and colorfastness to gas, light, perspiration, salt (sea) water, washing, and dry cleaning.

Tests to Determine Colorfastness. Beauty of color in any fabric is of no value to the consumer unless the dye may be considered fast under the conditions in which the fabric will be used. Color must meet such tests as washing, ironing, steaming, perspiration, strong light, and dry cleaning. The United

States Government tests fabrics for colorfastness to maintain and enforce trade standards. Retail stores often have laboratories for testing consumers' goods to maintain merchandise standards for their own protection as well as to give their customers proper value for the price paid. The consumer may also test fabrics for colorfastness at home. Garments will give additional wear and retain a fresh, new appearance if samples of the fabrics are tested before the garments are subjected to cleaning at home or commercially.

• *Fastness to Washing*. The usual method for determining fastness to washing is to wash and then iron under a white cloth a sample of the fabric while it is still wet. If the dye bleeds on the cloth, the color cannot be considered fast. Home washing is not a rigorous enough test for fabrics that will be washed in commercial laundries. A more adequate test is to immerse the sample in water containing a bleach, such as Clorox, or in Javelle water, because similar strong compounds are used in the laundries.

• *Fastness to Ironing*. To test for fastness to ironing, iron the sample with a very hot iron. After the sample has cooled, compare it with the original fabric. If the color is unchanged, the fabric is fast to ironing.

• *Fastness to Steaming*. To test for fastness to steaming, place a sample between the folds of a white cloth, and steam it over a teakettle. If the color is fast, it should be unchanged, and no dye will show on the white cloth.

• *Fastness to Light*. To test for fastness to light, cover half a sample of fabric with opaque paper and expose it to outdoor light for perhaps 20 days. Then compare both halves. If the exposed portion shows perceptible fading, the fabric is not fast to light. A more specific time for exposure cannot be given, because the intensity of sunlight varies in different localities. Usually, resistance to exposure of 20 days is considered good.

This test is performed in a much shorter time in textile testing laboratories by the use of the Fade-Ometer, an apparatus having very strong electric lamps or a special carbon arc light. If a fabric can withstand an exposure of 40 hours in this machine with no perceptible loss of color, it is said to have superlative fastness to light. A fabric has good fastness to light if it withstands an exposure of 30 hours.

• *Fastness to Perspiration*. To test for fastness to perspiration, soak a sample of the dyed fabric for 10 minutes in a weak acid, such as a dilute acetic acid solution. Do not rinse. Roll the sample in a piece of undyed cloth. Permit gradual drying, and leave the material rolled for a few days. If comparison with the original color shows that the shade of the dyed fabric has changed, or if the dye appears on the cloth in which the sample was rolled, the color is not fast to perspiration.

The Fade-Ometer is used for testing colorfastness to sunlight. Samples of fabric are placed between slides and are exposed to the rays of a sun lamp for a period of hours or days. After removal, the samples are compared with an unexposed piece of fabric to determine the extent of loss of color.

Courtesy American Viscose Corp.

The effects of both acid and alkaline perspiration can be determined by the standard Government test, which recommends the use of two solutions. *For acid perspiration:* 10 grams sodium chloride; 1 gram lactic acid, U.S.P. 85 per cent; 1 gram disodium orthophosphate, anhydrous. Make up to 1 liter with water. *For alkaline perspiration:* 10 grams sodium chloride; 4 grams ammonium carbonate, U.S.P.; 1 gram disodium orthophosphate, anhydrous. Make up to 1 liter with water. Samples of the dyed fabric are placed against pieces of undyed cloth and left for a few days in each solution. The pieces of dyed fabric and undyed cloth are then squeezed and allowed to dry. Any indication of staining denotes poor fastness to perspiration.

• *Fastness to Crocking.* To test for fastness to crocking, rub a dry sample against a white cloth; make the same test with a wet sample. If the color does not rub off on the white cloth, the color is fast to rubbing or crocking.

• *Fastness to Gas Fading.* Flames from heating appliances cause nitrogen in the atmosphere to unite with oxygen, forming nitrogenous compounds that cause some acetate dyes to lose color if the fumes come in contact with the fabric. This is known as gas fading or acid fading in acetate; blue is especially susceptible. An antifume finish of an alkaline nature can be applied to a fabric to minimize gas fading, by the use of an inhibiter in the dye. Fabrics can be tested to determine the permanency of their antifume finish by exposure for about 20 hours in a chamber containing the combustible fumes of a gas burner.

ARTIFICIAL DYES RANKED BY COST AND DEGREE OF FASTNESS[1]

Type of Dye	Home Washing	Commercial Laundry	Light	Slashing	Bleaching (Chlorine)	Cross-Dyeing	Mercerizing
Direct	Good in light shades; poor in heavy shades	Poor	Some poor, some good	Good in light shades; heavy require care	Bad	Bad	Some good
Basic	Poor	Bad	Bad	Require extreme care	Bad	Bad	Bad
Sulphur	Good	Fair to poor	Good	Excellent	Bad	Good	Good
Developed	Good	Fair to poor	Poor	Excellent	Bad	Good	Good
Naphthol	Excellent	Excellent	Very good	Excellent	Excellent (not good to peroxide)	Excellent	Excellent
Vat	Excellent	Excellent	Excellent	Excellent	Excellent	Excellent	Excellent

[1] Courtesy Franklin Process Company. The sequence runs from the less expensive direct dyes to the more expensive vat dyes.

▶ TEST YOURSELF ON THIS CHAPTER

1. What are the essential differences between stock, yarn, and piece dyeing?
2. Explain the importance of dyeing from the consumer's point of view.
3. What is vat dyeing? When would it be used?
4. Discuss both the limitations and the advantages of direct dyes.
5. Discuss the advantages and the limitations of acid dyes.
6. When is cross-dyeing used?
7. Explain the following terms: fugitive, crocking, bleeding, gas fading.

8. What is a mordant? Explain how it is used in dyeing.
9. Why may warp yarns be dyed in the fiber stage or in the yarn stage instead of using the piece-dyeing method entirely?
10. What two factors enter into the selection of a dye?
11. What type of fabrics need to be colorfast to washing? to light? to perspiration?
12. What kinds of dyes are used for the animal fibers? for the vegetable fibers? for man-made and synthetic fibers?
13. Why is salt often put into a dye bath?
14. What happens to sulphur-dyed fabrics if stored for a long time?
15. Why are direct dyes the least desirable for the general consumer?
16. Why are vat-dyed fabrics the most desirable for the general consumer?
17. What is solution dyeing? What are its advantages?
18. What characteristic is common to yarn dyeing and skein dyeing?
19. What factors determine the durability of a dye?
20. Explain the difference between dyeing and printing.
21. Describe briefly the methods and stages of dyeing.
22. Explain how to test colorfastness to: (*a*) light, (*b*) washing, (*c*) crocking.
23. Obtain small samples of colored fabrics, and test them for colorfastness. Report the procedure used in your test and your findings.
24. Examine the labels on three pieces of apparel or household furnishings. Copy each label on a sheet of paper, and write your interpretation of each label in terms of the textile information that you have acquired.

8 · DECORATION | With Color Design

The yarns produced in the spinning process create some form of decoration in the fabric. Later, in the weaving process, decoration is also obtained by the pattern of the weave. The checkerboard pattern of the plain weave, the variations of the basket construction, the diagonal of the twill weave, and the luster of the satin weave produce simple designs. This type of decoration becomes more elaborate as fabric construction advances to the use of the third dimension in the pile weave, to the open-mesh lacelike effect of the lappet weave, and to the intricate effects of the Jacquard weave as seen in damask, brocade, and brocatelle fabrics.

When fabric passes through finishing operations, it is given lustrous effects that contribute further to its final appearance. Other finishing processes create the additional effects of soft napped surfaces and the crinkled designs seen in seersucker, matelassé, and similar crepes. Dyeing makes an important contribution to fabric decoration by the many beautiful colors it produces and the color harmonies obtained by combinations of the various dyeing methods. Fabric can be still further enhanced or decorated by printing color designs on the finished cloth.

Methods of Decoration with Color. One form of applying color decoration to a fabric after it has otherwise been finished is called *printing*. Fabric that is to be printed must be singed, bleached, and cleaned. The methods producing color designs are:

Block printing
Roller printing
Duplex printing
Discharge or extract printing
Resist printing
Stencil printing
Screen printing

Warp printing
Photo printing
Batik dyeing
Tie dyeing
Composition or paste designs
Spray painting

In most of these methods, the dye is imprinted on the fabric in paste form; and any desired pattern may be produced. Paste dyes require a sizing, such as cornstarch or wheat starch, which acts as a binder. In this method of applying color, thorough penetration of the dye is not necessary.

Courtesy Celanese Corp. of America

Machine-printed fabrics.

Distinguishing Printing from Dyeing. To know whether a fabric has been dyed by immersion or whether the color has merely been printed on the cloth, examine the outline of the design. On the printed fabric, the outline or edges of the design are sharply defined on the right side. The entire design seldom penetrates to the wrong side.

On sheer fabrics, the design may show up favorably on the wrong side because dyestuffs will penetrate sheer construction. Such fabrics may intentionally simulate woven designs, which use yarn-dyed warp and filling. Examine some of the raveled yarns. If the design has been imprinted, the yarns will show areas on which the color is not equally distributed.

Block Printing. The oldest method of printing designs on fabric is the hand method called *block printing*. This method is not commercially important because it is too slow—printed fabric cannot be produced inexpensively in large enough quantities by the hand-blocked method. Block printing has usually been done in countries where labor is less costly than in the United States. Today, fabric is block-printed only in comparatively short lengths of material. Block printing is found chiefly in decorative pieces for the home or in expensive linens for upholstery purposes.

To make hand-blocked prints, the design must first be carved on a wooden or metal block. The dyestuff is applied in paste form to the design on the face of the block. The block is pressed down firmly by hand on selected portions of the surface of the fabric, imprinting the carved design as many times as desired on a specific length of cloth. To obtain variation of color in the same design, as many additional blocks must be carved as there will be additional colors. The portions of the design that will appear in different colors must be separately imprinted by hand before each design is complete. The more colors used, the more valuable and expensive the hand-blocked print will be, because of the enhanced beauty of design as well as the labor involved in the hand printing.

You can recognize hand-blocked prints by noting slight irregularities in the detail and in the repetition of the design and by comparing areas for slight variations in color. These irregularities are imitated by machine printing, however, to give machine prints the characteristic appearance of expensive hand-blocked prints.

Roller Printing. *Roller printing* is the machine method of printing designs on cloth. It turns out color-designed fabrics in vast quantities at the rate of thousands of yards an hour. This method of producing attractive designs is relatively inexpensive when compared with any hand method. It is a machine counterpart of block printing. In roller printing, engraved copper cylinders or rollers take the place of the hand-carved blocks. Just as there must be a separate block for each color in block printing, so must there be as many engraved rollers in machine printing as there are colors in the design to be imprinted.

Each of the engraved rollers first comes in contact with a companion roller that has been submerged in the dye paste to be used for its part of the design. A sharp blade, called the *doctor blade,* scrapes the dye from the part of the roller upon which there is no design, so that other portions of the fabric will not come in contact with the dyestuff. As the fabric passes between the engraved rollers, the design is imprinted on it. A mordant is generally used in the dye paste to fix the color.

Duplex Printing. *Duplex printing* simulates a woven pattern by printing the fabric on both sides. The fabric may be passed through the roller-printing machine in two separate operations or through a duplex printing machine in a single operation. Duplex printing produces an equally clear outline on both sides of the fabric. The design is applied so skillfully by careful registration of the printing cylinders that the result may be mistaken for a woven design. But the difference can be detected by raveling a yarn.

• *Blotch Prints.* Blotch prints may have a colored background as well as a colored design. Both may be printed at the same time. This method is used chiefly for cottons and linens.

Discharge or Extract Printing.

The *discharge* or *extract* method of printing cloth receives its name from the fact that color is discharged or extracted from fabric that has first been piece-dyed. Basic or direct dyes are used because they can be removed easily. The chemical that discharges the dye tends to weaken the fabric, however, in the area of the design. Because the background dye is not fast and the construction may be weak in parts, the consumer should not buy fabrics printed by the discharge method if he wants serviceability and durability. Discharge prints are found in cottons and rayons and in some patterned silks with dark backgrounds.

In extract printing, the cloth is put through rollers that exude a bleaching agent, such as zinc oxide paste or hydrosulphite, in the form of a small pattern, reproducing it on the fabric by bleaching the dye. This method is chiefly employed where a light design is required against a dark background, because the bleaching produces an off-white color in the design. A light polka-dot pattern on a dark ground is an example of discharge printing.

Resist Printing.

In *resist printing,* bleached goods are run through cylinders

This fabric was discharge-printed. The chemical used to bleach the design on the fabric was too strong, causing the design area to deteriorate.

Courtesy U.S. Department of Agriculture

that stamp a pattern on the fabric in the form of a resist paste, a resinous sub-stance that cannot be penetrated when the fabric is subsequently immersed in a dye. The dye will affect only the parts that are not covered by the resist paste. After the fabric has passed through a subsequent dyeing process, the resist paste is removed, leaving a pattern on a dark ground. In the discharge method, the fabric is first dyed, and the color is then extracted by an imprinted chemical; in the resist method, a resist paste is first imprinted, and the fabric is then dyed. The durability of the fabric is not affected by the resist method.

Stencil Printing. *Stencil printing* originated in Japan. Its high cost limits its use and importance in the United States. In stencil printing, the design must first be cut in cardboard, wood, or metal. The stencil may have a fine, delicate design, or there may be large spaces through which a great amount of color can be applied. A stencil design is usually limited to the application of only one color and is generally used for narrow widths of fabric.

Screen Printing. The chief advantage of screen printing is individuality of design. The method is especially adapted for printing large designs having elaborate effects. The expense of the process limits its use to the printing of comparatively short yardages. The process is not used for mass production.

In *screen printing,* the design is drawn on an intermediary cloth or screen, which serves as a stencil. A lacquer coating is applied to all parts of the under-side of the screen on which the design does not appear. The fabric is spread on

In screen printing, the dye is forced through the screen with a squeegee. A different screen is used for each color of the pattern.

Courtesy Owens-Corning Fiberglas Corp.

a long table, sometimes several hundred feet long. The screen is placed on a small portion of the fabric. The printing paste or dye is poured on and forced through the unlacquered portion of the screen onto the fabric with a wooden or rubber paddle or squeegee. The frame is then raised and placed on the next section of the fabric, and the operation is repeated until the entire length of the cloth is printed with that one color. This process must be repeated for each color to be used in the design.

In screen printing, it is possible to have designs consisting of squares, circles, and ovals because the areas not to receive the dye are painted out by the lacquer. If clearly defined geometric designs were attempted in cardboard or metal stencils, obviously, the cut area would fall away.

On a knitted fabric, such as jersey, screen printing is the only printing method that can be used. Other methods smear the dye, as a knitted fabric stretches when it receives the impact of the rollers.

Warp Printing. *Warp printing* is roller printing applied to warp yarns before they are woven into fabric. Fine white or neutral-colored filling yarns are generally used, so that the design on the warp will not be obscured. This method produces designs with soft, nebulous, but striking, effects. Great care must be taken to keep the warp yarns in their proper position so the outline of the design will be preserved. Warp printing is used for expensive cretonnes and upholstery fabrics.

Photo Printing. In *photo printing,* the fabric is coated with a chemical that is sensitive to light. Any photograph may be printed on the fabric. The results are the same as when printing photographs on paper. All details can be reproduced if the photographer and technician are careful.

Batik Dyeing. The hand method of producing designs, known as *batik,* originated in Java. It enjoys frequent renewal of popularity in the United States. Batik is somewhat similar to the machine method of resist printing. The design is drawn on the fabric, and beeswax containing paraffin is deposited through a small cup-shaped instrument on the areas that are not to be colored. The fabric is then immersed in a tepid dye bath, and the wax resists penetration of the dye. After the fabric is dried, the wax is removed by applying heat or benzine. The result is a silhouette design on a dyed background. The process is repeated if additional colors are to be added.

Sometimes, in the last application of color, the wax is permitted to crack, and the last dyestuff partially penetrates the other dyed portions, producing the multicolored design characteristic of batik. The American method differs from the Oriental in that light colors are applied first, followed by the wax; then the deeper shades are built in. In the Oriental method, the dark shades are applied first, and the portions to be kept light are waxed.

Tie Dyeing. The results of tie dyeing are similar to batik, but the designs can be only circular in form, as the dye is resisted by knots that are tied in the cloth before it is immersed in the dye bath. The outside of the knotted portion is dyed, but the inside is not penetrated if the knot is firmly tied. Partial penetration occurs when the knot is not tight, causing gradations and irregularities of color that produce indistinct but attractive designs. The process is repeated as many times as desired by making new knots in other parts of the cloth and immersing the fabric in additional dye baths. This gives a characteristic blurred or mottled effect, the result of the dyes running into each other. Like other hand methods, tie dyeing is expensive. Because the method creates interesting designs, the patterns are duplicated in roller printing.

Composition or Pasted Designs. The rollers or cylinders used to imprint color by means of dyes, chemicals, or resist pastes can also apply lacquer or colored paste to fabric as small designs, called *flocked dots*. Considering that the dots are only glued on, this method is surprisingly lasting. It is not used on fabrics that are expected to withstand laundering, however. Even for the dry cleaner, it presents a problem. Substances that can be baked into the fabric are also used for this decorative effect. When this is done, the designs become so much a part of the cloth that they may be considered permanent, seldom being destroyed by washing or dry cleaning.

Spray Painting. Designs may be hand-painted on fabric, or the dye may be applied with a mechanized airbrush, which blows or sprays color on the fabric. Spray painting is used when surface coloring is to be done quickly and economically; for example, designs on tablecloths. Direct, acid, or vat dyes dissolved in water, alcohol, or other organic solvent may be used.

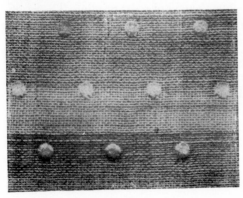

Pasted designs, like the dots in this fabric, may disappear in laundering.

Courtesy U.S. Department of Agriculture

DECORATION OF FABRIC BY PRINTING AND DYEING

Type of Decoration	Hand Method	Machine Method
Block printing	Design carved on blocks; dye applied to block; block pressed on fabric	
Roller printing		Design etched on roller; companion roller transmits dye to etched roller, which transmits it to fabric
Discharge printing		Bleached goods first dyed; chemical bleach printed on fabric; color discharged
Resist printing		Resist paste put on fabric; fabric dyed; paste removed
Stencil printing	Design cut in stencil; color applied over stencil	
Screen printing	Design sketched on sheer silk or nylon for screen; lacquer applied to background of design; color applied to screen as stencil and forced through screen	
Warp printing		Engraved rollers print design only on warp yarns; fabric then woven, using white or neutral filling yarn
Duplex printing		Design printed back to back on both sides of fabric; gives effect of woven pattern
Photo printing	Photographs printed on sensitized fabric	

DECORATION OF FABRIC BY PRINTING AND DYEING

Type of Decoration	Hand Method	Machine Method
Batik dyeing	Design put on fabric; wax deposited on background of design; fabric dyed; wax removed	
Tie dyeing	Fabric knotted or tied in parts with string; dipped into dye; fabric untied	
Composition or paste designs		Lacquer figures or colored paste glued or baked on surface of fabric
Spray painting	Mechanized airbrush applies surface coating	

▶ TEST YOURSELF ON THIS CHAPTER

1. Explain roller printing and duplex printing.
2. Differentiate between discharge and resist printing.
3. Describe warp printing and its result.
4. Compare and contrast the batik method and the resist method of decoration.
5. Describe tie dyeing, and explain why it is expensive.
6. What is meant by block printing?
7. What are the several methods of hand decoration with color?
8. Why are most fabrics machine-printed?
9. How could one determine whether a color design is printed or woven?
10. Name and describe five types of printing on fabrics.
11. How do screen printing and stenciling differ?
12. What are the characteristics of a well-printed fabric?
13. How can spinning and weaving processes produce decoration in fabrics? finishing processes?
14. Why is the discharge-printed fabric the least desirable?
15. What is the difference between a blotch and a duplex print?

9 · COTTON | Universal and Economical

Ancient historical records show that cotton was first cultivated in Oriental countries at least three thousand years ago. India is believed to be the oldest cotton-growing country. Cotton was known and used in all the Mediterranean countries, being introduced into Italy by the Arabs and into other parts of Europe by the Crusaders. The use of cotton in England is mentioned in writings of the thirteenth century, although its use did not become general until the first half of the sixteenth century. In the United States, cotton was cultivated in the early seventeenth century. The impetus of the Industrial Revolution, represented in the cotton industry by the invention of the spinning frame and the spinning mule in England, and by the invention of the cotton gin in the United States, resulted in vastly increased cotton production and manufacturing. Today, cotton fields extend across the southern section of the United States from Virginia to California.

Cotton fabrics have been so well known and so extensively used throughout the world for hundreds of years that the spinning of the cotton fiber into yarn, the weaving of cotton yarn into fabric, and many of the finishing processes used for cotton goods come first to mind and naturally serve as foremost examples in a study of fiber and fabric. Cotton has been of service to mankind for so long that its versatility is almost unlimited. New uses are constantly being discovered. Cotton is considered nature's most economical fiber; it is low-priced as a raw material and as a finished product. It can be depended on to serve many purposes. Not only is cotton a textile in its own right, but its by-products form the base for some of the man-made textile fibers.

Cultivation of Cotton. Cotton can be cultivated only in warm places, which is the reason for its cultivation in the southern part of the United States. Cotton requires about two hundred days of continuous warm weather with adequate moisture and sunlight; frost is harmful to the plant. The ground must be thoroughly plowed, and the soil pulverized. In the United States, usually in March or April, carefully selected cotton seeds are planted in rows. Approximately thirty-five days pass before the seeds develop. The plants require careful

135

Courtesy Deere & Company

This mechanical cotton picker can pick cotton bolls from two rows of cotton plants at one time. Upper left: *cotton bolls;* upper right: *baled cotton.*

fertilization. When they are about 3 inches high, they are weeded and thinned out. The plant begins to bloom in June or July, about four months after planting. Creamy white blossoms appear first, change to a reddish purple in about two days, and fall off, leaving seed pods that grow to full size by August or September, a month or more after blossoms first appeared. Before maturing, the cotton bolls must be protected against the boll weevil, which is attracted to the plant at this stage.

When fully grown, the cotton plant may be from 3 to 6 feet in height. Its wide green leaves conceal some of the bolls, which begin to burst with fleecy white cotton fiber. This indicates that the cotton is ready for harvesting.

• *Harvesting.* Not all cotton bolls open at the same time. Only those that burst, thus exposing the fiber, are ready for picking. A cotton field must be gone over several times. Consequently, harvesting the cotton fiber requires a large amount of labor as picking is mainly done by hand. The picking is the most expensive operation in cotton production. A machine picker has been developed that can pick cotton from plants 2 to 4½ feet in height. The mechanical picker,

Cotton fiber, which has entered the top of the cotton gin from a pneumatic conveyor, is here seen falling on covered gin saws after sand and coarse soil have been removed. The saws separate the seeds from the fiber. The fiber is removed from the saw teeth by a blast of air and is whisked toward the back. The seed falls into a conveyor at the bottom of the machine.

however, represents a large capital investment for the owner of a comparatively small cotton tract. Co-operatively owned mechanical pickers might be economical.

Ginning and Baling. When the raw cotton is harvested, it contains seeds, leaf fragments, dirt, and other material that must be removed before the fiber can be baled. Cotton seeds alone constitute approximately two-thirds of the weight of the raw cotton when first picked. The seeds are removed by the cotton gin, a machine having rows of revolving saw-toothed bands that pull the fiber away from the seeds as well as remove other extraneous material. The cotton seeds are one of the valued by-products. The cotton fiber is compressed into rectangular bales, which are covered with jute bagging and bound with iron bands. These bales weigh about 500 pounds each.

By-products of Cotton. The raw cotton passes through several cleaning processes before it is baled as well as after it is unbaled at the cotton mill. As a result, the grower obtains valuable by-products that amount approximately to one-sixth of the entire income derived from the cotton plant. Cotton is therefore important because of its contributions to other industries as well as to the textile industry.

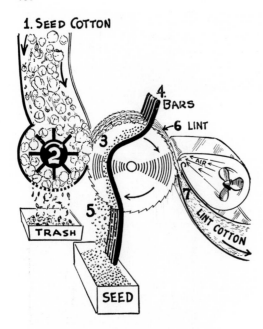

1. SEED COTTON

This drawing shows the basic principle of operation of the cotton gin. (1) Seed cotton enters gin. (2) Roll throws seed cotton against fast-turning saws. (3) Saw teeth take cotton up and against bars. (4) Bars near saws on both sides let lint pass through but hold back seed. (5) Seed falls into conveyor. (6) Lint on saw teeth is struck by blast of air and blown into (7) lint cotton conveyor pipe.

Courtesy Bibb Manufacturing Co.

• *Cotton Linters.* Linters are the short, fuzzy, hairlike fibers that remain on the seeds after they have been separated from the fiber in the cotton gin. The cotton linters are removed by a second ginning process. They are used in the manufacture of rayon, other synthetics, plastics, shatterproof glass, guncotton, photographic film, fast-drying lacquers, and for other purposes.

• *Hulls.* The hulls, which are the outside portion of the cotton seeds, are obtained after the linters have been removed. The hulls, rich in nitrogen, an important plant food, are used as fertilizer, and also in the manufacture of paper, plastics, cattle feed, and as a base for explosives.

• *Inner Seeds.* The meat of the seed inside the hull yields *cottonseed oil,* which is used in cooking oils and compounds and in the manufacture of soap. The residue of the inner seed becomes cattle feed.

Varieties of Cotton. Soil and climatic conditions affect the length and the character of cotton fibers. The relative fineness of the fiber seems to vary directly with the length of staple, the shortest staple being the coarsest type. The names of countries or sections where cotton is produced usually indicate the quality and the kind of cotton. Cottons of high quality have been successfully transplanted. The name of the place of origin is usually retained. The better-known cottons in the United States are described here according to their rank.

• *Sea Island Cotton.* Sea Island cotton received its name from Sea Island off the coast of Georgia. This cotton is now successfully grown on other islands off the southeastern coast of the United States as well as along the seacoast of the mainland. As nearness to the ocean provides the moisture so necessary to the proper development of good-quality cotton, Sea Island cotton has an extremely fine long staple, ranging from $1\frac{1}{2}$ to $2\frac{1}{2}$ inches in length. Wherever this variety has been successfully transplanted, it has produced the finest and the longest staple of all cotton fibers. Sea Island cotton is used for the highest-quality cotton fabrics, including laces, fine sewing thread, and imitations of silk.

• *Sakel (Sakellaridis).* This is the best variety of Egyptian cotton. It is a lustrous, light-cream-colored, fine fiber with a length of $1\frac{3}{8}$ to $1\frac{17}{32}$ inches. Its fineness and strength permit the spinning of Sakel into yarns of 200s, which can be used for the manufacture of the very best sheerest cotton fabrics. It is also used for fine-quality white-on-white and broadcloth. Through crossbreeding, Sakel has given rise to the best American Egyptian cottons, which are used in making the finest cotton goods today.

Due to its low yield per acre, its low resistance to wilt disease and boll damage, the production of Sakel is, however, only about 1.5 per cent of the entire cotton crop of Egypt. There are two other very good varieties of Egyptian cotton. But the label "Egyptian Cotton" does not necessarily indicate superiority, since there are many varieties of Egyptian cottons. Some of these are excellent to very good. Others are only average quality.

• *Pima.* There are several strains of this variety of cotton, but two are outstanding. One of the successful strains is Pima 32. It is the result of a series of crossbreeding of original Sakel and Pima (an American cotton). It is grown in the Upper Rio Grande Valley in Texas and New Mexico and in Arizona. Pima is a fine, lustrous, almost white fiber with a length of $1\frac{7}{16}$ to $1\frac{9}{16}$ inches and is very strong. Since there is more Pima cotton available than either the Sea Island or Sakel cottons, it is more commonly known and more popular. Pima cotton is used for high-quality white-on-white, and for broadcloth and other fabrics.

In recent years, a new strain, Pima S-1, has been developed in Arizona. It is a little coarser than the other strains of Pima. There is some controversy at present concerning the scientific accuracy of tests to prove that Pima S-1 is stronger than Sea Island or Sakel cotton. Certainly, this controversy is an indication of the high strength of Pima S-1, which is greater than all other varieties of cotton. Pima S-1 is also lustrous, silky, and almost white, making it highly desirable. It is a long staple fiber averaging about $1\frac{13}{32}$ inches in length. Farmers producing this fiber have formed the SuPima Association of America and now advertise their fiber under the trade name of SuPima.

• *Amsak*. Amsak, another variety of American Egyptian cotton, is the result of a series of crossbreeding involving Sakel and a strain of Pima. It is a very good quality of cotton about $1\frac{1}{2}$ inches in length.

• *Malaki*. Malaki owes its origin to crossbreeding between Sakel and Sea Island. Its fineness and strength are in close competition to that of Sakel. However, it is dark brown in color, a serious disadvantage since strong bleaching is required. The fiber length is $1\frac{7}{16}$ to $1\frac{21}{32}$ inches. Malaki represents about 8 per cent of the total Egyptian cotton acreage. It is used for a wide variety of cotton fabrics.

• *Karnak*. The largest acreage in Egypt is given to Karnak, a long-staple cotton. It also has the third largest acreage of the Egyptian cottons. Karnak is about as fine as Sakel and is $1\frac{3}{8}$ to $1\frac{5}{8}$ inches in length. It is light brown in color and must be thoroughly bleached to obtain the desired white.

• *Ashmouni*. A good-to-fair variety of Egyptian cotton is Ashmouni. It is not as strong as Karnak nor quite as fine. It is also shorter in length, averaging about $1\frac{5}{32}$ inches.

• *Giza 30*. Another widely used variety of Egyptian cotton is Giza 30. It is of fair strength but not as strong as Ashmouni; it is finer in diameter and consequently produces a thinner, though weaker, yarn. The staple length of Giza 30 cotton fiber averages about $1\frac{7}{16}$ inches.

• *Peeler*. This cotton is grown in the Mississippi Delta and in the low wet portions of the southern states. It is valued because of its fairly long length of $1\frac{1}{8}$ to $1\frac{1}{4}$ inches and is considered as the best of the varieties of cotton grown in the states east of the Mississippi River. Peeler cotton is used for better-quality sheer fabrics and for broadcloth.

• *Upland*. American Upland cotton supplies the bulk of the United States cotton crop. It yields a soft, fairly strong fiber and has a staple length of $\frac{3}{4}$ to $1\frac{1}{16}$ inches. Upland is used for most popular-priced cotton fabrics.

• *Peruvian Cotton*. Peruvian cotton is harsh and wiry; its staple is from 1 to $1\frac{1}{4}$ inches in length. Its rough, crimpy texture makes it resemble wool, and it is sometimes mixed with wool for the purpose of adulteration. Peru also produces cotton of finer quality.

• *Asiatic Cotton*. Asiatic cotton is grown in India, China, Asia Minor, Iran, Indo-China, and Japan. Of relatively short staple, nearly all being less than 1 inch in length, its use is limited to low-grade cotton goods.

Manufacturing Processes of Cotton.

Because cotton is such a universal fiber, its manufacture into yarn was used in Chapter 4 to illustrate the spinning process. Cotton fabrics may be produced in any weave. In the finishing processes, they may be given:

Full bleaching—for clear white-
ness
Mercerizing—for strength, luster,
and affinity for dyes
Singeing—for smoothness
Sizing—for stiffness, smoothness,
and body
Weighting—for bulk
Preshrinking—for serviceability
Sanforizing—for maximum pre-
shrinking

Calendering—for luster
Schreinerizing—for luster
Beetling—for flattened effects
Napping—for softness, warmth,
and absorbency
Crepe effects—for wrinkle resist-
ance
Water repellency—for resistance to
water and rain
Drip-dry—for no ironing
Embossing—for decoration

The types of dyes used for cotton and their degree of fastness to light and to washing were explained in Chapter 7.

• *Simulating Linen*. Cotton yarn can be spun to simulate the irregularities characteristic of linen fiber. The fabric is woven in the damask and other patterns usually associated with linen fabrics and is then sized, beetled, and calendered similarly to linen.

• *Simulating Wool*. Cotton fibers can be treated with chemicals to give them the roughness characteristic of wool fibers. The fibers are spun into thick yarns to increase the similarity. The finished fabric is napped or roughened to produce a wool-like surface. Because Peruvian cotton fiber has crimp, an inherent similarity to wool fiber, it is sometimes mixed with American Upland cotton to simulate wool.

• *Simulating Silk*. The highest quality of cotton fiber, when spun to a high yarn count and then mercerized, simulates silk. The use of the satin construction in weaving produces a silklike luster. The cotton fabric may be singed and calendered to smooth its surface and to increase the luster. Cotton fabrics are frequently schreinerized to obtain an added lustrous effect.

Judging Cotton Fabrics.

Many manufacturers now place labels on finished consumers' goods to give such information as the thread count, fiber content, shrinkage to be expected, permanency of crispness (if any), and fastness of dye to strong light, washing, and dry cleaning, with general instructions on the maintenance and care of the fabric. Such labels are designed to protect the consumer. If he understands them, he will know how long the fabric or garment that he is purchasing may be expected to give good wear. These labels also protect the manufacturer from the consumer's possible misunderstanding of the quality and durability of a fabric and from complaint if it is improperly handled when washed or dry-cleaned.

The information gained in the first chapters of this book concerning the essential qualities of the fibers and their spinning into yarn and weaving into fabric can now be applied to the actual purchase of consumers' goods, based on the following summary.

• *Strength.* Compact construction, represented by high thread count, helps a fabric keep its shape and give longer wear. Strength is also judged by the character of the cotton yarns, which should be of long staple and tightly twisted. A sample of the fabric may be tested for strength by holding it in both hands and pressing down firmly with the thumbs while pulling. If the cloth gives easily, it will not stand the strain of wear.

• *Amount of Sizing.* If a cotton fabric is oversized, rubbing or tearing a sample swatch will cause shedding of excess starch. Holding the fabric to the light will reveal defects in construction that may have been concealed by sizing. Washing a sample will remove excess sizing, showing sleazy construction. An absolute test for starch is made by dipping a sample in a very dilute iodine solution; a dark-blue color indicates starch.

• *Crease Resistance.* The tendency of cotton fabrics to wrinkle easily may be offset by finishing processes that give a crease-resistant quality.

• *Heat Conductivity.* Cotton fabrics make excellent summer clothing because cotton is a good conductor of heat. Crisp, clean, fine cotton fabrics look cool as well as feel cool. Napped or pile-weave cotton fabric has a warmth-giving quality.

• *Absorbency.* Cotton is not naturally a highly absorbent fiber, but certain finishing processes, such as kiering, mercerizing, and napping, increase the absorbency of cotton fiber and fabric.

• *Cleanliness and Washability.* Although cotton attracts dirt particles because of its roughness, this disadvantage is offset by the washability of the fiber. Cotton fabrics are not injured even in strong, hot solutions of alkalies; therefore, they can stand laundering with strong soap. They withstand rough handling and considerable heat in ironing. Because of low resistance to acids, cotton deteriorates when constantly exposed to perspiration. Mercerizing and new types of finishes, however, in many cases offset this.

• *Shrinkage.* A great amount of shrinkage will occur if cotton fabric is loosely woven and stiffened with starch, which is usually lost in washing. Preshrinking finishing processes minimize shrinkage in cotton fabrics.

• *Fastness of Color.* Fastness of dye to washing can be tested by washing a sample in hot water. Fastness to light can be tested by exposing a sample to light for a week or more. Penetration or thoroughness of dye can be tested by raveling a yarn and examining its unexposed surfaces.

• *Resistance to Mildew.* Cotton fabrics, especially sized fabrics, mildew readily when permitted to remain in a damp condition. New processes, in many cases, offset this tendency to mildew.

• *Resistance to Moths.* Cotton is not digestible to moth larvae, so that the fabric will not be attacked by moths. But in fabrics containing cotton and wool, the larvae may damage the cotton to get at the wool.

• *Reaction to Alkalies.* Cotton is not harmed by alkalies. In fact, a solution of sodium hydroxide is used to mercerize cotton, making it stronger, smoother, and more lustrous.

• *Reaction to Acids.* Although unaffected by cold weak solutions, cotton is quickly damaged by hot dilute or cold concentrated acids.

Construction of Sheets.   As sheets are an important item in the budget of the American family, the labeling of sheets is explained here.

• *Thread Count.* Sheets are labeled as belonging to one of seven types: backfilled, 112, 128, 140, 180 carded, 180 combed, and 200. The figures are obtained by adding the number of warp and filling yarns to the square inch, which represents the thread count. The higher the count, the closer and more uniform the weave; the more compact the weave, the greater the resistance to wear. Types including backfilled, 112, 128, and 140 are known as *muslin,* which is made from cotton yarns that have been carded but not combed. Of these types, 140 represents the best quality, giving greater durability, because such sheets are made from good-quality carded cotton yarns that are coarser and heavier and more compactly constructed than the first three types. Heavy muslin sheets are practical and economical because they are moderately priced and withstand wear longest, particularly when subjected to hard laundering.

Types including 180 carded, 180 combed, and 200 are known as *percale.* Percale is woven from fine-quality long-staple cotton yarns. In the case of 180 carded percale, the sheet is woven with 180 carded threads to the square inch. The 180 combed percale is woven with 180 combed threads to the square inch. Combed yarns are smoother, more lustrous, and stronger than yarns that are merely carded. The 180 combed percale is therefore superior and a little more expensive than the 180 carded percale. The 200 percale, woven with 200 combed threads to the square inch, is constructed of the finest cotton yarn and is considered the most luxurious of sheets. The thread count is high in all percale sheets because of the fineness of the yarns and their compact construction. Such yarns make lightweight sheets of fine texture, desirable for summer use. There is a gain in luxury but a slight sacrifice in durability because, all other conditions being equal, the heavier fabric gives the longer wear.

Sheets are generally labeled. But you can always examine the sheet itself for quality. By holding it up to the light, you can determine whether it is firmly, closely, and uniformly woven. It should look smooth. Lengthwise and crosswise threads should be of the same even thickness, rather than thick or thin in spots.

	Grade	Weave or Thread Count	Points to Consider in Buying	Price
	Back-filled muslin	Woven with less than 112 threads to each square inch	Loosely woven; excess starch washes out, leaves sheets sleazy	Lowest
	Light-weight muslin	Woven with not less than 112 threads to each square inch	Wears well considering low price. For limited household service	Low
	Medium-weight muslin	Woven with not less than 128 threads to each square inch	Strong; gives satisfactory wear. Widely used for everyday household service	Medium
	Heavy-weight muslin	Woven with not less than 140 threads to each square inch	Sturdy; longest wearing muslin. Used where durability is prime consideration, as in hospitals, many hotels, etc.	Highest price muslin
	Percale (carded)	Woven with carded yarns not less than 180 threads to each square inch	Lightweight; durable. Smooth, pleasant to sleep on. Easy and economical to launder	Medium
	Percale (combed)	Woven with all combed yarns. Not less than 180 threads to each square inch	Lightweight, extremely strong and durable. Soft and unusually smooth. Easy and economical to launder	Medium
	Finest quality percale	Not less than 200 threads to each square inch	The finest, most luxurious sheets available. Light, fine, soft texture, beautiful appearance. Made of finest all combed yarns	Highest price percale

Courtesy Cannon Mills, Inc.

There should be no weak places, knots, or slubs, and the yarns should run straight and unbroken.

• *Selvage.* Sheets should be made with a tape selvage in which extra threads are woven. The selvage should be firm and strong, clean, neat, and with no loose threads.

• *Weight.* Many weights of sheets are available, varying from $3\frac{1}{4}$ to $5\frac{1}{4}$ ounces per yard. But good weight should be the result of compact construction, not of excessive sizing. Government regulations on sheets permit a certain amount of sizing depending on the grade of the sheet. In the lowest grade of sheet, an excessive amount of sizing may be used to give the material greater body. Since this washes out, leaving the sheet thin and sleazy, it is advisable for the consumer to test sheets for sizing by rubbing parts of the sheet together over a dark surface. If much of a white powdery substance comes out, the sheet is "loaded" or sized. Sometimes, sheets are labeled "no weighting," which indicates no overdose of sizing.

• *Length and Width.* Sheets should always be long enough and wide enough to tuck underneath a mattress at least 6 inches on all sides. The better grades of sheets are torn to size to make certain that the length is absolutely even; therefore, the size is given as a torn size, which means before hemming. After hemming, sheets are shorter; top hems are usually 3 inches wide on muslin, 4 inches wide on percale sheets; bottom hems are 1 inch wide. After washing, there is another decrease in length of approximately 5 inches, or 5 per cent, due to shrinkage.

Sheets 108 inches long should be selected. As about 10 inches must be deducted from the stated torn size for hems and shrinkage allowance, 98 inches remain for use. The average mattress is 74 inches long and 6 inches thick. Thus, 6 inches will be left for tucking under when a sheet is used to cover the mattress directly, and when used as an upper sheet, there will be a sufficiently wide turnover to protect blankets.

Careful consideration should be given also to the width of sheets. For a double bed, a sheet should be 81 to 90 inches wide. A three-quarter bed requires a sheet 72 inches wide, and a single bed a width of 63 to 72 inches.

There are also mortised sheets, the corners of which conform to the shape and size of the mattress. When buying these contour sheets, you need to know only the size of the mattress, that is, whether the sheet is for a single, three-quarter, or double bed.

Construction of Terry Towels.
The primary function of a terry towel is to absorb moisture from wet skin. It must, however, be strong enough to withstand the strain of the rubbing and pulling, twisting and tugging of the user

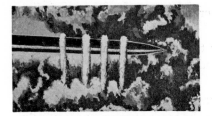
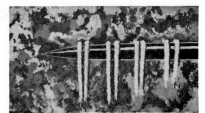

Magnified view showing comparison between single- and double-loop construction in terry cloth.

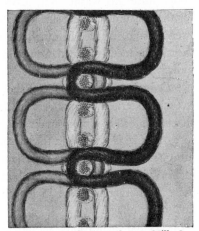

Enlarged view showing how the loops (uncut pile) in terry cloth are formed.

Cross section showing how terry loops are formed on both sides at the same time.

Loops do the drying.

Ground weave does the wearing.

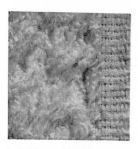  

Courtesy Cannon Mills, Inc.

Fast selvage   *Overedged selvage*   *Hemmed selvage*

and of constant laundering. A terry towel, therefore, should be constructed of an uncut pile with a sound underweave. One cannot purchase towels merely by a brand name because the name identifies only the manufacturer, not a particular quality. A company may manufacture many different grades and qualities of towels under the same brand name.

• *Weave.* The underweave, which supplies the strength of the towel, should be firm, close, and tight, preferably of a twill weave. It is difficult to examine the weave because the loops hide it. It can be more readily seen in the plain portion or near the hem or selvage of the towel. To examine the weave better, the towel should be held up to the light. If light shows through in tiny and regular pin points, the weave is uniform and good; if the light shows loose and open spots, then the weave is poor.

The loops of the pile, which absorb the moisture, should be closely packed. In a well-constructed towel, the moisture absorbed remains in the surface loops and does not reach the underweave. A better-quality towel, therefore, will absorb more moisture and dry faster after use. Another consideration is that the longer the loops, the greater the absorbency of the towel. Also, loosely twisted loops are more absorbent than tightly twisted ones. On this point, however, personal choice must be a factor, since some people prefer soft towels with loosely twisted loops, some prefer medium-soft towels, and others prefer a rough, hard towel with tightly twisted loops. In a well-constructed towel, good absorbency may be expected, since the close weave will result in a close, thick pile.

• *Hem and Selvage.* The hems of the towel should be sewn with small close stitches and finished with the edges either backstitched at the corners or turned and continued across the width of the hem. There are three types of satisfactory selvages, if properly made. One is the fast selvage, which is the ordinary type of selvage found on any fabric. It should be closely woven. The second is an overedged selvage, and the third the hemmed selvage.

• *Length and Width.* Terry towels are divided by size into five groups: guest, small, bath, extra large, and beach. The guest towels are 11 × 18 inches. The small size, used for hands and face, are from 16×26 to 18×36 inches. The bath size are from 20×40 to 22×44 inches. The extra-large-size bath towel is 24×46 to 25×48 inches. The beach size is 35×70 to 36×72 inches.

GLOSSARY OF COTTON FABRICS[1]

airplane fabric. Plain weave. Closely woven, desized, durable medium-weight and lightweight fabric used in the manufacture of airplane wings and parts. Made of combed and mercerized yarns; usually in square weave. Many fabrics go under this name. Most important is fancy, irregular broken weave.

armure. Drapery fabric with a small woven design, usually on a rep foundation. Can be either Jacquard or dobby weave. Pattern is made by floating warp threads over the surface, giving a raised effect.

backing or back cloth. Gray goods, usually print cloth, used to take up surplus dye and to reinforce fabric on the printing machine.

balloon cloth. Plain weave. Of finest Pima yarns. High thread count. The extremely fine yarns give the fabric luster. Usually mercerized. When used for balloons, given a special coating. Also used for frocks, shirts, typewriter ribbons.

batiste. Plain weave. A sheer, soft-finished fabric of the lawn family. Comes in various grades from coarse to very fine. Generally woven of combed yarns, but occasionally of carded. Often given high mercerization, bleached, dyed, or printed. Sometimes embroidered.

beach cloth. A strong, coarse fabric of plain weave, heavy yarns, and low thread count. Has the appearance of crash. There are a number of versions of this fabric.

Bedford cord. A carded yarn, wale, or cord material. Two-ply warp yarns and heavier single or ply yarns used as a backing. These heavy yarns are caught at intervals in the weaving of the fabric. Single yarns sometimes used in cheaper versions; the effect of the cord is obtained in the weaving. Wale runs in warp. Can be napped in back, bleached, dyed, or printed. Often the face of the fabric is given a suede finish.

bengaline. Rib effect in filling with a high luster. Has somewhat the appearance of grosgrain. For draperies and frocks.

bird's-eye (diaper cloth). Fabric woven on a dobby loom of carded yarns in tiny geometric designs that look like the eye of a bird, or in diamond effect. Heavier filling yarns are loosely twisted, making the fabric absorbent.

blanket cloth. Plain or twill weave, 60×80 inches and over. Coarse, soft filled yarns, filling heavily napped both sides. Generally bleached, yarn-dyed in plaids or stripes, or with colored filling edge.

book cloth. Coarse, plain-weave print cloth or sheeting. Dyed, heavily sized, often pyroxylin coated, or embossed.

box loom. Fabrics made with right-hand and left-hand twist in filling, no-

---

[1] Specially prepared by The Cotton Textile Institute, Inc.

tably box-loom crepe. Such fabrics as ginghams and plaids are also made on box looms.

broadcloth. Plain, closely woven fabrics of either carded or combed yarns with a rib effect fillingwise. Originally a poplin or adapted from poplin construction, broadcloths are of lighter weight with a finer rib. Ribs are made by using finer warp yarn and medium filling. Many more warp threads than filling. Better broadcloths are combed ply yarns and high thread counts. Coarser fabrics often have both ply and single carded yarns.

brocade. Basic weave is satin. Elaborate lustrous design woven on a Jacquard loom. Has a raised appearance, usually on a sateen ground but often on twill or rep. The design is on the surface only. Multicolored yarns used.

brocatelle. A heavier version of brocade. Woven on a Jacquard loom with two, three, four, or more shuttles. Ordinary warp yarns but fewer twists in filling yarns. Has extra backing threads. The floating warp yarns over the backing yarns make the design stand out in relief.

bunting. Plain weave, in low or medium thread count. Open weave similar to cheesecloth or scrim. Dyed or printed.

calico. A low-count or medium-count cotton print cloth with special designs called calico designs. Many Early American designs are in use.

cambric. Originally linen, now cotton print cloth or lightweight sheeting construction. Given special sizing and calendered finish.

canton flannel. Warp-faced twill flannel with a heavy, soft filling yarn and lighter warp than filling yarn. Has a long nap on one side only. Comes unbleached or bleached. For men's work gloves, infants' wear, linings.

challis. Plain or twill weave, printed or dyed. Given a soft finish and very slight nap.

chambray. Pattern is formed by the use of colored yarn warp and natural or white filling. This gives a tiny check or mottled effect. There are endless variations of this fabric, such as stripes, satin stripes, and so on. The end-to-end chambrays are woven with alternate colored and natural or white yarns in warp and all natural or white yarns in filling, or vice versa. Many novelties on the market.

cheesecloth (and tobacco cloths). Loose, open, plain light weave with low thread count. Print cloth yarns. Cheesecloths range from 25 to 55 inches in width. Tobacco cloths are 36 inches and over in width with a somewhat lower thread count than cheesecloths. When bleached, starched, or permanently finished, known also as scrim. Other names, depending on finish, are gauze, bunting.

chenille. Fluffy or fuzzy faced fabric made with a cotton warp yarn and a cotton chenille filling yarn that has a fuzzy pile protruding from all sides. Some imitations made by tufting, using no chenille yarn.

cheviot. A strong twilled fabric woven with a colored stripe or check.

chiffon. A sheer voile with a dull finish; of fine, hard-twisted yarns. Often dyed or printed.

chintz. A print cloth or high-count fine sheeting with bright attractive floral or geometric designs, both large and small. Often given a permanent or semi-permanent glaze; then known as glazed chintz. For draperies, slip covers, frocks.

clokay. A plain woven fabric with an embossed surface of some geometric pattern. Rather compact weave. Embossed design is permanent if the fabric is laundered only in lukewarm water with a mild soap.

corduroy. A ribbed pile fabric with a high, soft luster. Made with extra filling threads or extra warp threads. In weaving, the extra filling yarns form loops or floats over the ground threads. After weaving, the loop threads are cut on a special machine. Threads are then brushed, forming a pile.

cottonade. Generally three-harness, left-hand, warp-faced twill of coarse yarns. Comes mostly in dark stripes on a solid or medium-dark ground. Durable finish.

coutil. A strong three-harness herringbone or reverse-twist twill weave of high count. For suits, corsets, and other purposes requiring a durable fabric.

covert. A medium-weight or medium-lightweight fabric with warp-faced left-hand twill. Usually of two-ply warp yarns and single or two-ply filling. Mixed yarns, such as natural and color in warp and matching color alone in filling. Has a mottled appearance. Often made with slack-twisted single yarns consisting of two rovings, one white and one color in warp and all color in filling.

crash. Name given to fabrics having coarse, uneven yarns in both plain and twill weaves. Usually sheeting, osnaburg, or twill-weave constructions with a special finish. Used for toweling and drapery purposes. In lighter weights used for suits and dresses.

crepe. Has a pebbly or crinkled surface produced by use of special crepe yarns. Can be either crepe, granite, or plain weave. Generally, mixed-twist crepe yarns used in both warp and filling, occasionally crepe yarns used only in the warp or the filling. Mostly woven on a box loom.

cretonne. Generally a medium or heavy sheeting or osnaburg printed in bold, bright designs. Used for draperies and other household articles.

crinoline. Cheesecloth, tobacco cloth, or loosely woven sheetings given a stiff starched or plastic finish. Gives a firm appearance and feel.

damask. Design, woven on Jacquard loom, on both sides of the fabric. Usually given a lustrous, smooth finish when used for tablecloths and a soft or lustrous finish for draperies or upholstery.

denim. A durable fabric of the twill family. Usually of single hard-twisted yarns with colored warp and natural or white filling.

dimity. A sheer white, dyed, or printed fabric of plain weave with a spaced rib made with warp cords. This rib may be single, double, or in groups. Comes also in checks and other novelty versions. Coarser small-check dimities are known as pajama checks.

dobby. Woven on a dobby loom. All material with small figures, such as dots and geometric designs; floral patterns woven in the fabric, such as certain shirtings, huck towels, diaper cloth, certain dress goods, drapery and upholstery fabrics. Can be dyed, bleached, or yarn-dyed in many colors.

domett flannel. See also "outing flannel." Plain or twill weave. Generally white with a longer nap than outing flannel, although the names are interchangeable. Soft filled yarns of medium or light weight.

dotted swiss. Generally a voile or lawn construction woven with either clip spots or swivel dots. The clip spot is the more popular version. The fabric is given a crisp, clear finish, which may be permanent or semipermanent. Often yarn-dyed dots are woven on a white ground, or a dark ground has white dots. Many imitations on the market, pigment dots, wool dots, and others.

drill. A durable fabric of medium weight. Usually, three-harness warp-faced twills made of carded sheeting yarns. Comes in various weights and thread counts. When dyed, known as khaki, tickings, silesia, herringbones. One thread goes over two filling yarns, then under one.

druid's cloth. See "monk's cloth."

duck. The name duck covers a wide range of fabrics. It is one of the most durable fabrics made. A closely woven, heavy material. The most important fabrics in this group are known as *number duck, army duck,* and *flat* or *ounce duck.* Number and army ducks are always of plain weave with medium or heavy ply yarns; army ducks are the lighter. Ounce ducks always have single warp yarns woven in pairs and single or ply filling yarns. Other names for variations of these fabrics are sail duck, belt duck, hose duck, tire duck (such as breaker, cord, chafer), wide and narrow duck, biscuit duck, harvester duck, oil press duck, wagon duck, enameling duck, boot duck, canvas, and so on. Generally of ply yarns in warp and yarns of various sizes and weights in filling.

duvetyn. See "suede cloth."

éponge. See "ratiné."

express stripe. Warp-faced twill with a woven stripe. A durable fabric. An even number of unbleached and blue yarns are used in the pattern, forming a stripe.

friezette. An uncut loop or pile ribbed fabric similar to a heavy rib or rep. Of heavy yarns, usually mixed in color.

gabardine. A distinctive steep-diagonal warp-faced twill of carded or combed yarns. Twill is to the left if made with all single yarns, and to the right when ply warp and single filling are used.

gauze. See "cheesecloth." Usually bleached; often specially treated, as when used for bandages. Better cheesecloths are also used for less expensive infants' items under trade names.

gingham. Plain-weave, medium-weight, or lightweight fabrics. Can be either combed or carded yarns. Usually woven on a box loom. Colored and white yarns or multicolored yarns form the pattern. Same number and variation of yarns in the warp as in the filling, forming squares, plaids, and similar patterns. Strange to say, a solid-color gingham is called a novelty gingham. Endless variations in color and design. Tissue ginghams are sheer ginghams made with lighter-weight yarns.

glazed chintz. Generally a print cloth or percale or a lightweight sheeting having bright, attractive floral or geometric designs. The fabric has a semipermanent or permanent glaze finish. Sometimes calendered or given a plastic finish. Fine twills are also used for this purpose.

granite. See "mummy cloth."

grosgrain. Plain-weave fabric similar to poplin but with a heavier rib effect and coarser, lower thread count. Made with single or with ply filling.

hickory cloth. Resembles ticking somewhat, but of lighter weight and not so firm a weave.

holland. Usually a low-count print cloth or high-count cheesecloth, heavily sized and glazed. Occasionally, sheeting constructions are used.

hopsacking. Made of yarns about the same weight as osnaburg in a loose and low thread count. Sometimes made with spiral yarns. It has a soft texture and is of the homespun family of cottons. Sometimes made with fine warp and heavier filling. Many versions of this fabric.

huck. Small-figured dobby weave used for towels. Has a rough surface. Comes bleached or with yarn-dyed striped border.

Indianhead. A porous fabric of a plain weave. The yarn is somewhat thick. The fabric feels wiry, resembling butcher linen but not as stiff or as lustrous.

jaspé. A durable, narrow woven stripe made on a dobby loom with multi-colored threads or with different shades of the same color. Has a shadow effect. Sometimes printed versions are shown in the market. Often small dots are woven into the fabric. Used for draperies and slip covers.

jeans. Three-harness warp-faced twills of lightweight sheeting yarns. One warp thread goes over two or more filling threads, then under, moving one pick higher for each return filling thread. Sometimes made in chevron or herringbone versions.

kasha cloth. Flannel with napped face and mottled color. Usually tan or brown. An unbleached soft filled sheeting. Mixed yarns are used with sized warp yarns that take dye and filling yarns with natural wax that do not take dye. When bale-dyed, has a mottled appearance.

khaki. See "twill."

lawn. Sheer and medium-sheer plain-weave fabrics made with lightweight yarns and medium to high count. Can be bleached, dyed, or printed. When finished, it is also known by the name of such special finishes as batiste, organdy.

linene. See "osnaburg."

longcloth. Also known as *fineplain*. A plain-weave, closely woven, high-count fabric. The weight is between a print cloth and lawn. Generally combed finer yarns, and with more threads to the square inch than percales. A few are made of print cloth yarns.

madras. Usually woven in stripes, cords, dobby, and Jacquard. Mostly all white, but in a number of cases done with a patterned warp and white filling, such as white and color warp, or color-and-color warp and white filling, or vice versa. Often a stripe is woven in solid colors. A number of variations of the above.

*From Flax to Fashion.
From flax straw, to roughly
combed fibers, to fine flaxen
"tresses," to bleached yarn,
to crisp linen for suits and
dresses.*

Courtesy Irish Linen Guild

grown in Canada and in the United States (Michigan, Minnesota, and Oregon), but chiefly for its seed.

Qualities and Grades of Flax. Courtrai flax, which comes from the Lys district in Belgium, produces the finest and strongest yarns. The water of the Lys River in Belgium and of the Scheldt River in The Netherlands is free from minerals and has proved especially desirable for decomposing the woody tissues of the plant, a necessary step in treating the linen fiber.

Belgium has a reputation for producing the best quality of linen, but Ireland is noted for the best workmanship. Irish linen is also prized for its fine white color and strength. The flax is spun while it is wet, and the cloth is grass-bleached, two processes reserved for good-quality linen.

Scotch linen is lighter in color than Irish linen. It is used extensively in making heavy-grade fabrics, such as twine and canvases for tarpaulins.

French linen ranks high. It is characterized by fine designs and the use of round yarns, as the cloth is not put through the beetling process.

Russian flax is used for medium and coarse yarns, which are dark gray in color. Russian linen sometimes cracks because the fiber is not so carefully processed as in the countries that have a reputation for fine-linen production.

Courtesy Irish Linen Guild

Harvesting flax.

German linen is generally of medium grade. Austria, Czechoslovakia, and Poland also produce medium-quality flax.

Cultivation of Flax. The flax plant requires deep, rich, well-plowed soil and a cool, damp climate. Premature warm weather affects the growth and the quality of the fiber. Level land with a plentiful supply of soft fresh water is essential. As the soil in which flax is grown must be enriched for six years before it will yield a good harvest, only one crop in seven years can be raised on a specified portion of land. The crops, therefore, must be carefully rotated. Shorter periods of rotation have been tried with success.

The flaxseeds are sown by hand in April or May. When the plants are a few inches high, the weeds must be pulled by hand with extreme care to avoid injury to the delicate sprouts. In three months, the plants become straight, slender stalks from 2 to 4 feet in height, with tapering leaves and small blue or white flowers. The plant with the blue flower yields the finer fiber. The white-flowered plant produces a coarse but strong fiber.

• *Harvesting.* By the end of August, the flax turns a brownish color, which indicates that the plant is about to mature; it is ready for harvesting. There must be no delay at this stage; otherwise, the fiber will lose its prized luster

Courtesy Irish Linen Guild

Flax being stacked in a retting dam.

and soft texture. The plants are often pulled out of the ground by hand; however, there is a machine which can efficiently pull the flax. If the stalk is cut, the sap is lost; this loss affects the quality of the fiber. The stalk must be kept intact, and the tapered ends of the fiber must be preserved, so that a smooth yarn may be spun. The stalks are tied in bundles, called *beets,* in preparation for extraction of the fiber.

Preparation of the Fiber. The seeds and the leaves are removed from the stems of the flax plant by passing the stalks through coarse combs. This process is called *rippling.* The bundles of plants are then steeped in water. The plants are weighted down with heavy stones to insure complete immersion. This allows the tissue or woody bark surrounding the hairlike flax fiber to decompose, thus loosening the gum that binds the fiber to the stem. This decomposing or fermentation is called *retting*.

• *Dew retting* is the method used in Russia. The flax straw is spread on the grass and is exposed to the atmosphere for 3 or 4 weeks. This method produces strong flax, dark gray in color.

• *Pool,* or *dam, retting* is done in Ireland. It requires less time than dew retting, from 10 to 15 days. As stagnant pools of water are used, this method sometimes causes overretting, which is responsible for brittle and weak flax fibers. Pool retting darkens the flax, giving it a bluish-gray color.

• *Stream retting* produces the best quality of flax fiber, as the process of fermentation can be retarded and easily controlled. The flax straw is placed in streams of cool, soft running water for 5 to 15 days. This method produces superior strong linen of a pale yellow color.

• *Chemical retting* can shorten the retting process, but chemicals affect the strength and color of the flax fiber. The use of soda ash, oxalic soda, and caustic soda in warm water, or boiling in a dilute sulphuric acid solution, are the chemical methods used.

• *Mechanical retting* also shortens the retting process, but the subsequent fabric is susceptible to mildew and mold.

Retting only loosens the woody bark. If flax is not retted enough, the removal of the stalk without injury to the delicate fiber is difficult. If flax is overretted, the fiber is weakened. The retting operation, as well as all other processes for producing linen fabric, therefore, requires great care.

Courtesy Irish Linen Guild

After retting, flax is shaken out by hand and spread on the fields to dry.

Courtesy Irish Linen Guild

After scutching, the fibers must be roughly combed by hand by drawing them over sets of steel combs, ridding them of further pieces of straw and clearing the main tangles.

The stalk becomes partially separated from the fiber when the wet plants are laid in the fields to dry. When the decomposed woody tissue is dry, it is crushed by being passed through fluted iron rollers. This *breaking* operation reduces the stalk to small pieces of bark called *shives*.

• *Scutching.* The scutching machine removes the broken shives by means of rotating wooden paddles, thus finally releasing the flax fiber from the stalk. This operation can be done by hand as well as by machinery.

• *Hackling.* The simple combing process known as hackling straightens the flax fibers, separates the short from the long staple, and leaves the longer fibers in parallel formation. For very fine linen, hackling is usually done by hand and is repeated, a finer comb being used with each hackling treatment. Coarse linen is hackled by machine.

Classification of Flax Fibers.

The short-staple flax fibers, called *tow,* are used for the spinning of irregular linen yarns. Tow is put through a carding operation, similar to the carding of cotton staple, which straightens the fibers and forms them into a sliver ready for spinning into yarn. The long-staple

Flax in the hackling machine.

fibers are used for fine linens. These are called *line,* sometimes *dressed flax.* Line fibers are from 12 to 20 inches in length. They are put through machines, called *spreaders,* which combine fibers of the same length, laying them parallel so that the ends overlap. The sliver thus formed passes through sets of rollers, making a rove for the final spinning process, which inserts the necessary twist.

Spinning Flax Fiber into Yarn.   Although flax is one of the strongest fibers, it is inelastic and requires carefully controlled warm, moist atmosphere for the spinning operations. Two methods are used.

• *Dry spinning* does not use moisture. It produces rough, uneven yarns, which are not especially strong. These yarns are used for making coarse, heavy, and inexpensive linen fabrics.

• *Wet spinning* requires a temperature of 120 degrees Fahrenheit, which is conducive to the production of soft, fine, even yarns. By passing the roving through hot water, the gummy substance on the fiber is dissolved, permitting drawing out the roving into a fine yarn of high yarn count.

Linen Yarn Count.   The standard measure of flax yarn is the *cut.* If 1 pound of flax fiber is drawn out to make 300 yards, the yarn is known as No. 1s. When drawn out to make twice 300 yards, it is labeled No. 2s. The higher the yarn count, the finer the yarn. Exceptionally fine linen yarns for fine laces have been spun as high as 600s.

Weaving Linen Yarns. The inelasticity of the flax fiber presents a problem also in the weaving process because the fiber breaks easily under strain. A dressing, applied to the warp yarns by passing them over rotating brushes, helps linen yarns to withstand the strain of being lifted by the heddles during weaving. A very moist atmosphere is also required.

Linen fabrics usually have a balanced or squared construction, with the exception of double damask and certain sheer linens. The thread count, therefore, is always expressed as one number.

With the exception of some toweling, linen is seldom made in the pile weave. The pile weave increases absorbency, and this quality is already possessed to a large degree by any linen fabric. The twill weave is seldom used, as the fiber possesses natural strength; for the same reason, ply yarns are not necessary. The plain, satin, and Jacquard weaves are predominant. The twill weave, however, is used for linen drills in the South American market.

• *Table Linens.* Fine table linens are always woven with the Jacquard construction; there are two kinds of construction, depending on the weave. The designs in damask result from the manner in which the warp yarns pass over the filling yarns. The background is always the same on both sides.

A five-shaft satin construction on the Jacquard loom is used for *single-damask linen.* Most single damasks have the same number of warp and filling yarns, and the thread count ranges from 100 to 200 to the square inch. Some single damasks may be overwefted about 10 to 15 per cent, but the cheaper qualities are usually underwefted; that is, some skimping is done with respect to the equalization of filling and warp.

The weave used for *double-damask linen* is an eight-shaft satin construction on the Jacquard loom. There are twice as many filling yarns as warp yarns, which gives greater distinctness to the pattern. The thread count ranges from 165 to 400 to the inch.

Originally, double-damask linen was considered superior to single damask. Today, the weave alone does not produce a superior product, because inferior yarns as well as high-quality yarns are used in all weaves. Double damask may range in quality from mediocre to excellent, and is superior to single damask only if good yarns and quality construction are used.

If single and double damasks having thread counts approximately the same are compared, the single damask is preferable because shorter floats give greater

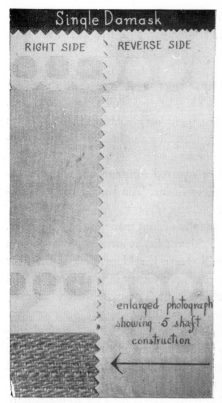

The construction and appearance of single damask may be compared with double damask.

Double damask is superior to single damask only if good yarns and quality construction are used.

serviceability. The threads hold more firmly. A double damask with a thread count less than 180 threads is not advisable for home use.

Finishing Linen. Linen is usually bleached in the piece, except yarns for dress linens. Two methods are used. *Grass bleaching* produces the finest re-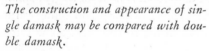sults. *Chemical bleaching* is chiefly used but may adversely affect the durability of the finished fabric. Bleaching produces four grades in the finished product: fully bleached, three-quarters bleached, half or silver bleached, quarter bleached. Unbleached linen makes a fifth grade. A fully bleached linen fabric is less enduring than any other grade. Unbleached linen is the strongest because the natural strength of the fiber has not been weakened by the bleach. It is sometimes called gray linen or brown linen. The natural characteristics of linen are enhanced by the finishing processes listed on page 168.

Courtesy Irish Linen Guild and British Information Service

Above, linen is laid "on the green" for sun bleaching. Below, modern chemicals do the job.

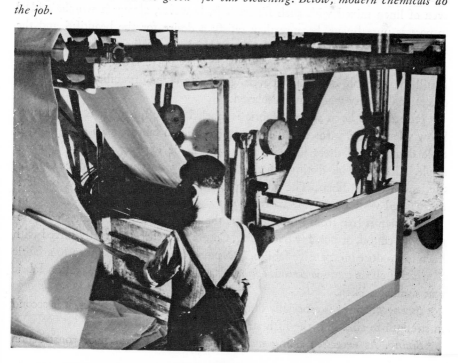

Beetling—for flexibility and uniform thickness
Calendering—for luster and smoothness } Finishing Processes
Mercerizing—for luster
Sizing—for added body

Linen is never napped. The fiber does not lend itself to this process, nor would napping be desirable for long-staple yarns of hard surface. Where some crease resistance is obtained by reducing the yarn to short staple, strength, which is the chief attribute of linen, is sacrificed. Thus, any fuzziness in a linen fabric indicates the use of short staple or the presence of cotton.

Dyeing Linen. Linen is seldom yarn-dyed. The surface of the natural flax fiber is hard and nonporous and is, therefore, impenetrable to dyes. The cells of the fiber are held together with tissue that can be broken down only in a severe bleaching process. Highly colored linens, therefore, will not give lasting service because they must have been fully bleached to absorb the dye.

Judging Linen Fabrics. The term "linen" has long been used to refer to such household necessities as tablecloths, napkins, towels, pillowcases, sheets, and decorative coverings. Every consumer knows that these articles are not necessarily made of pure linen. They may be made of cotton or spun rayon, even of linen mixed with such fibers. It is, however, always a woman's ideal to possess pure linens, because they satisfy a desire for the beautiful and the luxurious and may remain in families as heirlooms. When linens are chosen wisely, their additional cost is well worthwhile. There is no doubt that linen is still the best fabric for table covering because of its durability as well as its exceptional beauty when thus displayed.

• *Pure Linen.* Even when a fabric is labeled "pure linen," it is necessary to know whether the yarns are line or tow. Fine linen fabrics, such as high-grade table damask and dress linens, are usually made of line, the long uniform staple. Line may be distinguished from tow by untwisting and examining the length of the fibers. The popular peasant linen is made of tow, but it is constructed with a very fine weave.

Pure linen is free from lint; therefore, the presence of lint indicates adulteration with cotton, or possibly oversizing. Cotton yarns are frequently mixed with linen to produce inexpensive fabrics. The name *Union Linen* is given to a fabric of which half or more is cotton. *Linene* is a trade name for an all-cotton fabric that simulates linen.

• *Strength.* Linen is especially durable. Among the natural fibers, it is second in strength to silk. It is the fifth strongest of all fibers.

• *Sizing.* As excessive sizing indicates the probability of poor construction or imperfections in weave, a sample may be tested for oversizing by holding it to the light, by rubbing, or by washing.

• *Weight.* In linen, weight may be considered a criterion of durability. Damask weighs from 4 to 7 ounces to the square yard.

• *Crease Resistance.* The inelasticity of the flax fiber causes linen to wrinkle easily, which somewhat offsets its otherwise excellent qualities as a fabric for summer apparel. But it is possible to buy dress linens that have been given one of the patented crease-resistant processes described in Chapter 6.

• *Heat Conductivity.* Linen is most suitable for summer apparel, as it allows the heat of the body to escape.

• *Absorbency.* When absorbency is the main consideration, linen is preferable to cotton. It absorbs moisture and dries more quickly. It is therefore excellent for handkerchiefs and towels.

• *Cleanliness and Washability.* Linen launders well and gives up stains readily; its softness is enhanced with repeated washings. Linen can be boiled and made absolutely sterile. It is desirable for surgical dressings and bandages. Bacteria do not thrive on linen because of its hard, smooth surface.

• *Shrinkage.* Linen does not shrink a great deal; in fact, less than cotton.

• *Fastness of Color.* When buying colored linens, look for the words "Guaranteed Fast Color" on the label, or get a guarantee of colorfastness from the store. If a label states that the fabric is vat-dyed, it has been given the fastest color possible to withstand washing.

• *Resistance to Mildew.* Like cotton, linen is vulnerable to mildew.

• *Resistance to Moths.* Also like cotton, linen is not damaged by moths.

• *Reaction to Alkalies.* Linen, like cotton, is highly resistant to alkalies. Linen may also be mercerized.

• *Reaction to Acids.* Linen is damaged by hot dilute acids and cold concentrated acids. Cold dilute acids will not harm linen.

GLOSSARY OF LINEN FABRICS[1]

art linen. Closely woven round-thread linen, used chiefly for embroidery, generally in the plain weave. Bleached, unbleached, and colors. Also used for dresses and table linens.

bisso linen. Fine, sheer linen; sometimes called altar linen. Made of wiry yarns. Has a crisp feel. Used for altar cloths.

cambric. Fine, closely woven fabric with a high thread count. Plain weave; white and colors. Used chiefly for handkerchiefs.

canvas. Many fabrics come under this heading. Two principal types: (1) Open-mesh canvas; used for embroidery; made of hard-twisted yarns;

[1] Specially prepared by the Linen Trade Association.

very durable. Most popularly known in this group is Java canvas. (2)
Close-woven canvas; made from coarse hard-twisted yarns in the plain
weave; in various weights. Finishes range from heavily sized to soft.

crash. A relatively coarse fabric made of uneven slack-twisted yarns. Made in
various qualities; plain weave. Used for towels, suitings, dresses, depending on the weight.

damasks. In satin weave as well as the Jacquard pattern. Two types: single
damask and double damask. Single damask has a five-shaft satin construction; if given a high thread count is more durable than double damask.
Double damask is more lustrous because of the longer float of the eight-
shaft construction; reversible because the design is made on both sides.

handkerchief linen. Same as linen cambric. Sometimes called *linen lawn* or
linen batiste. Plain weave, often corded.

huckaback. Coarse fabric, having rough surface. Variations in weave; may
have small figures. Color range semibleached to white.

sheeting. Firmly constructed plain-weave cloth. Used industrially. The closer
constructions used for bed linens. May be unbleached or white.

toweling. General name that covers all types of linen woven in special
widths for towels. Some are terry, huckaback, crash, bird's-eye, glass.

► TEST YOURSELF ON THIS CHAPTER

1. Why is linen a desirable fiber?
2. Why is linen not used as frequently as cotton?
3. What disadvantages may there be in the use of linen fabrics?
4. Why are linens expensive?
5. What kind of climate is necessary for the growth of flax?
6. What are the methods of retting? Which method is used in Russia? in Ireland?
   in Belgium?
7. Which method of retting produces the finest linen?
8. From what part of the flax plant is the fiber taken? From what part of the
   cotton plant is the fiber taken?
9. What are line and tow?
10. Would you prefer a cotton blouse to a linen blouse? if so, why?
11. What country grows the flax plant for its seed? What is the seed used for?
12. Why should the short fibers be separated from the long fibers? What process
    accomplishes this?
13. What characteristic of the linen fiber makes it difficult to spin? Why would a wet
    fiber be more easily twisted?
14. In what weaves are linen yarns woven? Name some fabrics in each weave.
15. What finishing processes are given to linen fabrics?

11 · WOOL | Warm and Resilient

Originally, wool was borne on wild species of sheep as a short, fluffy undercoat concealed by hair. When wild sheep were killed by primitive man for food, he used the pelts as covering for his body. The fluffy undercoat probably became matted by usage, thus giving early man the idea of felting it into a crude cloth. It is believed that ancient shepherds in the first century A.D. discovered that Merino sheep could be bred to improve the fleece.

At first, wool was a very coarse fiber. Its development into the soft, fleecy coat so familiar on domesticated sheep is the result of long-continued selective breeding. The quality has been greatly improved by careful crossbreeding of fine-wool and long-wool sheep. The breeding of the animals and the production of the wool fiber into fabric are more costly processes than the cultivation of plant fiber and its manufacture. Consequently, wool fabrics are more expensive than cotton and linen. But wool provides warmth and physical comfort that cotton and linen fabrics cannot give. These qualities, combined with its soft resiliency, make wool a necessity for apparel as well as for such household uses as rugs and blankets.

Wool is not overabundant. This factor adds to its cost. It is also a delicate fiber. This makes intelligent buying and care necessary if the consumer wishes serviceability and durability.

Wool and Hair. Wool fiber and hair fiber differ in basic structure. Wool is distinguished from hair by its overlapping scales, which give wool fiber its felting property. Hair is straight, lustrous, and comparatively inelastic; it is smoother than wool. Strictly speaking, such animal hairs as camel's hair, mohair, cashmere, llama, alpaca, and vicuna differ enough from wool to be classified as *hair fibers*. As these hairs are included, however, by the United States Government under specification standards for wool fabrics, they are described at the end of this chapter. They have all the qualities of wool. In general, they are even more expensive than wool. Vicuna is the world's costliest textile product and surpasses all other textiles in fineness and beauty. These hairs are often mixed with wool, adding rather than detracting from the quality of any wool fabric in which they appear.

Wool-producing Countries. The quality of the wool fiber is determined by the breeding, climate, food, general care, and health of the sheep. Cold weather produces a hardier and heavier fiber. Excessive moisture dries out natural grease. Insufficient or poor food retards growth. Certain countries are suitable for large-scale sheep raising and consequently produce the greatest quantities of wool. The chief wool-producing countries are Argentina, Australia, British Isles, India, South Africa, and the United States.

Classification of Sheep Bred for Wool. There are about forty breeds of sheep. Counting the crossbreeds, there are over two hundred distinct grades of sheep. Those that produce wool may be classified into four groupings according to the quality of the wool produced.

• *Merino*. Merino sheep produce the best wool. The variety originated in Spain and was so prized for its outstanding quality that during the Middle Ages it was a capital offense to export a Merino sheep from Spain. The staple is relatively short, ranging from 1 to 5 inches, but the fiber is strong, fine, and elastic and has good working properties. There is a maximum number of serrations, totaling as many as 3,000 to the inch. Merino is used in the best types of wool clothing. The Ohio Merino, Austrian Silesian, and French Rambouillet all are Merino sheep. Other types are now found in Australia, New Zealand, South America, South Africa, and Spain.

• *Class-Two Wools*. These sheep originated in England, Scotland, Ireland, and Wales. They have helped make the British Isles famous for their fine wool fabrics. They are, however, no longer limited to that area and are now raised in many parts of the world. While not quite as good as the merino wool, this variety is nevertheless a very good quality wool. It is 2 to 8 inches in length, has a large number of serrations per inch, and has good crimp. The fibers are comparatively strong, fine, and elastic and have good working properties. Some of the better-known sheep of this variety include Bampton, Berkshire, Blackface, Cornwall, Devonshire, Dorset, Hampshire, Hereford, Exmoor, Kent, Norfolk, Shropshire, Southdown, Sussex, Oxford, Welsh Mountain, Wiltshire, Westmoreland, Irish, and Ryeland.

• *Class-Three Wools*. These sheep originated in the United Kingdom. The fibers are about 4 to 18 inches long, are coarser, and have less serrations and less crimp than merino and the class-two wools. As a result, they are smoother, and therefore have more luster. These wools are less elastic and resilient. They are nevertheless of good enough quality to be used for clothing. In fact, some of these sheep, such as Leicester, Cotswold, Cheviot, Harris, Lewis, and Shetland, have given their names to wool fabrics.

Cheviot ram..

Southdown ewe.

Merino ram.

Courtesy American Cheviot Sheep Society, Inc., American Southdown Breeders Assn., Australian News and Information Bureau, American Suffolk Sheep Society, Continental Dorset Club.

Blackface ewe.   *Dorset ram.*

• *Class-Four Wools.* This class is actually a group of mongrel sheep some-times referred to as half-breeds. The fibers are from 1 to 16 inches long, are coarse and hairlike, have relatively few serrations and little crimp, and are therefore smoother and more lustrous. This wool is less desirable, having the least elasticity and strength. It is used primarily for carpets, rugs, and inex-pensive low-grade clothing.

Classification of Fleeces. Sheep are generally shorn of their fleeces in the spring, but the time of shearing varies in different parts of the world. In the United States, shearing takes place in April or May; in Australia, in Septem-ber; in Great Britain, in June or July. Texas and California sheep are shorn twice a year because of the warm climate.

Sheep are not washed before shearing. Sometimes, they are dipped into an antiseptic bath, but this is done only when prescribed by law. Formerly, sheep were shorn by hand, but today the fleeces are removed in one piece by machine clippers, which shear closer as well as faster than hand clippers.

Wool shorn from young lambs differs in quality from that of older sheep. Also, fleeces differ according to whether they come from live or dead sheep. This necessitates standards for the classification of fleeces.

• *Lamb's Wool.* The first fleece sheared from a lamb about six to eight months old is known as *lamb's wool* and sometimes referred to as *fleece wool,* or *first clip.* This wool is of very fine quality; the fibers are tapered because the ends have never been clipped. Such fibers produce a softness of texture in fabrics that is characteristic only of lamb's wool. Because of its immaturity, however, lamb's wool is not as strong as fully developed wool of the same sheep.

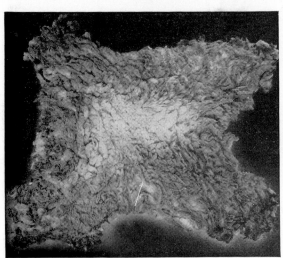

A fleece after shearing.

Courtesy U.S. Department of Agriculture

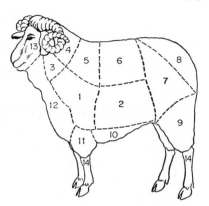

One fleece produces different qualities of wool fiber. The parts are here numbered according to softness, fineness, and length of fiber, No. 1 yielding the best quality.

• *Hogget* (*Hogg or Teg*) *Wool.* This wool comes from sheep, 12 to 14 months old, that have not been previously shorn. The fiber is fine, soft, resilient, and mature, and has tapered ends. Hogget wool is a very desirable grade of wool and, because of its strength, is used primarily for the warp yarns of fabrics.

• *Wether Wool.* Any fleece clipped after the first shearing is called *wether wool.* This wool is usually taken from sheep older than 14 months. These fleeces contain much soil and dirt.

• *Pulled Wool.* When sheep are slaughtered for meat, their wool is pulled from the pelt by the use of lime, by sweating, or by a chemical depilatory. Such wool fiber, called *pulled wool,* is of inferior quality for two reasons: (1) because sheep that are raised for meat generally do not have a good quality of wool, (2) because the roots of the fibers are generally damaged by the chemicals and the tension exerted in pulling.

• *Dead Wool.* The grade of wool fiber known as *dead wool* is sometimes mistaken for pulled wool. The term is correctly used for wool that has been recovered from sheep that have died on the range or been accidentally killed. Dead-wool fiber is decidedly inferior in grade; it is used in low-grade cloth.

• *Cotty Wool.* Sheep that are exposed to severe weather conditions or lack of nourishment yield a wool that is matted or felted together and is hard and brittle. This very poor grade is known as *cotty wool.*

• *Taglocks.* The torn, ragged, or discolored parts of a fleece are known as *taglocks.* These are usually sold separately as an inferior grade of wool.

Government Classificition of Wool.

There has never been a sufficient supply of new wool stocks to take care of a steadily increasing demand for wool. To meet this situation, wool fibers have had to be recovered from old clothing, rags of all kinds, and waste from wool manufacturing; all are important sources. This wool is variously called "salvaged," "reclaimed," "re-worked," or "remanufactured," but it is best known in the textile industry as *shoddy*. This term is misunderstood by the average consumer, who is inclined to believe that wool fabric containing remanufactured fibers is necessarily of inferior quality. This is not so.

The hardier, though less resilient, remanufactured fibers when obtained from good original stock and combined with new wool from lamb, hogget, or wether fleeces, add durability to the soft new wool. Thus, remanufactured fibers contribute ability to withstand hard wear, although there is some sacrifice in warmth, softness of texture, and resiliency. They also make wool clothing available to consumers who cannot afford expensive wool fabrics.

To correct wrong impressions concerning the use of remanufactured wool, and also to protect consumers against unscrupulous practices, the United States government passed the Wool Products Labeling Act. This act provides that every article of wool clothing must be labeled according to the type of wool used in its manufacture. The label must state: (1) amount of wool fiber in the fabric; (2) percentage by weight of "new or virgin wool" fibers; (3) percentages of "reprocessed" fibers or "reused" fibers; (4) percentage of each fiber other than wool, if such fibers constitute 5 per cent or more of the total; (5) aggregate of other fibers; (6) nonfibrous loading, filling, or adulterating substance.

Note that the law does not require labeling as to the type of sheep or the type of fleece from which the wool has come. It is therefore of only partial and limited value to the consumer. New definitions of the type of wool fibers used in labeled garments were established by this act.

• *Wool*. The simple term "wool," according to government standards, must always mean "new wool" that has not been made up in any form of wool product. New wool comes directly from a fleece. It has never been previously spun, woven, felted, or worn.

• *Reprocessed Wool*. According to the government classification, "reprocessed wool" is fiber that has been reclaimed and remanufactured from "unused" wool materials. Such materials may be combings and scraps of wool obtained during the manufacturing processes, sample swatches, or pieces of all-wool cloth from apparel manufacturing.

• *Reused Wool*. The government gives the special classification of "reused wool" to fiber salvaged from all kinds of "used" consumers' goods.

Virgin Wool. The term *virgin wool* is now used by the textile industry to designate new wool from a sheep's fleece, but the term is too all-inclusive to serve as a criterion of quality. Although the term testifies to the fact that virgin wool does not contain remanufactured wool fibers, it can be used to identify the less desirable fibers of a fleece as well as a specially fine quality of wool. Virgin wool may also include pulled or dead wool, which may be of definitely inferior stock. You should not feel that a fabric labeled "100 per cent new wool" is necessarily more serviceable than one containing any of the remanufactured wool fibers, for there are many different grades of new wool. It is important to remember that a high grade of reprocessed wool makes a more serviceable fabric than one having a low grade of new wool.

Garnetting. Reprocessed and reused wool fibers are obtained by separately reducing the unused and used materials to a fibrous mass by a picking and shredding process called *garnetting*. The fibers are then put through a dilute solution of sulphuric or hydrochloric acid, which destroys any vegetable fibers that may be contained in the raw stock. This process is known as *carbonizing*, and the resultant wool fibers are called *extracts*. The new staple ranges from $\frac{1}{4}$ inch to $1\frac{1}{2}$ inches in length.

The quality and cost of reprocessed and of reused wool fibers depend on the original stock from which they were obtained. A good grade of reprocessed wool may cost five times as much as a poor grade of virgin wool.

Preparation of Wool Fiber. Domestic wool reaches the mill in loosely packed bags; imported wool comes in tightly compressed bales. Each fleece contains different grades or *sorts* of wool; and the raw stock must be carefully graded and segregated according to length, diameter, and quality of the fiber. The raw wool or newly sheared fleece is called *grease wool* because it contains the natural oil of the sheep. When wool in the grease is washed, it loses from 20 to 80 per cent of its original weight. The grease, known as *yolk*, is widely used in the pharmaceutical and cosmetic industries for lanolin compounds because it can be absorbed by the human skin.

• *Sorting.* Wool sorting is done by skilled workers who are expert in distinguishing qualities by touch and sight. As many as twenty separate grades of wool may be obtained from one fleece if the sorting is especially rigid. Each grade is determined by type, length, fineness, elasticity, and strength. Wool from different parts of the body of the sheep differs greatly. The shoulders and sides generally yield the best quality of wool, as the fibers from those parts are longer, softer, and finer.

• *Scouring.* The next step in preparing raw wool for manufacturing is a thorough washing in an alkaline solution; this process is known as *scouring*. The scouring machines contain warm water, soap, and a mild solution of soda

At the upper right of the picture, wool is dropping into the first tank for the scouring process. The raised spikes move slowly toward the rear of the tank, drop, and then move forward to force the wool through the solution. This action is constantly repeated.

Courtesy Wool Bureau, Inc.

ash or other alkali; they are equipped with automatic rakes, which stir the wool. Rollers between the vats squeeze out the water. If the raw wool is not sufficiently clear of vegetable substance after scouring, it is put through the carbonizing bath of dilute sulphuric acid or hydrochloric acid.

For some consumers' goods, the term "naphthalated wool" is used, which means that the grease and dirt found in the fleece when originally sheared from the sheep's back have been removed by a series of naphtha baths, followed by clear water which removes the naphtha. When wool has been thus treated by a cleansing agent, dyestuff penetrates better.

• *Drying.* Wool is not allowed to become absolutely dry. Usually, about 12 to 16 per cent of moisture is left in the wool to condition it for subsequent handling.

• *Oiling.* As wool is unmanageable after washing, the fiber is dipped in, or sprayed with, a light emulsion of virgin olive oil or mineral oil to prevent it from becoming brittle and to lubricate it for the spinning operation.

Dyeing. If the wool is to be dyed in the raw stock, it is dyed at this stage. The advantage of stock dyeing has been described in Chapter 7. Some wool fabrics are piece-dyed, some are yarn- or skein-dyed, and some are top-dyed.

Blending. Wool of different grades may be blended or mixed together at this point. It is not uncommon for taglocks and inferior grades of wool to be mixed with the better grades. The use of a mixture with a coarser grade of fiber is a legitimate practice if the purpose is to make a hardier product and a less expensive one, provided the label on the finished goods indicates a true

Various types of scoured wool are blended on a combination scale that indicates the amount of each type of wool to be used in the blend.

Courtesy Wool Bureau, Inc.

description of the raw materials used. In the manufacture of *Union* fabrics, a small amount of cotton is blended with raw wool. A greater amount of twist can be given to such yarns, with a resultant increase of strength in the fabric. Because of its crimp, Peruvian cotton is frequently mixed with raw wool stock. Such mixtures have a place in certain finished goods, but the amount of cotton used must be indicated on the label.

Carding. The carding process introduces the classifications of *woolen yarns* and *worsted yarns*. Manufacturing processes from this point differ, depending on whether the wool fiber is to be made into a woolen or a worsted product.

In the manufacture of woolen yarns, the essential purpose of carding is to disentangle the fibers by passing the wool fibers between rollers covered with thousands of fine wire teeth. Incidentally, this action also removes some dirt and foreign matter from the fibers. As the wool fibers are brushed and disentangled by these wires, they tend to lie parallel, which would make woolen yarns too smooth. Since woolen yarns should be somewhat rough or fuzzy, it is not desirable to have the fibers too parallel. By use of an oscillating device, one thin film or sliver of wool is placed diagonally and overlapping another sliver to give a crisscross effect to the fibers. This permits the fibers to be disentangled and somewhat parallel and at the same time provides a fuzzy surface to the yarn. After this carding process, the woolen slivers go directly to the spinning operation.

In the manufacture of worsted yarns, the essential purpose of carding is also to disentangle the fibers by passing the wool fibers between rollers covered with fine wire teeth. Since worsted yarns, however, should be smooth, the

Carded wool in fine spider-web form is being drawn from the cylinder at the left into wool sliver (at right).

Courtesy *National Association of Woolen Manufacturers*

fibers are made to lie as parallel as this process will permit. Following this operation, the wool goes to the gilling and combing processes.

Gilling and Combing. The carded wool, which is to be made into worsted yarn, is put through gilling and combing operations. The *gilling* process removes the shorter staple and straightens the fibers. This process is continued in the combing operation, which removes the shorter fibers of 1 to 4 inches in length, called *combing noils,* places the longer fibers, called *tops,* as parallel as possible, and further cleans the fibers by removing any remaining loose impurities.

The short-staple noils are not necessarily of poor quality. Combing noils may well be of good quality, depending on the original source of the wool. They may be used as filler for other types of wool fabrics; however, such fibers must be classified as reprocessed wool.

The long-staple tops, which are over 4 inches in length, excel in color, feel, and strength. They are used in the production of such worsted fabrics as serge, whipcord, gabardine, and covert.

Drawing. Drawing is an advanced combing operation which doubles and redoubles slivers of wool fibers. The process draws, drafts, twists, and winds the stock, making the slivers more compact and thinning them into slubbers. Drawing is done only to worsted yarns.

Roving. This is the final stage before spinning. Roving is actually a light twisting operation to hold the thin slubbers intact.

Spinning. In the spinning operation, the wool roving is drawn out and twisted into yarn. Woolen yarns are chiefly spun on the mule spinning machine. Worsted yarns are spun on any kind of spinning machine—mule, ring, cap, or flyer. There are two different systems of spinning worsted yarns.

How the manufacture of woolen and worsted yarns differs.

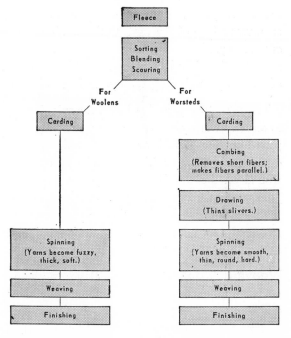

1. In the English system (Bradford), the yarn is oiled before combing, and a tight twist is inserted. This produces smoother and finer yarns. The more tightly twisted yarn makes a stronger, more enduring fabric.
2. In the French system, no oil is used. The yarn is given no twist; it is fuzzier, and therefore suitable for soft worsted yarns.

The differences between woolen and worsted yarns are given here.

Woolen Yarn	*Worsted Yarn*
Short staple	Long staple
Carded only	Carded and combed
Slack twist	Tightly twisted
Weaker	Stronger
Bulky	Finer, smoother, even fibers
Soft	Hard
Uneven twisting	Even twisting

Yarn Count. The fineness or thickness of wool yarns is based on different systems for woolen and worsted. One pound of worsted yarn yielding 560 yards is identified as No. 1s. Ply yarns are numbered according to the number of the single yarn from which they are spun. Thus, 2/60s worsted means two-ply yarns of No. 60 singles, twisted together.

In woolens, the size of the yarn is based on two separate systems: the cut, and the American run. The latter is more generally used.

The *cut system,* sometimes called the *Philadelphia* because of its use in that area, uses a base of 300 yards to the cut. Thus, 1 pound of woolen fiber drawn out to 300 yards sets a standard for No. 1s.

In the *American run system,* sometimes called the *New England,* 1 pound of woolen yarn yielding 1,600 yards is identified as No. 1s.

Warping. The yarn that leaves the spinning frame is not of sufficient length to serve as warp yarn on the loom. It is first wound on bobbins or spools and placed on a large rack or frame called a *creel.* As in the warping operation explained in Chapter 4, the warp yarns on the bobbins or spools are evenly wound on the warp beam. They may be immersed in a solution of starch, gum, or similar compound to make them smooth and strong for weaving. In the production of better-quality wool fabrics, a hard-twisted two-ply yarn is frequently used for the warp yarn, as the plied construction gives greater strength.

Weaving Woolen Fabrics. Basically, the weaving process for wool resembles the process described in Chapter 5. The short, curly woolen yarns obtained in the carding process are made into woolen fabrics by using the plain weave, sometimes the twill. The weave pattern is not always discernible because woolen fabrics often have a napped surface. The thread count of woolens is usually less than that of worsteds because the construction is not so compact.

Woolen fabrics are soft, fuzzy, and thick; they are warmer than worsted, but not so durable. Napping gives woolens a soft surface, which acts as a protection against objectionable luster. But napping can conceal poor construction and the quality of the yarns used; therefore, woolens can be more easily adulterated than worsteds. The napped surface tends to catch and hold dirt, but stains can be easily removed. If poorer yarns have been used in woolens, the fabric is less expensive than worsted. Woolens are desirable for sportswear, jackets, sweaters, skirts, blankets, and similar general use.

Weaving Worsted Fabrics. The worsted yarns, which have been specially carded and combed, are woven into fine worsted fabrics with distinctive patterns, chiefly by means of the twill weave. The plain weave is infrequently

Long-staple fibers produce the smooth worsted yarn shown in the upper part of this drawing. Short-staple fibers produce an uneven yarn with protruding short ends, as in the lower drawing.

used. The thread count of worsteds is higher than that of woolens because the finer yarn is more closely constructed.

Worsted fabrics are flat, rough, and harsh when worn next to the skin. They are more durable than woolens and more resistant to dirt. They wrinkle less and hold creases and shape, but they become shiny with use.

Worsted fabrics are costlier than woolens. They are appropriate for tailored and dressy purposes, for spring and summer coats and suits, and for tropical suits. They are suitable for business wear.

Fulling. After the weaving process, woolen and worsted gray goods are placed in warm soapy water and are pounded and twisted to make the wool fibers interlock. This application of heat, moisture, and pressure, followed by a cold rinse, is called *fulling* (also *felting* or *milling*). Sometimes, chemicals are used to help moisten, soften, and lubricate the fibers so that matting will occur.

Fulling produces a desired shrinkage and gives the fabric additional thickness and a firmer, fuller texture. The longer the fulling operation, the greater the shrinkage, with consequent increase in the strength of the fabric.

The fulling process and other finishing operations for woolens and worsteds

Woven pieces are sewed end to end and fed into the fulling machine where, in moisture and heat, the cloth is tumbled and pounded. This shrinks the fabric in length and width to give it body and evenness.

Courtesy Wool Bureau, Inc.

yield *flocks,* extremely short staple ranging from ⅛ to ¾ inch in length. Flocks are felted into the poorer grades of woolens to add weight. They are also blended with other raw wool stocks. Other waste material reclaimed from fulling is termed *mungo.* This is the lowest grade of waste. It is used for blending and is combined with yarn for low-grade wool fabrics.

Crabbing. To set the cloth and the yarn twist permanently, wool fabric is passed over several cylinders that rotate in hot water and is then immersed quickly in cold water. The cloth is held firmly and tightly to avoid wrinkling. Repetition of the treatment with increased pressure results in setting the cloth and the finish.

Unfinished Worsteds. Unfinished worsteds have the durability and tailored appearance characteristic of worsted fabrics and the comfort, greater warmth, and freedom from luster characteristic of woolens.

The soft texture of unfinished worsteds is due to additional manufacturing processes, such as fulling, brushing, or napping. Since they require more processing, the term *unfinished* gives a wrong impression.

The napped surface in the unfinished worsted gives softness of texture, serves the functional purposes of napped fabrics, and gives the beauty found in woolens. In addition, the fabric possesses the durability of worsteds. With continued wear, however, the nap rubs off, and these areas show an objectionable luster or shine. Such consumers' goods can be renapped by a cleaning establishment, but this is generally avoided since the renapping can weaken the cloth. You can enjoy longer serviceability by selecting an unfinished worsted in a light color. Light colors, such as gray, do not show luster as readily as the darker shades.

Additional Finishing Processes. Woolen fabrics are also given the following finishing processes:

Perching—examining cloth for defects while it is run over two rollers
Burling—removing loose threads and knots
Mending—darning flaws and defects, if any
Shearing—cutting and shaving for a uniform surface
Singeing and steaming—for hard finish of worsted fabrics
Pressing—improving appearance and giving final shape to the cloth
Steaming, sponging, or shrinking—removing excess glaze, setting cloth to proper width
Decating, or decatizing—may be done wet or dry. The cloth is shrunk by winding it under tension on a perforated cylinder through which steam is forced. The process frequently serves as a substitute for London shrinking.

Judging Wool Fabrics. The presence of reprocessed or of reused wool in a fabric does not condemn it so long as the product is properly labeled and the

Courtesy Wool Bureau, Inc.

The drying machine permits the cloth to be dried to a predetermined width before going into the dry-finishing department.

consumer understands the limitations as well as the advantages of such wool fabrics. A fabric made of new or virgin wool may be of inferior quality if it is made of inferior grades or of extremely short staple.

• *Strength.* As wool is the weakest of the natural textile fibers, the fabric is made more durable by the use of selected grades of reprocessed or reused wool, although the durability is gained at the expense of texture and resiliency. To determine whether strength has been given by the use of flocks, brush and whip the fabric vigorously. Then examine the surface and selvages for powdery particles, which are the signs of short staple. Also examine the structure of the fabric to determine whether it has been weakened by excessive napping.

Wool fabric is strengthened by the use of ply yarns. A hard-twisted two-ply yarn may be regarded as an assurance of durability. Tightly twisted single yarns also make a strong fabric.

• *Crease Resistance.* Because wool fiber has a high degree of elasticity, wool fabric wrinkles less than some others; wrinkles disappear when the garment or fabric is steamed. Good wool is very soft and resilient; poor wool is harsh. When buying a wool fabric, grasp a handful to determine its quality. If the fabric retains the wrinkles and feels inelastic, this may indicate a mixture with cotton or an inferior grade of reused wool.

• *Heat Conductivity.* As wool fibers are nonconductors of heat, they permit

DIFFERENCES BETWEEN WOOLEN AND WORSTED FABRICS

	Woolen Fabrics	Worsted Fabrics
Fiber	Short, curly fibers	Long, straight fibers
Yarn	Carded only; slack twist; weaker yarns	Carded and combed; tightly twisted; greater tensile strength; generally yarn-dyed
Weave	Indistinct pattern; usually plain weave, sometimes twill; thread count generally less than worsteds	Distinct pattern; chiefly twill weave, infrequently plain weave; more closely woven than woolens
Finishing	Soft finish; fulling, flocking, napping, steaming; as napping can conceal quality of construction, woolens are easily adulterated	Hard finish; singed, steamed; unfinished worsteds are napped; adulteration more difficult as fillers would be easily discernible
Appearance and touch	Soft, fuzzy, thick	Flat, rough, harsh
Characteristics	Warmer than worsteds; not so durable; nap acts as a protective agent against shine; soft surface catches and holds dirt; stains easily removed	Wrinkle less than woolens; more durable; hold creases and shape; become shiny with use; feel harsh when next to skin; more resistant to dust
Uses	Generally less expensive than worsteds if poorer yarns are used; desirable for sportswear, jackets, sweaters, skirts, blankets, winter use	Costlier yarns; appropriate for tailored and dressy wear; spring and summer coats and suits, tropical suits; good for business wear
Typical fabrics	Tweed, homespun, flannel, broadcloth, shetland, cassimere	Gabardine, whipcord, serge, worsted cheviot, tropical worsted, Bedford cord

the body to retain a temperature close to the 98.6 degrees required for health. Wool garments are excellent for winter clothing and are protective on damp days throughout the year. Lightweight wool of sheer construction may be worn in the summer for its thermostatic quality.

• *Absorbency.* Wool fabric absorbs a great deal of moisture without feeling damp; it dries slowly. This makes it most suitable for bathing apparel.

• *Cleanliness and Washability.* Dirt tends to adhere to wool fabric. Unless thoroughly cleaned, wool retains odors. Consequently, wool requires frequent dry cleaning, or washing if the fabric is washable. Extreme care is required in laundering. Wool is softened by moisture and heat, and shrinking and felting occur when the fabric is washed.

• *Shrinkage.* Shrinkage is greater in woolens than in worsteds, but all fabrics made of wool are subject to shrinkage; they will shrink less if dry-cleaned. "Chlorinated wools" have been subjected to good preshrinkage, but the strength of the fabric is diminished.

• *Fastness of Color.* Because of their high affinity for dyes, wool fabrics dye well and evenly. The use of chrome dyes assures fastness of color.

• *Resistance to Mildew.* Wool is not ordinarily susceptible to mildew; but if left in a damp condition, mildew develops.

• *Resistance to Moths.* Wool fabrics are especially vulnerable to moths. They should be protected in some manner as discussed in Chapter 6.

• *Reaction to Alkalies.* Wool is quickly damaged by strong alkalies. It is imperative to use a mild soap or detergent when laundering wool fabrics.

• *Reaction to Acids.* Although wool is damaged by hot sulphuric acid, it is not affected by other acids, even when heated. This property permits wool to be carbonized without damage.

HAIR FIBERS: WARMTH WITHOUT WEIGHT

Hair fibers that have the qualities of wool are obtained from certain kinds of animals throughout the world. The hair of these animals has been so adapted by nature for the climate in which they live that the cloth produced from the fiber gives warmth without weight. Some of these animals are used primarily as burden carriers; others are bred for their fleeces, which produce the most expensive fibers in the textile industry.

These hair fibers are used alone or are combined with sheep's wool for construction into fabrics whose cost varies according to the amount and quality of the blend. The consumer must be careful to analyze descriptions of certain of these blends. Parts of the names of rare animals are sometimes used to convey false or nonexistent values to mixtures of cotton and wool that contain such insignificant quantities of the lowest grade of hair fibers that they could not possibly add quality to the fabrics.

Camel's Hair. Camel's hair is a fine hair that is known to the American consumer chiefly in the form of high-quality coat fabrics. This textile fiber is obtained from the two-humped Bactrian camel, which is native to all parts of Asia. The climate of the desert countries, where the camel is used as a burden carrier and as a means of transportation, is exceedingly hot during the day and extremely cold at night. This constant change has produced a protective hair covering that is a nonconductor of both heat and cold; it is also naturally water-repellent. In the spring, the year's growth of hair, which hangs from the camel in matted strands and tufts, falls off in clumps to make room for the new growth. Masses of hair that are shed throughout the year are also accumulated. The camel is sometimes plucked to obtain the down or underhair.

Camel's-hair fabrics are ideal for comfort, particularly when used for over-coating, as they are especially warm but light in weight. Camel's hair is characterized by strength, luster, and smoothness. The best quality is expensive when used alone. It is often mixed with wool, thus raising the quality of the wool fabric by adding the fine qualities of camel's hair. The price of a mixed cloth is naturally much less than that of a fabric that is 100 per cent camel's hair.

In the textile industry, camel's hair is divided into three grades. Grade 1 is the soft and silky light-tan underhair found close to the skin of the camel. This is short staple or noil of 1 to 5 inches but is the choicest quality. Until recent years, it was the only true camel's hair used in the manufacture of apparel. In wool, noils represent the less valuable short staple; but in the hair fibers, the short fibers are the prized product and are the only ones used in high-grade hair fabrics.

Grade 2 is the intermediate growth, consisting partly of short hairs and partly of coarse outer hairs. Grade 3 consists entirely of coarse outer hairs measuring up to 15 inches in length and varying in color from brownish black to reddish brown. This grade has no value for apparel manufacture; it is suitable only for cordage and for low-quality rugs.

Mohair. Mohair is the hair of the Angora goat, native to the province of Angora, Turkey. This species of goat is now raised in the United States, principally in Oregon, California, and Texas. Some of the domestic mohair, particularly that obtained from Texas, is of excellent quality. Imported mohair

Courtesy S. Stroock & Co., Inc.

Sources of fine hair fiber are the camel (top left), the llama (top right), the angora goat (center), the vicuna (bottom left), and the alpaca (bottom right).

is of long staple, 9 to 12 inches long, and represents a full year's growth. The domestic goat is shorn twice a year, yielding a shorter staple, from 8 to 10 inches. Imported mohair can be spun to a fineness of 60s in yarn count. The highest count possible for domestic fiber is 40s. The domestic fiber has a great amount of coarse, stiff hair, known as *kemp,* which does not process readily or allow thorough penetration of dye.

Mohair is a smooth, strong, and resilient fiber. It does not attract or hold dirt particles. It absorbs dye evenly and permanently, and its fine silklike luster permits unusual decorative effects. Mohair fiber is more uniform in diameter than wool fiber. Under the microscope, it shows almost no serrations; its indistinct scales do not project from the shaft as is characteristic of wool fiber. Mohair, therefore, does not shrink or felt as readily as wool.

When mohair is used in pile fabrics, the naturally strong fiber combined with the strength of the pile weave makes an especially durable and serviceable fabric. Mohair fabrics are wrinkle-resistant and do not mat readily because of the natural resiliency of the fiber. The fabric can be made mothproof. Because mohair is very resilient and is stronger than wool or the other hair fibers, it is used to great advantage in quality floor coverings, better grades of upholstery and drapery materials, and summer suitings.

Cashmere. The Cashmere goat is native to the Himalaya region of China and India. The fleece of this goat has long, straight, coarse outer hair of little value; but the small quantity of underhair, or down, is made into luxuriously soft wool-like yarns with a characteristic highly napped finish. This fine cashmere fiber is not sheared from the goat but is obtained by frequent combings during the shedding season. The microscope reveals that cashmere is a much finer fiber than mohair or any wool fiber obtained from sheep. The scales are less distinct and are farther apart; the fiber appears to be made of sections placed within each other.

Cashmere first became familiar in the beautiful soft, light cashmere shawls for which India has been famous. Today, it is used for such garments as sweaters, sports jackets, and overcoats. Cashmere is desirable because it is soft, lighter in weight than wool, and quite warm; however, because it is a soft, delicate fiber, fabrics produced from cashmere are not as durable as wool.

Llama. The llama is allied to the camel in species, having many of the characteristics of that animal, but being about one-third its size. The llama is the traditional burden carrier in the higher parts of the Andes Mountains in South America and therefore has not been bred for its fleece. Its hair fiber is generally coarse and brownish in color and is valued because it may be mixed with the hair of the alpaca, an animal of the same species that is raised for its fleece alone. Some noils are obtained from the undercoat of the llama.

When llama is part of a blend of fibers, it gives exquisite natural colors that can be found in few fabrics. Llama mixtures have a characteristic high insulative property with little weight and are used for high-quality coat fabrics, as they embody the essential qualities of wrinkle resistance, fastness of color, and extreme durability.

Alpaca.   In the higher regions of the Andes, 14,000 feet above sea level, is found another fleece bearer, the alpaca, a domesticated animal that resembles the llama and is related to the camel. The fiber is valued for its silky beauty as well as for its strength. The hair of the alpaca is stronger than ordinary sheep's wool. It is also water-repellent and has a high insulative quality. The staple is relatively long, ranging from 6 to 11 inches; yet it is as delicate, soft, and lustrous as the finest silk.

Alpaca consists of two varieties of fiber: soft, wool-like hair, and stiff beard, or outer hair. Of the many colors obtainable, ranging from white to brown and black, the reddish-brown variety is considered the most valuable.

A more highly selected type of alpaca is the *suri*—a superbreed just as the Merino is the highest type of sheep. The fiber of the suri is sought by manufacturers of outer apparel because the staple is longer, silkier, and finer and has curl throughout its length. A crossbreed, with the alpaca as sire and the llama as dam, produces the *misti*. Another crossbreed, the *huarizo,* is the result of breeding a llama sire and an alpaca dam.

Vicuna.   The rare animal whose fiber makes the world's most costly and most exquisite cloth, surpassing all others in fineness and beauty, is found in an almost inaccessible area of the Andes Mountains, at altitudes between 16,000 and 19,000 feet. The vicuna, one of the wildest of animals, is less than 3 feet high and weighs 75 to 100 pounds. A single animal yields only ¼ pound of hair; thus forty animals are required to provide enough hair for the average coat. To preserve the species, the vicuna is now under the protection of the Peruvian and Bolivian governments. Attempts to domesticate this animal have not been very successful but are still being made in Peru. The fiber of the vicuna is the softest and most delicate of the known animal fibers; yet it is strong for its weight, is resilient, and has a marked degree of elasticity and surface cohesion. It is used in costly suitings and overcoat fabrics.

GLOSSARY OF WOOL FABRICS[1]

alpaca. The lower grades of alpaca were originally used as linings, and the better grades for fine dress goods. The fabrics currently being sold as alpaca merely resemble an alpaca fabric in finish; the use of the term for such fabrics is incorrect.

astrakhan. Rough fabric with closely curled face resembling Astrakhan lamb's pelt. Often made with cotton warp or cotton back.

batiste (wool). Lightweight wool fabric in plain weave similar to plain cambric. Should be all wool unless otherwise described.

Bedford cord. Vertically ribbed fabric of substantial construction used for severe wear. Rib is pronounced and runs in same direction as warp. Originally an all-wool fabric, now also made of other fibers. Term describes weave rather than material.

bengaline. A thin fabric made generally of silk and wool, usually with a relatively inconspicuous rib running at right angles to the warp. The name does not denote any particular fiber blend.

bolivia. A soft plushlike fabric of wool, usually containing some special wool fiber, such as alpaca or mohair. The term is properly applied only to an all-wool product, closely woven and of fine stock.

bouclé. A fabric woven from curled or specially twisted yarn in such a way as to produce small loops on the surface, giving a kinky appearance. The curled nap does not cover the entire surface but occurs at intervals, distinguishing it from astrakhan. Usually made in coating weights but also in lighter weights for dress goods.

broadcloth. A fine wool fabric openly woven and then fulled to achieve uniform texture. The surface is then napped, closely sheared, and polished. The term originally was applied only to wool fabrics, but it is also applied to a cotton fabric used principally for men's shirtings. Not only is the fiber content of these fabrics wholly dissimilar but also the construction, finish, and use, so that they cannot be confused.

camel's hair. In undyed form, camel's hair is light tan. Fabrics that merely have this distinctive color cannot be correctly called camel's hair. The best grade is very expensive, and even then camel's hair is sometimes mixed with sheep's wool or other fibers.

candlewick. A soft woolen dress fabric made in imitation of the candlewick bedspread, with tufted patterns similarly applied.

cashmere. A real cashmere fabric is woven only from the hair of the Cashmere goat. It is of fine close twill weave and extremely soft. The total amount of cashmere wool available is strictly limited.

cassimere (not to be confused with cashmere). Cassimere is a woolen fabric closely woven with a plain twill weave, and fulled. Most unclassified woolen fabrics are referred to as cassimeres.

challis. A lightweight sheer fabric of all wool or of silk and wool. Sometimes made with a woven pattern but more often printed with designs

---

[1] Courtesy of Associated Wool Industries.

after weaving. The designs are commonly of the type found in silk goods. Challis is made of fine yarn; it is very thin, light in weight, and soft and pliable.

cheviot. Rough, somewhat harsh woolen fabric, woven from finer yarns than used in typical tweeds. Usually in plain colors or herringbones but may be in other fancy patterns. Woven from woolen yarns except for more expensive cheviots made from worsted yarns, generally in high colors, and referred to as worsted cheviots.

chinchilla. A thick, heavily napped fabric with a close curled surface in imitation of chinchilla fur. The tufts are close together, covering the entire surface. Generally dyed in the piece in solid colors. Used for women's and children's coats and hats.

covert. Twilled fabric made from highly twisted woolen or worsted yarns, usually of two colors, which give it a speckled appearance. Closely woven with a fine, smooth face. Used largely for men's topcoats and women's coats or mannish tailored suits.

crepe (wool). Wool crepe is a lightweight worsted fabric with a more or less crinkly appearance, obtained by using warp yarns that are tightly twisted in alternate directions. The term is often applied to lightweight worsted fabrics for women's wear that have little or no crepe surface.

doeskin. A very close and compact wool fabric with exceptionally smooth face. The weave is similar to a satin, but the smooth finish generally obliterates any trace of the weave on the face.

flannel. A fulled and napped woven fabric, made generally of woolen yarn but sometimes with worsted yarn used in the warp or filling. Usually woven with a twill weave, which may be obscured by the nap. Distinguished for its softness. Used for bathrobes, skirts, men's suits and trousers. Cotton flannel or flannelette is not dissimilar in appearance.

fleece. Wool fabric with deep, soft nap. Term properly applied to flat woven or knit woolen fabrics as well as to those woven on the pile principle. The long nap or pile provides many air spaces, resulting in a fabric with high insulative properties.

gabardine. A firm, hard-finished worsted fabric in the twill weave with a fine diagonal wale.

homespun. A coarse and loosely woven woolen material made to simulate homemade cloth—in effect, a coarse, rough tweed. Yarn is usually heavy and contains coarse wool fiber unevenly spun.

hopsacking. A rough open-weave woolen fabric made of coarse yarn, usually in a basket weave. Used for novelty effects.

jersey. Elastic knitted fabric made from either woolen or worsted yarn. The rib is clearly discernible on one side of the fabric.

kersey. A medium-weight woolen fabric, well fulled in the finishing, with a napped and closely sheared surface that obscures the weave. Used extensively for military and civil uniforms.

mackinaw. A heavy woolen fabric, heavily fulled or felted, sometimes napped, with the result that no weave is apparent on the surface. In general construction, the same as melton except that the latter is usually made in plain colors, whereas mackinaw cloth is commonly woven with large distinctive plaids or color effects. Usually made of the coarser wools.

melton. Well-fulled or felted overcoating fabric with smooth finish and close-cropped nap. Generally in plain colors. Coarser meltons similar to mackinaw cloth, but sometimes made of fine, soft wools to produce smooth coating fabric with finish similar to broadcloth.

mohair. Yarns and fabrics of mohair are bright and lustrous. Warp yarns of cotton or worsted generally used in flat mohair fabrics. Mohair pile fabrics used in automobiles and for upholstery usually have pile introduced as warp, but in such fashion that the special system of threads is not subjected to severe tension.

nun's veiling. A fine, lightweight plain-weave woolen fabric, very soft and thin, originally for veils but now used for women's and children's dresses. Plain colors.

plaid back. A type of construction used in overcoatings. The face may be finished like melton, fleece, or similar fabrics. The back is a fancy or tartan plaid.

poplin (wool). Originally a fabric having a silk warp and a filling that consisted of a wool yarn heavier than the silk, thus producing a ribbed surface something like a rep. Now made of different fibers or combinations.

rabbit's hair. Rabbit's hair is used in combination with other fibers. It is soft and lustrous. In the better fabrics, enough hair may be present to justify the use of the term.

ratiné A rough, pebbly woolen fabric the surface interest of which is obtained by the use of novelty yarns with a fancy twist.

Saxony. A term applied to certain flannels and to smooth woolen fabrics made from fine wools similar in nature to Saxony wools.

serge. A fabric with a diagonal twill and a smooth finish. The twill is visible both on the face and on the back. Dark blue is the color most commonly used, but other plain colors are made for certain purposes.

sharkskin (wool). A term descriptively applied to wool fabrics woven in a 2 and 2 right-hand twill, with a 1 and 1 color arrangement of yarns in the warp and filling. This combination of weave and color results in color lines running diagonally to the left, opposed to the direction of the twill lines, and a distinctly sleek appearance and feel that suggests the texture of the skin of the shark. Modifications of this design are often loosely designated as sharkskin.

sheers (wool). General classification for thin lightweight women's-wear fabrics. Usually woven from worsted yarns, although some woolen fabrics are sufficiently thin to be classified as sheers.

shetland. The term is now applied to fabrics made of wool with the characteristics of Shetland Islands wool. Shetlands are extremely soft. The herringbone weave is common.

snow cloth. Fabrics designed for outdoor winter use. May be meltons, kerseys, heavy flannels, and similar fabrics. Often indicates these fabrics have been given water-repellent finish.

suede (wool). A fine soft fabric with closely clipped nap made to imitate suede leather.

tropical weights. Lightweight suitings of woolen or worsted, usually the latter, used for men's and less frequently for women's summer suits. The weave should be firm but open, as the fabric is especially designed for hot-weather wear.

tweed. A term broadly applied to the sturdier types of fabrics made of the coarser grades of wool. Tweed fabrics originally derived their interest from the color effects obtained by mixing stock-dyed wools. More recently the term includes monotones, which derive their interest from weave effects. The most popular weaves for tweeds are the plain, the twill, and variations of the latter.

velour (wool). A smooth, sleek fabric with a closely cut pile face. The upright pile, which yields in any direction, gives the fabric an exceedingly smooth feel.

vicuna. Short, soft, exceedingly fine hair fiber, very valuable because of the limited supply. It is rarely used by itself, although a few vicuna coats are manufactured each year. Sometimes mixed with wool to produce special soft coating fabrics. The term and certain derived and coined names have been much misused.

whipcord. Sturdy wool fabric with pronounced diagonal wale, closely woven and smooth-finished. Used for riding habits and other garments subjected to hard wear; in heavier weights for upholstery.

▶ **TEST YOURSELF ON THIS CHAPTER**

1. What are the advantages of wool fabrics?
2. Name the classification of fleeces according to quality.
3. What countries supply the world with wool?
4. Explain the United States government classifications of wool.
5. What qualities are found in fleece wool?
6. How are grease and dirt removed from the fleece? What by-product is obtained from the grease?
7. Name six differences between woolens and worsteds.
8. Name three woolen fabrics and three worsted fabrics.
9. What are unfinished worsteds?
10. How would you judge quality wool fabrics?
11. What finishing processes are used for woolens?
12. Which finishing processes are used for worsteds? Why?
13. How do worsteds compare with woolens as to appearance and touch?
14. Which type of wool fabric is warmer? Why? Which stronger? Why? Which higher in price? Why?
15. Discuss the qualities of the hair fibers, their sources, and how they are used.

12 · SILK | Soft, Strong, Luxurious

The possibility of making cloth from the filament that the silkworm spins into a cocoon was first discovered in China about 2600 B.C. The Chinese cultivated the silkworm and developed a silk industry, endeavoring to keep the source of the raw material a secret. They succeeded for many years, but eventually Chinese emigrants introduced the silkworm into Japan in A.D. 300.

Eggs of the silk moth were smuggled out of China into southeastern Europe in A.D. 550. Spain began to produce silk in the eighth century, and Italy in the twelfth. It was the sixteenth century before the industry developed in France and England.

Attempts have been made to cultivate the silkworm in the United States, but they have not succeeded commercially because of the higher labor and production costs in this country. The silk industry is an important one, however, because the United States has become the greatest importer and consumer of silk. That part of the industry that manufactures raw silk into fabrics closely touches the lives of American consumers. The possession of silk fabrics has always represented an ideal of luxury to Americans, perhaps more than to the inhabitants of other countries. Silk will probably always be prized by the consumer even though man-made and synthetic fibers now have qualities that were formerly possessed only by silk.

Silk-producing Countries. When farmers in the Asiatic countries first raised silkworms, the many diseased worms and defective cocoons resulted in poor grades of finished goods. The farmers were raising silkworms only as an additional means of support. Japan was the first country producing silk in large quantities to use scientific methods in cultivating the silkworm on farms as well as in factories. Japan has therefore always ranked highest in the production of fine silk, although satisfactory types are made in other silk-producing countries—China, Italy, Spain, France, Austria, Iran, Turkey, Greece, Syria, Bulgaria, and Brazil. The cultivation of the silkworm requires extreme care and close supervision, and the reeling of the filament from the cocoons can be undertaken only by skilled operators whose training is the result of many generations of experience.

Cultivation of Silk Cocoons.

Since the discovery, so many years ago, that the fiber, or filament, composing the cocoon of the silkworm can be unwound and constructed into a beautiful and durable fabric, silkworms have been bred for the sole purpose of producing raw silk. The production of cocoons for their filament is called *sericulture*. The cocoon of the silkworm is the second stage of development of the life cycle of the *Bombyx mori,* a species of moth. Experiments have proved that this moth produces the finest quality of raw silk. In sericulture, all four stages of the life cycle of this moth are important, because some of the better cocoons must be set aside to permit full development, thus supplying eggs for another hatching. Under scientific breeding, silkworms may be hatched three times a year; under natural conditions, breeding occurs only once a year. The life cycle is:

1. The egg, which develops into the larva or caterpillar—the silkworm
2. The silkworm, which spins its cocoon for protection, to permit development into the pupa or chrysalis
3. The chrysalis, which emerges from the cocoon as the moth
4. The moth, of which the female lays eggs, so continuing the life cycle

Within three days after emerging from the cocoons, the moths mate, the female lays 350 to 400 eggs, and the moths die. Each healthy egg hatches into a grub, or larva, about $\frac{1}{8}$ inch long. The larva requires careful nurturing for approximately twenty to thirty-two days. During this period, the tiny worm has a voracious appetite. It is fed five times a day on chopped mulberry leaves. After four changes of skin, or moltings, the worm reaches full growth in the form of a smooth grayish-white caterpillar about $3\frac{1}{2}$ inches long. Its interest in food ceases. It shrinks somewhat in size and acquires a pinkish hue, becoming nearly transparent. A constant restless rearing movement of the head indicates that the worm is ready to spin its cocoon. Clusters of twigs or straw are provided for this purpose.

Of importance to the silk industry is the small opening under the caterpillar's jaws, called the *spinneret*. The silkworm begins to secrete a proteinlike substance through its spinneret, and with a bending motion the filament is spun around the worm in the form of the figure eight. The silkworm is hidden from view within twenty-four hours; in three days, the cocoon is completed. It is about the size and shape of a peanut shell. The filament is in the form of a double strand or *fibroin,* which is held together by a gummy substance called *sericin,* or *silk gum.* The liquid substance hardens immediately on exposure to the air. If left undisturbed, the chrysalis inside the cocoon develops into a moth within two weeks. To emerge, the moth must break through the top of the cocoon by excreting an alkaline liquid that dissolves the filament. As this cutting through damages the cocoon so that the filament cannot be unwound in one

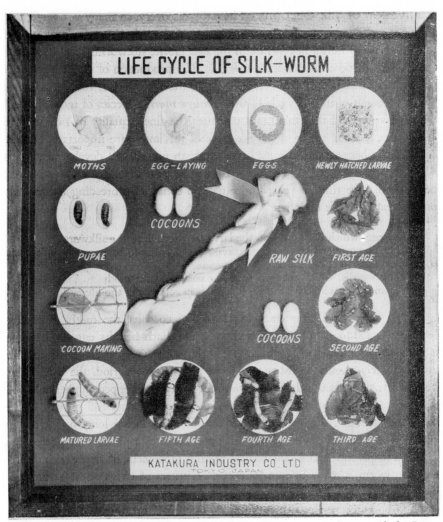

Courtesy Charles Roman

long thread, the life cycle is terminated at this point by a process known as *stoving* or *stifling.* The cocoons are heated to suffocate the chrysalis, but the delicate silk filament is not harmed.

Filature Operations. The cocoons that are raised by silk farmers are delivered to a factory, called a *filature,* where the silk is unwound from the cocoons and the strands are collected into skeins. Some cocoons are scientifically bred in such factories.

• *Sorting Cocoons.* The cocoons are sorted according to color, size, shape, and texture, as all these affect the final quality of the silk. Cocoons may range

Cocoons are being picked from nests of twigs originally provided to aid the silkworms in their spinning.

from white or yellow to grayish, depending on the source and the type of food consumed during the worm stage. Cocoons from China are white; Japanese cocoons are creamy white and yellow; Italian are yellow.

• *Softening the Sericin.* After the cocoons have been sorted, they are put through a series of hot and cold immersions, as the sericin must be softened to permit the unwinding of the filament in one continuous thread. Raw silk consists of about 80 per cent fibroin and 20 per cent sericin. At this time, only about 1 per cent of the sericin is removed because this silk gum is a needed protection during the further handling of the delicate filament.

• *Reeling the Filament.* The process of unwinding the filament from the cocoon is called *reeling.* The care and skill used in the reeling operation prevent defects in the raw silk. As the filament of a single cocoon is too fine for com-

Reeling silk cocoons.

Skeins of reeled silk.

Courtesy The Central Raw Silk Assn. of Japan

mercial use, three to ten strands are usually reeled at a time to produce the desired diameter of raw silk thread. The cocoons float in water, bobbing up and down, as the filaments are drawn upward through porcelain eyelets and are rapidly wound on wheels or drums while the operator watches to detect flaws. As the reeling of the filament from each cocoon nears completion, the operator attaches a new filament to the moving thread. Skilled operators have an uncanny ability to blend the filaments, always retaining the same diameter of the rapidly moving silk strand. The sericin acts as an adhesive. It aids in holding the several filaments together while they are combined to form the single thread. On old-style reeling machines, at high speed, an operator could handle five to seven threads; on the newest models, he can handle twenty-five threads.

The usable length of the reeled filament is from 1,000 to 2,000 feet, approximately a quarter of a mile long. The remaining part of the filament is used as valuable raw material for the manufacture of spun silk.

The term *reeled silk* is applied to the raw silk strand that is formed by combining several filaments from separate cocoons. It is reeled into skeins, which are packed in small bundles called *books,* weighing 5 to 10 pounds. These books are put into bales, ranging in weight from 135 to 145 pounds. In this form, the raw silk is shipped to all parts of the world.

Manufacture of Silk Yarns.   From the filature, the books of reeled silk go to the throwster.

• *Silk Throwing.* Reeled silk is transformed into silk yarn—also called silk thread—by a process known as *throwing.* The term is derived from the Anglo-Saxon word "thrawn," meaning "to twist." Persons engaged in this work are called *throwsters.* Silk throwing is analogous to the spinning process that manufactures cotton, linen, or wool fibers into yarn. Unlike those fibers, the manu-

Books of reeled silk.

Courtesy The Central Raw Silk Assn. of Japan

facture of silk yarn does not include carding, combing, and drawing out, the usual processes for producing a continuous yarn. The raw silk skeins are sorted according to size, color, and length or quantity, then soaked in warm water with soap or oil. This softening of the sericin aids in handling the thread. After mechanical drying, the skeins are placed on light reels, from which the silk is wound on bobbins.

During this winding operation, single strands may be given any desired amount of twist. If two or more yarns are to be doubled, they are twisted again in the same direction or in a reverse direction, depending on the kind of thread to be made. To equalize the diameter, the thread is run through rollers. The thread is then inspected and packaged ready for shipment to manufacturers for construction into fabric.

Kinds of Thrown Silk Threads. Several kinds of silk yarns or threads are used in the manufacture of silk goods. The type of yarn and the amount of twist depend on what the weaver desires.

• *Singles.* Usually, three to eight strands of silk filaments are twisted together in one direction to form a yarn called a single. Loose-twist singles, having two or three twists per inch, are used primarily for the filling yarns in many silk fabrics. Hard-twist singles, having a much greater number of twists per inch, are used in the sheer fabrics.

• *Tram.* Tram is used only as a filling yarn. Usually, two to four untwisted singles are combined with only a slight twist of about three to five turns per inch. The number of turns may be increased for especially heavy silk fabrics. Tram is rarely twisted more than five turns to the inch, except in such fabrics as radium and taffeta, which use a special hard-twisted tram of about thirty turns per inch.

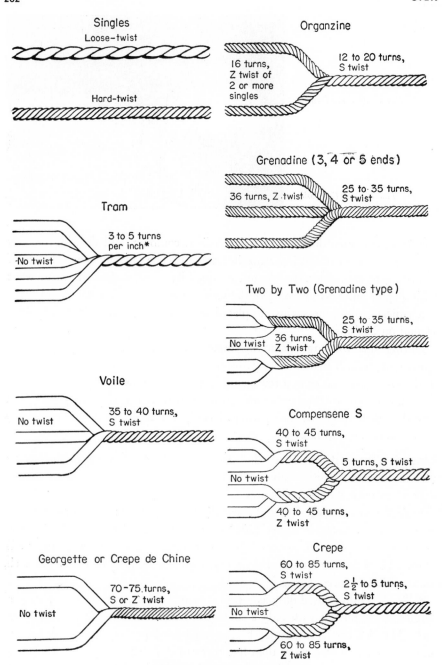

Types of thrown silk yarns.

* *Descriptions of all turns are per inch.*

• *Voile.* This yarn is used for such sheer crepes as voile. It is composed of three untwisted singles combined with thirty-five to forty S turns per inch.

• *Georgette or Crepe de Chine.* This yarn is composed of two untwisted singles combined with a very hard S or Z twist of seventy to seventy-five turns per inch. The result is a very fine, strong, elastic yarn used for warp yarns and for such sheer fabrics as georgette or crepe de chine.

• *Organzine.* Organzine is used primarily for warp yarns. It is composed of two or more singles, each of which has sixteen Z turns per inch. These singles are then combined by twisting them around each other in the opposite S twist twelve to twenty turns per inch, which causes them to interlock more tightly, resulting in a firmer, stronger yarn.

• *Grenadine.* This yarn is composed of three to five singles, each given a twist of about thirty-six Z turns per inch, then combined by being twisted around each other in the opposite S direction twenty-five to thirty-five turns per inch. Although these yarns have a high twist, they are nevertheless fine and are used for such sheer fabrics as organdy and grenadine.

• *Two by Two* (*Grenadine Type*). Each of two pairs of untwisted singles is twisted about thirty-six Z turns per inch, then twisted around each other twenty-five or thirty-five turns in the S direction. These yarns are consequently much like the grenadine yarns but are heavier. Their weight, body, and high twist make them desirable for crepe fabrics.

• *Compensene S.* This yarn is made of each of two pairs of untwisted singles. One pair is twisted together forty to forty-five S turns per inch; the other is twisted the same number of Z turns per inch. These twisted pairs are then twisted around each other five S turns per inch. The opposing directions of these twists prevent kinking but give elasticity. These yarns are often used for knitted fabrics.

• *Crepe.* Some crepe fabrics are made of crepe yarns. These yarns are composed of each of two pairs of untwisted singles. One pair is twisted sixty to eighty-five turns per inch in the S direction; the other is twisted the same number of turns per inch in the Z direction. They are then twisted around each other two and one-half to five S turns per inch.

Yarn Count of Silk Threads. The size or the yarn count of silk threads is based on a system of weight known as the *denier*. A denier represents a weight of 5 centigrams; that is, .05 or $\frac{1}{20}$ gram. The standard length of a raw silk skein is 450 meters. A 450-meter skein weighing $\frac{1}{20}$ gram contains a 1 denier thread, which is an extremely fine thread. To find the denier of 450 meters of silk thread weighing 70 centigrams (the usual weight of skeins from Japan), divide 70 by .05, or $\frac{1}{20}$. The result is 14. The denier is expressed as 13/15 to allow for variation in the diameter of the thread.

In the laboratory, the denier size of a silk thread is obtained by a different method of figuring. The weight of a 450-meter skein is multiplied by 20 because 20 denier equals 1 gram, as 1 denier equals $\frac{1}{20}$ gram. For example, if the 450-meter skein weighs 2.16 grams, multiplying this weight by 20 gives 43.2, which is expressed as a 42/44 denier to allow for variation.

The most common size of raw silk from Japan was 13/15 denier. This is as fine as a 350s cotton yarn. In the spring crop, a 13/15 denier requires four to five cocoons to a thread, whereas the summer and autumn crops require five to six cocoons to the thread. As each cocoon comprises two filaments, a 13/15 denier may contain eight to ten or twelve to fourteen filaments, depending on the season. The greater the number of cocoons used, the coarser the thread and the higher the denier.

Degumming. Thrown silk threads still contain some sericin, which must be removed in another soap bath to bring out the natural luster and the soft feel of the silk. As much as 25 per cent of the weight is lost by the degumming process. When the gum has been removed, the silk fiber or fabric is a creamy-white color, beautifully lustrous and luxuriantly soft.

Degumming may take place after the silk thread is thrown in order to prepare it for yarn dyeing, or it may be done in any finishing process after the fabric is woven. For example, the tightly twisted yarns used for crepe effects still contain sericin. A small amount of sericin is sometimes left in the yarn or in the fabric to give the finished product added strength or a dull finish. Ecru and souple are examples of silk fabrics from which sericin has been partially removed.

Weighting. The amount of weight that silk loses in the degumming process is an appreciable factor in manufacturing costs because the manufacturer buys silk by weight. As is customary in any business, the price of the finished product must offset this loss; therefore, silk has always been an expensive fabric. The weighting of silk fabric with metallic substances to make up for the weight lost by degumming is an accepted practice in the silk industry. This procedure lowers the cost of silk to the consumer.

Weighted silk is less compactly woven than unweighted silk, and less silk is used in the construction of the cloth. In other words, weighting rather than compact construction gives firmness and body to the fabric. Weighting is done by the dyeing process. To weight colored silks, stannic chloride is used, followed by treatment with sodium phosphate. Black silks are weighted with metallic mordants, such as iron salt and logwood.

A small amount of metallic weighting, correctly applied to a fabric that is well woven to hold the weighting, is not considered injurious. In addition to lowering the cost, it is claimed that weighting gives silk crispness, luster, and firmer body and feel. When weighted silk is pleated, the crease is retained. Weighted silk, however, loses the natural elasticity of the silk fiber and is subject to deterioration when exposed to sunlight, perspiration, and dry cleaning. When the fabric is not properly constructed, threads shift. If the fabric is not woven sufficiently wide to allow for natural shrinkage, there is an unsatisfactory amount of shrinkage.

Taffeta is a commonly used fabric that is usually heavily weighted, because today there is little demand for pure-dye taffeta. Weighted taffeta is apt to crack and split at the places subjected to the strain of wear and when folded for a length of time. (Rayon and acetate taffeta do not contain any metallic weighting.) Because the consumer cannot determine the percentage of weighting in a silk fabric, the Federal Trade Commission ruled in 1938 that weighted silk must be marked as such, and the percentage of weighting must be indicated on the label.

Pure-Dye Silk. As silk is weighted during the dyeing process, the term *pure-dye silk* indicates that weighting was not added at that time. According to the Federal Trade Commission rulings, pure-dye silk is defined as a fabric made exclusively of silk fibers containing *no metallic weighting whatsoever*. But the use of such water-soluble substances as starch, glue, sugar, or gelatin in the dyeing and finishing processes is allowed. Such foreign substances are limited to 10 per cent for white or colored silks and 15 per cent for black silks. Well-constructed pure-dye silk requires a greater amount of silk thread than weighted silk because pure-dye silk is usually more compact. Thus it is generally superior, having the qualities of elasticity and durability, because the natural elasticity of the silk fiber has not been lessened, and its great natural strength has been retained.

Spun Silk. Short lengths of inferior silk filaments obtained from waste material are not used in producing reeled silk. After the short lengths have been carded and combed, they are spun together much as cotton, linen, or wool yarns are spun. Spun silk threads are soft, but they are less lustrous than reeled silk and are not as strong or elastic. Spun silk fabric tends to become fuzzy after wearing because the yarn is made of short staple.

There are several sources of staple silk: (1) pierced cocoons, the result of breeding moths that have emerged from their cocoons; (2) double cocoons, the result of two cocoons having been spun by two silkworms too close together; this is sometimes called *doupioni* silk; (3) floss, brushed from cocoons before reeling; (4) frison, the coarse and uneven silk fiber at the beginning and end of each cocoon; (5) scrap, the machine waste left from reeling, throwing, and the like.

Spun silk is less expensive than reeled silk. Although spun silk has less strength and elasticity than reeled silk because of the shorter staple used, it possesses all the general characteristics of reeled silk. Tub silk fabric, for example, is made of spun silk, yet it gives good service when the quality of the fiber is good. Spun silk is used for shantung and pile fabrics; for dress trimmings, linings, elastic webbing, and sewing silk; for summer wash silks, for velvets, for umbrella fabrics, and for insulative materials.

• *Yarn Count of Spun Silk Threads.* The method of determining the size of spun silk thread is similar to that used for cotton yarn. In cotton, the term 2/60s signifies a two-ply yarn consisting of two single strands twisted together, each having a yarn count of 60.

In spun silk, a two-ply yarn is indicated by the figures 60s/2. Although this term appears to be only the reverse of the cotton term, it does not mean the same. In spun silk, 60s/2 means that two yarns with a separate yarn count of 120 have been doubled, producing a ply yarn with a new count of 60.

Wild, or Tussah, Silk. The silkworms that hatch from a wild species of moth, the *Antheraea mylitta,* live on oak leaves instead of the mulberry leaves that form the food of the cultivated species. This coarser food produces an irregular and coarse filament that is hard to bleach and hard to dye. The tannin in the oak leaves gives wild silk its tan color, and the silk is commonly woven with the naturally colored thread; it is rarely dyed except in solid shades. Wild silk is less lustrous than cultivated silk as only a low percentage (about 11 per cent) of sericin is removed in the degumming process. Wild silk fabrics are durable and have a coarse irregular surface. They are washable and are generally less expensive than pure-dye silk. Typical fabrics are rajah, shantung, tussah, and pongee.

The standard wild silk thread differs from the standard reeled silk thread in size, as it is made from eighteen cocoons. It averages 32/34 denier.

Finishing Processes. Finishing processes that enhance the appearance of fabrics and add to their serviceability are given to silk fabrics. Special finishes are used to make the fabric water-repellent. The most essential finishes are:

Singeing—for smoothness
Bleaching—very little required when silk is completely degummed
Stiffening—for cheaper grades
Embossing—if such patterns as moiré are desired
Calendering—for enhancing luster

Steaming—for pile weaves

Wringing and stretching—softening the fiber and increasing the luster

Pressing—removing wrinkles from finished fabric by passing it through heated rollers. The fabric is soaked in dilute acid to develop luster

Judging Silk Fabrics. In spite of its high cost, silk has been one of the most popular fabrics because of its unique properties. Soft, supple, strong, and lighter in weight than any other natural fiber, silk is prized for its lightness with warmth, sheerness with strength, and delicacy with resiliency.

• *Strength.* Silk is very durable when the fabric is well constructed. Its use for parachutes is the highest recommendation that can be given for the strength of its filament. The great length of the filament, a factor in strength, imparts smoothness to the constructed cloth. There are fewer fiber ends in silk fabrics than in any fabric made of other natural fibers.

• *Crease Resistance.* Silk fabrics retain their shape, resist wrinkling, and recover easily from creasing because of the natural elasticity of the fiber. This is particularly true of the fabrics made from pure-dye silk and from wild silk. Those that contain a large percentage of weighting or those made from the short-staple spun silk do not have this degree of elasticity.

• *Heat Conductivity.* Like wool, which is also a nonconductor of heat, silk is desirable for winter apparel. Even silk fabrics of sheer construction are comfortably warm when used for lingerie and linings. Silk is worn in the summer because of its smoothness and crease resistance, which help to retain a fresh appearance. The warmth-giving quality is lessened by weighting, as the metallic content causes the fabric to become a conductor of heat.

• *Cleanliness and Washability.* Silk is a hygienic material because its smooth surface does not attract dirt, and any that gathers is given up readily when silk is washed or dry-cleaned. All silks are easily spotted by water, but subsequent washing or dry cleaning restores the appearance of the fabric. Weighted silks preferably should be dry-cleaned, but wild silk and spun silk fabrics may be washed. As perspiration deteriorates silk, undergarments should be washed immediately after each wearing.

• *Shrinkage.* Because of the straightness of the filament, smooth-surfaced silk fabrics have only a normal shrinkage, which is easily restored by ironing. Crepe effects shrink considerably in washing, but careful ironing with a moderately hot iron will restore the fabric to its original size.

• *Fastness of Color.* Dyed silk is colorfast under most conditions, but its resistance to light is unsatisfactory. The resistance of weighted silk is particularly poor; therefore, silk is not recommended for window curtains. Pure-dye silks may be redyed by the consumer, provided a suitable commercial dye is used and the directions on the container are carefully followed.

• *Resistance to Mildew*. Silk will not mildew unless left for some time in a damp state or under the extreme conditions of tropical dampness.

• *Resistance to Moths*. Silk is not attacked by moths.

• *Reaction to Alkalies*. Silk is not as sensitive as wool is to alkalies but can be damaged if the concentration and temperature are high enough. Use mild soap and lukewarm water when laundering silk.

• *Reaction to Acids*. Concentrated mineral acids will dissolve silk faster than wool. Organic acids do not harm silk.

• *Reaction to Perspiration*. Silk fabrics are damaged by perspiration. The silk itself deteriorates, and the color is affected, causing staining.

GLOSSARY OF SILK FABRICS

bengaline. A ribbed fabric having cotton or wool yarns for the filling and silk for the warp. Similar to poplin but having a heavier ribbed effect. Used for coats, suits, dresses.

broadcloth. A fine, smooth, closely woven fabric in plain colors or in woven stripes; also known as silk shirting. It has a plain weave. Used for shirts and dresses.

brocade. Most figured silk fabrics in a Jacquard weave are known as brocades. The pattern is raised above the general surface of the fabric. Used mainly for elaborate evening wear.

canton crepe. Characterized by a heavy filling and a finer warp. Heavier than crepe de chine, having pronounced crinkle and greater durability. Used chiefly for dresses.

chiffon. A transparent sheer fabric in a plain weave. Extremely light in weight but very strong. It usually has a soft finish. Used for evening dresses, lingerie, blouses, and handkerchiefs.

China silk. A very soft, extremely lightweight silk made in a plain weave, used chiefly for linings. Irregularities of threads, caused by the extreme lightness and softness of China silk, are characteristic of the fabric.

crepe. Fabrics with a crinkled effect, produced either by the use of tightly twisted yarns or by the method of weaving.

crepe-back satin or satin crepe. Satin weave with a crepe-twist filling. As the fabric is reversible, interesting effects can be obtained by contrasting the surfaces. Used for dresses, blouses, linings.

crepe de chine. Soft but strong; lighter in weight than canton crepe. Has a fine crinkled effect produced by alternately twisted filling yarns. Popular for dresses, lingerie, blouses, and scarves.

crepe meteor. Similar to georgette in construction on the reverse side. Satin construction on its face, thus showing more luster than any of the flat crepes. Light in weight, drapes well, has a soft feel and finish.

damask. Reversible figured silk fabrics woven on the Jacquard loom. Pattern flatter than in brocade. Used for upholstery and draperies; the lighter weights, for dresses and lingerie.

ecru silk. Thrown silk with small amount of sericin removed.

faille. A silk fabric of the grosgrain type. In plain weave with flat ribs in the filling. Has good body and wears well if not too loosely constructed. Usually slightly lustrous finish. Used for dresses, coats, and handbags.

faille crepe. Lighter weight than faille with creped filling. Used for dresses.

faille taffeta. Stiff and crisp with a fine cross-ribbed appearance. Used for dresses and coats.

flat crepe. Similar to crepe de chine but with a flatter surface.

foulard. A lightweight silk fabric with a soft finish. Made with a twill weave. Usually printed with small figures on dark and light backgrounds. Suitable for dresses, robes, and scarves.

georgette. Highly creped sheer silk fabric, chiefly for dresses and blouses.

grosgrain. A fine cross-ribbed fabric of close texture having a heavy filling, which is sometimes made of cotton yarns. Ribs are rounder than in faille, heavier than in poplin. Used chiefly for ribbons and trimmings.

habutai. Similar to China silk but heavier. A closely woven, pure-dye fabric. Used for lamp shades, dresses, blouses, lingerie, curtains.

lamé. Silk in which metal threads form the pattern or the background. Used for evening wear.

marquisette. Very sheer silk fabric in the gauze weave. Sometimes called silk gauze. Used for evening dresses and trimmings.

matelassé. A fabric having a raised figured pattern in a blistered quilted effect. Woven on a Jacquard loom. Used for dresses and blouses.

merveilleux. An all-silk or silk-and-cotton mixture in twill weave. Used as lining in men's outer apparel.

moiré. Watermark designs embossed on plain-weave fabrics that have crosswise ribs.

mousseline de soie. Sheer transparent silk in a plain weave. Similar to chiffon but with a more open texture and a stiffer finish produced by the use of sizing. Used chiefly for evening dresses.

ottoman. Heavy plain-weave fabric with wide, flat crosswise ribs that are larger and rounder than in faille. Filling may be cotton, silk, or wool. Used for dress coats, suits, trimmings.

pongee. Also called *tussah silk*. Made from wild silk. Has a rough, uneven texture. Generally in its natural colors of cream to light brown, but may be dyed. Used for dress goods and household decoration.

radium. A lustrous, supple fabric having the drapability of crepe and the crispness of taffeta. Plain weave. Used for women's dresses, slips, negligees, blouses, linings, draperies.

satin. Silk fabric with a highly lustrous surface and usually a dull back. Made in different weights according to its uses, which vary from lingerie and dress goods to drapery and upholstery fabrics. May be made with a cotton back. Sometimes double-faced for use as ribbon.

shantung. Low in luster, heavier and rougher than pongee. A plain weave in which large, irregular filling yarns are used. Sometimes used to describe a heavy grade of pongee made in China.

souple silk. Silk dyed in the skein, only part of the sericin being removed.

surah. A soft, strong silk with a twill weave. Used for dresses and scarves.

taffeta. A smooth, closely woven fabric in a plain weave. Often weighted to produce its characteristic crispness. Sometimes has a moiré pattern. Used for dresses, suits, coats, and lingerie.

velvet. Silk velvet has a silk pile and a silk back. Some velvets are made with a silk pile and a rayon or cotton back. *Transparent velvet* is a sheer velvet having a rayon pile and a silk back. *Panne velvet* has a special luster that is produced by pressing the pile in one direction.

▶ **TEST YOURSELF ON THIS CHAPTER**

1. Name the silk-producing countries. What is the cultivation of silk called?
2. Describe the life cycle of the silkworm.
3. What process in the production of silk is analogous to the spinning process for other fibers?
4. What is the difference between weighted silk and pure-dye silk?
5. Describe the degumming process and its effects on various types of silk fabrics.
6. For what purpose would you select silk rather than other fabrics? Why?
7. What finishing processes are given to silk fabrics?
8. What is spun silk? How does it differ from thrown silk?
9. Why is silk weighted? What are the advantages of weighting? the disadvantages?
10. How does wild silk differ from cultivated silk? How does the difference affect the consumer?
11. Why are most wild silk fabrics tan in color?
12. Name some fabrics usually made from wild silk.
13. For what purposes is pongee most desirable?
14. Why is silk not recommended for window curtains?
15. List the essential qualities of silk, and show the effect of each quality on finished goods.

13 · RAYON, ACETATE, ARNEL

Cellulosic Fibers

The production of a fiber such as rayon, the first of the man-made fibers, had been prophesied as long ago as 1664 by Robert Hooke, the English naturalist. He believed that it was possible to make an "artificial glutinous composition, much resembling, if not full as good, nay better, than that excrement, or whatever other substance it be out of which the silkworm wire-draws his clew." In 1710, René A. de Réaumur, the French scientist, suggested the possibility of making silk filaments out of gums and resins; for example, threads of varnish. One hundred and thirty years later, in 1840, an apparatus was invented that drew synthetic filaments through small holes. In 1855, Georges Audemars, a Swiss chemist, discovered how to make cellulose nitrate. This was the first step toward the nitrocellulose process of making rayon. Almost thirty years later, in 1884, Count Hilaire de Chardonnet produced the first synthetic textile fibers from nitrocellulose. He became known as the "father of rayon." Chardonnet obtained the original French patent and won the financial support that built the world's first rayon factory. These and other chemists of their day, as well as those who are constantly experimenting today on new fibers, have been guided by a desire to produce beautiful, smooth, light, supple fabrics with just the right amount of luster—the characteristics for which silk has long been noted—at a price within the income of every consumer.

Man-made textile filaments were officially recognized in 1925, when the Federal Trade Commission permitted the use of the name *rayon* for yarns obtained from cellulose or its derivatives. As the production and types of man-made fibers had increased and been given various trade names, the Federal Trade Commission ruled again in 1937 that any fiber or yarn produced chemically from cellulose must be designated as rayon.

Over the period of the next fifteen years, however, confusion developed among garment manufacturers, and particularly among consumers, because there were as many as four different types of "rayon" with some similar and some different properties. Some rayons would fade faster than others; some would dry

Wood pulp and cotton, the sources from which rayon and acetate are made.

Courtesy American Viscose Corp.

more quickly than others; some would stick to the iron and melt, while others would iron nicely. The cause of this lay in the fact that there were basically two groups of rayons: one consisting of regenerated pure cellulose, the other of a cellulose compound. These different compositions gave different properties. The Federal Trade Commission therefore ruled that, as of February 9, 1952, there would be two categories of cellulosic fibers: rayon and acetate. All fabrics and garments containing rayon and/or acetate must be labeled as such and the per cent of content of each fiber must be indicated. The rules also incorporated the first official designation of rayon and acetate products as "man-made" rather than "synthetic." In the chemist's terminology, rayon and acetate are not synthetic because natural materials—cotton linters and wood pulp—are used in their manufacture, rather than chemical elements. This differentiation has been used in this text, but the reader should remember that in many other publications the two terms are used interchangeably.

RAYON

Basic Method of Producing Rayon Filament. The natural process by which the silkworm transforms the cellulose of mulberry trees into two fine filaments is simulated in the process of making rayon.

A liquid substance of cellulose is forced through a metal cap or nozzle about the size of a thimble. This nozzle is called a *spinneret* because it performs the same function as the silkworm's spinneret. The cap is usually made of platinum

The spinneret that forms the spinning solution into filaments.

because that metal is not affected by acids or alkalies; it is perforated with small holes that are almost invisible to the naked eye. Through each of the tiny holes, a filament is extruded, which is solidified by a liquid bath as it comes from the spinneret. This is similar to the hardening by air of the raw-silk substance spun by the silkworm. The number of holes in the spinneret may be varied, thus producing at one time any number of filaments of the same size. In a subsequent operation, these filaments are doubled and twisted to make any required size of rayon yarn.

Methods of Producing Rayon.

There are three principal methods of making rayon. The fibers differ in important characteristics because the methods differ in: (1) the raw material from which the cellulose substance is obtained; (2) the chemicals that change the cellulose into fluid form for spinning; (3) specific features of manufacture. These rayons, *viscose, cuprammonium,* and *nitrocellulose,* are classified as *regenerated rayons* because the original raw material, the cellulose, is changed chemically into another form, which is then changed (regenerated) into cellulose again. This second change produces the final product—purified cellulose in fiber form.

Nitrocellulose Rayon.

Although Chardonnet produced the first man-made textile fibers from nitrocellulose over seventy-five years ago, the nitrocellulose process is no longer a significant factor in the world production of rayon. In this process, cotton linters are treated with a mixture of nitric and sulphuric acids. The linters are dissolved in a mixture of alcohol and ether, which forms a spinning solution called *collodion*. As this solution is forced through the spinneret, the alcohol evaporates, and the filament hardens. Its nitrate element is removed by a sodium hydrosulphide treatment, yielding a filament of purified cellulose.

Viscose Rayon.

Viscose rayon is made from cotton fiber or wood pulp usually obtained from spruce, hemlock, and pine trees. The chemical process of dissolving wood pulp was first discovered in 1840 by F. G. Keller, a noted German weaver. The viscose method of using wood pulp to manufacture rayon

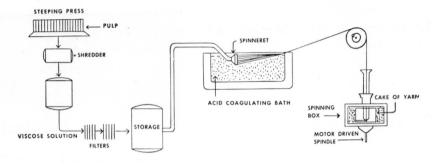

PRODUCTION OF VISCOSE RAYON YARN

Courtesy American Viscose Corp.

was developed in 1892, more than fifty years later, by C. F. Cross and E. J. Bevan, two English scientists. The first viscose manufacturing plant in the United States was established in 1910.

In the viscose process, the wood pulp or cotton fiber is soaked in caustic soda to produce alkali cellulose. This substance is broken up into fluffy white flakes or grains called cellulose crumbs, which are aged for two or three days under controlled temperature and humidity. Liquid carbon disulphide is then added. This turns the cellulose crumbs into xanthate, a light-orange substance, still in crumb form. The xanthate crumbs are dissolved in a weak solution of caustic soda and transformed into a thick viscous solution, called viscose, resembling honey in color and consistency. If the rayon is to be delustered, titanium dioxide is added at this point. The viscose is aged, filtered, and vacuum-treated to

Liquid viscose, after being forced through the many fine holes of the spinneret, in a short space becomes separate rayon filaments, which, farther on, form the rayon thread clearly shown in the gloved hand.

Courtesy E. I. du Pont de Nemours & Co., Inc.

remove air bubbles, as they would cause the filament to break. It is then forced through the holes of the spinneret into sulphuric acid, which hardens the newly formed rayon filaments. Twist is inserted in the hardened filament, which is finally washed, bleached, dried, and wound into skeins or on cones or spools ready for manufacture into fabric.

Cuprammonium Rayon.

The cuprammonium process of manufacturing rayon was first developed by L. H. Despaisses in France in 1890. This kind of rayon is made from cotton linters, which are boiled with caustic soda and soda ash, bleached with chlorine, and then washed and dried. The pulp is dissolved in copper oxide and ammonia, forming a solution ready for spinning. The name *cuprammonium* is derived from these two substances.

The spinning solution is forced through large holes in a spinneret, which are intentionally larger than the diameter of the filament will be. The filament is to be stretched and twisted to a finer diameter by a process called *stretch spinning,* which subjects the filament to tension while it is being hardened. This stretch-spinning feature was developed and patented by E. Elsaesser of Germany. As the solution is pumped through the large-sized holes of the spinneret, it passes into a glass funnel, through which flows soft deaerated water at a constant temperature. On its way through the funnel, the filament is stretched and twisted. As it leaves the funnel, the filament enters a bath of mild sulphuric acid, which removes the copper and ammonia, leaving a solidified filament of pure cellulose, which is ready to be wound in skeins or on cones for the finishing and weaving processes. Final washing and bleaching are not required because these are initial steps in the processing of the cotton linters.

The stretch-spinning feature of the cuprammonium process produces fine yarn that can be given a great amount of twist. For its weight, it has greater elasticity than viscose filaments. The fine threads can be woven into the sheerest of fabrics. The high twist contributes to drapability.

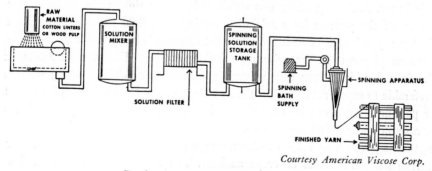

Courtesy American Viscose Corp.

Production of cuprammonium yarn.

Rayon Yarn Count. The count of rayon yarn is expressed in denier, the unit of weight explained in Chapter 12. The denier of rayon yarn is controlled by the size and the number of holes in the spinneret. The number of denier required to weigh one skein of yarn, 450 meters long (the standard length), is the denier that indicates the size of the yarn in that skein. Because the sizes of yarns differ according to the purposes for which the yarns are intended, the weights of the skeins differ, even though the skeins are of the standard length. The finer the yarn, the less the skein weighs, and the lower the figure that expresses its weight in denier.

Single rayon yarns may be composed of from 13 to 270 filaments, which may vary from 2.5 to 4 denier each. Thus, when 40 or more filaments are combined, the yarns will vary from 100 to 160 denier; these are the yarns generally used for rayon dress fabrics. Coarser dress-fabric yarns may run as high as 10 denier for a filament; the resultant denier of such yarns would naturally be higher than 160.

• *Monofilament Yarns.* Monofilament yarns are composed of a single filament. The viscous solution is extruded through a spinneret with only one hole. Spinnerets, each with a different-sized hole, are used, depending on the denier of yarn desired. Monofilament yarn is used for a variety of products including hosiery. The term *monofil* is applied to a type of monofilament yarn used in the millinery industry as a substitute for horsehair, which has limited use because of its short length.

• *Multifilament Yarns.* Multifilament yarns are composed of more than one filament, usually a great many twisted together. These filaments are extremely fine, sometimes less than 3 denier. Multifilament yarns are supple, pliable, and stronger than monofilament yarns of the same denier. They are used for a wide variety of fabrics including sheers.

Delustering. When rayon was first developed, the yarn had an objectionable luster. A dulling effect was obtained by using tight twist in the manufacture of the yarn or by a calcimine coating as a final finish on the fabric. Today, rayon is easily delustered while the filament is being made by including colorless pigments in the spinning solution; of these, the most important is titanium dioxide. Rayon thus treated is referred to as *delustered rayon*. It is preferable to rayon delustered in the finishing process by emulsions of oil, wax, or paraffin. Rayon can be manufactured to retain a permanently high luster or a semidull or a dull appearance.

Spun Rayon. The long, continuous rayon filaments produce rayon fabrics having smooth surfaces or crepe surfaces. The filament can be adapted for

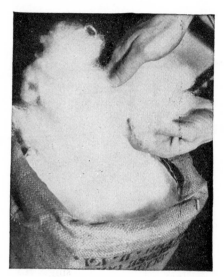

Staple fibers from which spun rayon is made.

Courtesy American Viscose Corp.

A cake of long-filament rayon yarn.

other effects by cutting it into short uniform lengths, usually 1 to 6 inches, and spinning it similarly to the spinning of cotton or wool. Such spun rayon yarns have a different character from the ordinary rayon yarns. According to the amount of twist inserted in the spinning process, spun rayon yarn can be made stronger, less lustrous, and adaptable to napping and other finishes, producing fabrics that resemble wool, linen, or cotton. Such short-staple rayon can also be combined with any of the other fibers to make effective and useful fabric. This blending would not be possible with the long rayon filament. Thus, spun rayon provides new finishes and a variety of low-priced fabrics that formerly were made only from natural fibers, with a consequently higher production cost.

Trade Names of Rayon Yarns. The many companies that manufacture rayon yarns use one of two methods of making the rayon: viscose or cuprammonium. They have given trade names to their rayon yarns, which the consumer often finds on labels or tags attached to garments and fabrics. The better-known trade names are classified on page 216 according to the type of filament.

Finishing Processes. The many types of yarn that can be made from rayon permit the production of a wide variety of fabrics. Spun-rayon yarns can be made into fabrics resembling cotton, linen, or wool; rayon filament yarns can be made into fabrics resembling silk. To enhance the appearance of these

VISCOSE

Bright Filament	*Semidull Filament*	*High Tenacity*
Briglo	Dulesco	Cordura
Crown	Newlow	Fortisan
Delray	Perlglo	Rayflex
DuPont		Super Narco
Enka	*Dull Filament*	Tenasco
Narco	Chalkelle	Tyron
Newbray	Chardonize	
North America	Dul-Tone	*Staple*
Premier	Englo	Avisco
Spun-lo	Newdull	Fibro
	Tubize	Tufton
	Veri-Dul	

CUPRAMMONIUM

Bright Filament	*Staple*
Aristocrat	Cupioni
Bemberg	Imperial
	Matesa

:abrics and to improve their serviceability, they can be given various finishes. The most common finishes are:

Calendering—for smoothness
Embossing—for decorative effects
Napping—only on spun rayons for softness and warmth and to improve re-
    semblance to wool
Sizing—for stiffness and body
Preshrinking—for greater dimensional stability
Water repellency—for resistance to water and rain
Wrinkle resistance—for better shape retention

These finishes are discussed in greater detail in Chapter 6. Printing and dyeing procedures are discussed in Chapters 7 and 8, respectively.

Judging Rayon Fabrics. In studying each of the natural fibers, cotton was rated highly for its economy and versatility. It was shown that linen excelled cotton in certain qualities, such as strength, luster, absorbency, cleanliness, and crispness. With respect to warmth and resiliency, wool and silk rank first.

The development of a man-made fiber possessing many of the above-mentioned prized qualities of the natural fibers is a tribute to the ingenuity of man. If the supply of natural fibers were insufficient or even nonexistent, man-made fibers could fully meet the situation.

The properties of viscose and cuprammonium rayons are essentially the same.

Of course, the type of yarn that is used, as well as how the material is woven or knitted, will contribute to the ultimate properties of the fabrics. The following discussion represents the general properties of rayon.

• *Strength*. Rayon is about half as strong as silk. It is also weaker than cotton and linen, but stronger than wool. Yet, although rayon is weaker than most natural fibers, it produces fairly durable, economical, and serviceable fabrics whose smoothness of surface favorably withstands the friction of wear.

Strength combined with sheerness of construction is possible in rayon fabrics by means of multifilament yarns. High-tenacity yarns afford a lightness with strength that is unsurpassed even by silk.

Smooth-surfaced rayon fabrics are unusually slippery; therefore, the seams of rayon garments will slip unless the French seam or the flat felled seam is used. Also, when cut on the bias, loosely constructed rayon fabrics may slip.

• *Elasticity*. Because rayon lacks the resilience natural to wool and silk, it creases readily; but it should be remembered that the resistance of a fabric to creasing depends on the kind of yarn, weave, and finishing process. For example, the extremely fine filaments used in multifilament rayons have a greater resistance to creasing. Any of the crepe surfaces produced by tightly twisted yarns also resist creasing. Fabrics treated with one of the better patented crease-resistant finishing processes are highly resistant to creasing. Also, a soft surface produced by napping, typical of spun rayon, has some degree of crease resistance because of the softness and flexibility of the short staple, which recovers easily from wrinkles.

• *Drapability*. Rayon possesses a marked quality of drapability because it is a naturally heavy pure-dye fabric. The filament can be made as coarse as desired, depending on the holes in the spinneret; and the yarn can be made heavy without the use of metallic filling, thus producing body substance in the fabric. Cuprammonium rayon is especially suitable for drapery fabrics because the numerous very fine filaments make the material extremely pliable.

• *Heat Conductivity*. Rayon is a good conductor of heat and is therefore appropriate for summer clothing. Spun rayon fabrics, however, are adaptable to winter apparel because they can be napped. The fuzzy surface provides some insulation, although the warmth will certainly not be as great as can be provided by wool or silk.

• *Absorbency*. Rayon is one of the most absorbent of all textiles. It is more absorbent than cotton or linen and is exceeded only by wool and silk in absorbency. The combination of high heat conductivity and high absorbency of rayon makes it very suitable for summer wear. One limitation in this regard, however, is that rayon loses up to 70 per cent of its strength while it is wet and therefore cannot take too much strain when it is wet.

• *Cleanliness and Washability.* The smoothness of rayon fibers helps to produce hygienic fabrics that shed dirt. Some rayon fabrics wash easily, depending on the finish that may be given to them. Rayon fabrics will not become yellow when washed or dry-cleaned. White rayon remains white and therefore needs no bleaching. Since rayon temporarily loses strength when wet, rayon fabrics must be handled with care when washed. When laundered, a mild soap and warm water should be used. The garments should be squeezed, not wrung, to remove the water. When in doubt about whether a rayon garment is washable, it is safer to dry-clean it. Rayon dry-cleans very well.

• *Shrinkage.* The percentage of shrinkage of rayon fabrics is similar to that of cotton. Crepe weaves and knitted fabrics always shrink more than flat woven fabrics because of the nature of the construction. Spun rayon fabrics shrink more than fabrics made of rayon-filament yarns. Spun rayon fabrics can be given a shrink-resistant finish, such as Sanforset, which makes them suitable for apparel that must be frequently washed. Spun rayon blended with wool tends to reduce the great amount of shrinkage characteristic of wool.

• *Fastness of Color.* Rayon fabrics absorb dyes evenly. Colored rayons have a high resistance to sunlight; they withstand strong light better than silk. This property makes rayon especially adaptable for window curtains. Of course, over a period of time rayon fabrics will fade. To overcome this, pigmented rayon, in which the dyestuff is put into the spinning solution thus becoming an integral part of the fiber, has been developed. Pigmented, or solution-dyed rayon, is absolutely fast to light, washing, atmospheric gases, perspiration, crocking, and dry cleaning. Two trade names for pigmented viscose rayon yarns are Jetspun and Coloray. A cuprammonium rayon yarn that is solution-dyed at varied intervals along its length has been produced under the trade name of Parfé. These solution-dyed rayons, however, are not produced in large quantities and are not widely used, because there is not a large sustained demand for specific shades.

• *Decorative Effects.* Rayon is often combined with other textile fibers to produce novel and decorative effects. This can be accomplished by combining different types of yarns as well as using such techniques as cross dyeing. Rayon can also be given a moiré finish, but it is not permanent and will come out with washing or dry cleaning.

• *Resistance to Mildew.* Like cotton, rayon has a tendency to mildew. Rayon fabrics should, therefore, not be allowed to remain damp for any length of time.

• *Resistance to Moths.* Moths are not attracted to rayon, and mothproofing treatments are not necessary.

• *Reaction to Alkalies.* Concentrated solutions of alkalies disintegrate rayon. A mild soap and lukewarm water is therefore recommended when laundering rayon garments.

• *Reaction to Acids.* Rayon reacts to acids in a manner similar to cotton. Being pure cellulose, the fabric is disintegrated by hot dilute and cold concentrated acids.

• *Resistance to Perspiration.* Rayon is fairly resistant to deterioration from perspiration. The color, however, usually is not as resistant as the fabric and will fade if not solution-dyed.

ACETATE

The Cellulose Acetate Process. The cellulose acetate process was developed in England in 1918 by Henri and Camille Dreyfus. In the United States, their product is known as Celanese. Acetates were developed much later by manufacturers in this country. Acetate is not a pure cellulose product like viscose and cuprammonium. Although it is made principally from the cellulose derived from cotton linters, the pulp is treated differently and becomes a chemical compound of cellulose. The pulp is steeped in acetic acid and allowed to age for a period under controlled temperature. After aging, it is mixed with acetic anhydride, which transforms it into a thick, clear liquid—cellulose acetate. After further aging, this solution is precipitated as pure white flakes by running through water. The flakes are dried and then dissolved in acetone, and filtered several times to remove impurities. The result is a clear, white spinning solution of the consistency of sirup. If delustered yarn is required, titanium dioxide is added at this stage.

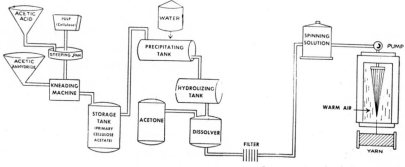

Courtesy American Viscose Corp.

Production of acetate yarn.

The spinning solution is then forced through a spinneret. Instead of passing through a liquid bath, it passes through warm air, which evaporates the acetone and solidifies the filament. It is then ready for winding on spools, cones, or bobbins. No washing or bleaching is required as the solution was cleaned and filtered before it passed through the spinneret. The filament produced by the acetate process differs from the rayons not only in the chemicals used to digest the cellulose raw material but in the chemical nature of the final product. It manifests different characteristics.

Delustering. In its natural form, acetate is highly lustrous, but this is not always desirable. The luster is, therefore, sometimes reduced by the addition of a delusterant, such as titanium dioxide, to the spinning solution before passing it through the spinneret. This delusterant has no effect on the characteristics or properties of acetate other than on the luster. Depending on the amount of the delusterant added to the spinning solution, acetate may be made in three types of brightness: bright, semidull, and dull.

The variation in the amount of luster given to acetate increases its versatility. It not only permits degrees of sheen in fabrics but also provides a wider use of acetate to simulate other fibers as well as for blending acetate with other fibers.

Types of Acetate Yarns. A wide variety of acetate yarns can be made in many different deniers depending on the number and size of the holes in the spinneret.

• *Monofilament Yarns.* The acetate solution may be extruded through a spinneret with one hole. This will produce a single, or monofilament, yarn. The denier of such a yarn can be regulated by the size of the hole in the spinneret. Monofilament acetate yarns are not very strong but provide good body and smoothness.

• *Multifilament Yarns.* The majority of acetate yarns are composed of two or more filaments extruded simultaneously from the same spinneret and then eventually twisted (thrown) around each other in a manner similar to silk yarns. The denier of the multifilament yarns is dependent on the denier of the individual filaments as well as on the number of filaments in the yarn. Multifilament yarns are stronger than monofilament yarns because of the greater number of filaments and the amount of twist given to the yarns. They also help in providing greater drape to fabrics.

• *Spun Yarns.* Acetate filaments may be cut into staple, generally from 1 inch to 6 inches in length, and spun into yarns. The staple can be spun on a system such as used for cotton or for wool to produce yarns that resemble these other textiles. Sometimes acetate staple is blended with other staples to obtain yarns and fabrics that will have characteristics of all the fibers used.

Trade Names of Acetate Yarns.

Acetate yarns are produced by many companies. Each company manufactures its acetate under its own trade name. Some of the better-known acetate yarns are:

Acele	Estron	Seraceta
Celanese	Koda	Teca (crimped staple)

Finishing Acetate Fabrics.

Acetate fabrics can be given various finishes depending on the kind of yarn used and the effect desired. The more common finishes are:

Embossing—for pattern or design
Moiréing—for permanent watermarking effect
Napping—on spun acetate for softness and warmth
Sizing—for stiffness and body
Heat setting—for crease and shape retention
Water repellency—for resistance to water and rain
Wrinkle resistance—for better shape retention

The characteristics of acetate are quite different from the other fibers considered thus far in this book. One of the most unique of these properties is that acetate is thermoplastic; that is, it can be softened by the application of heat and placed or pressed into a particular shape. This permits the permanent embossing and moiréing of acetate fabrics. Also, creases and pleats heat-set into acetate fabrics are relatively durable and are retained better than in cotton, linen, wool, silk, or rayon, although some amount of re-pressing is usually desirable.

Although acetate is not very absorbent, it does absorb some moisture. A water-repellent finish, such as Zelan, given to acetate fabrics makes them satisfactorily water-repellent.

Judging Acetate Fabrics.

The properties of acetate fabrics will vary to some extent depending on whether spun yarn or filament yarn is used, on the type of construction of the fabric, and on the finish that may be applied to the fabric. The general properties of acetate fabrics are given here.

• *Strength*. Acetate is not a strong fiber. It is weaker than rayon and is, in fact, one of the weakest textile fibers. Acetate has poor abrasion resistance and is therefore not suited for garments that are expected to take hard wear.

• *Elasticity*. Acetate is more elastic than rayon. It is also more wrinkle-resistant and will return to its original shape much better than will rayon after being pulled or crumpled. After wearing, acetate fabrics should be carefully hung to permit the yarns to relax and return to their original condition.

• *Heat Conductivity*. Acetate does not have as high a rate of heat conductivity as rayon and therefore is warmer. Acetate is consequently more useful for linings and warmer clothing, particularly if it is spun acetate. Of course, filament yarns woven or knitted into sheer fabrics will result in cooler fabrics because of their greater porosity.

• *Absorbency.* Acetate is not very absorbent. It absorbs only half as much moisture as rayon. This represents both advantages and disadvantages. Acetate fabrics get wet mostly on the surface and will not become saturated; therefore, they dry quickly. This makes acetate very suitable for shower curtains, umbrellas, and raincoats. It is also suited for bathing suits, particularly at the seashore because salt air does not have any deteriorating effect on acetate. On the other hand, acetate is uncomfortable in warm, humid weather because of its low absorbency. Acetate garments, such as blouses and lingerie, worn next to the skin feel clammy and uncomfortable because they do not absorb perspiration or atmospheric humidity.

• *Cleanliness and Washability.* The smoothness of acetate fibers helps to produce hygienic fabrics that shed dirt and wash easily. They will not become yellow when washed or dry-cleaned. White acetate remains white, and acetate fabrics need not be bleached. If bleaching is desired, it should be done with a very mild solution of hydrogen peroxide or a very dilute solution of sodium hypochlorite, such as a dilution of Clorox, Rose-X, or the like.

Since acetate temporarily loses some strength when wet, such fabrics must be handled with care when washed. When laundered, a mild soap and warm water should be used. The garments should not be rubbed vigorously or wrung but should be handled gently and squeezed to remove the water. They will dry readily and should be hung so that the water will drip off. Acetate fabrics will shrink less than rayon. Sometimes they are given a shrink-resistant finish.

Acetate fabrics need less ironing than rayon fabrics. A warm iron will easily smooth out an acetate fabric, particularly if the fabric is a little damp. If the iron is too hot, it will melt the acetate causing it to stick to the iron and make the fabric stiff.

When in doubt about the launderability of an acetate garment because of its tailoring or finish, it is always best to dry-clean it. Acetate dry-cleans very well.

• *Effect of Light.* Acetate is more resistant to the effect of light than is rayon; however, over a period of time, acetate will be weakened from exposure to light.

• *Resistance to Mildew.* Acetate is highly resistant to mildew. It is ideal for fabrics exposed to moisture, such as shower curtains.

• *Resistance to Moths.* Moths, carpet beetles, and similar insects will not attack acetate. Mothproofing of all-acetate fabrics is not necessary.

• *Reaction to Alkalies.* Concentrated solutions of alkalies disintegrate acetate.

A mild soap and lukewarm water is recommended when laundering acetate garments.

• *Reaction to Acids.* Acetate is more resistant to acids than rayon, but it will be decomposed by concentrated solutions of strong acids.

• *Affinity for Dyes.* Since acetate fiber is not very absorbent, special acetate dyes were developed; but acetate has still remained difficult to dye. The colors have not always been uniform, but there is improvement. The dyes are not as fast as one may wish. Acetate dyes are not fast to light, atmospheric gases, or perspiration. Some colors, particularly gray and blue, gas-fade badly and change color to red and purple.

To overcome this, the acetate solution may be pigmented before the fiber is extruded through the spinneret. Chromspun and Celaperm are two trade names for acetate yarns that are solution-dyed. They are colorfast to light, atmospheric fumes, perspiration, crocking, washing, and dry cleaning.

• *Resistance to Perspiration.* Acetate fabrics are fairly resistant to deterioration by perspiration, but the color will be affected if it has not been solution-dyed.

Acetate Fiber Blends. Acetate fibers are sometimes blended with other fibers to reduce the price of a fabric or to obtain a desired combination of acetate properties with the properties of other fibers.

• *Acetate and Wool.* Acetate will reduce the tendency of a fabric to shrink, felt, or pill when blended with wool. The combination provides good shape retention and holds creases well. Although such a fabric may be relatively inexpensive, it will not be as durable as an all-wool cloth.

• *Acetate and Rayon.* Of all the fibers thus far discussed, acetate fibers are most frequently blended with rayon. Acetate adds shape retention to fabrics. Garments made of such fabrics tend to wrinkle less because of the resilience of acetate. Such fabrics when pleated or creased tend to hold their shape well because of the thermoplastic characteristic of acetate. The easy care of rayon and acetate blended fabrics usually means little ironing for garments that have been laundered. Such fabrics, however, have reduced absorbency because of the acetate. They also may tend to shine when pressed if not given sufficient care.

GLOSSARY OF RAYON AND ACETATE FABRICS AND BLENDS[1]

The fabrics named in this glossary were formerly made only in the natural fibers—cotton, silk, linen, wool—or in blends. When rayon and acetate were de-

[1] Courtesy of American Viscose Corporation, adapted from *Rayon Fabrics.*

veloped, these man-made fibers were used alone, in combination, or in blends with the natural fibers. Now the synthetic fibers described in following chapters are being combined with rayon and acetate in new combinations and blends. The labels, required by the United States government, will identify the fibers used in any of these fabrics.

alpaca. A fabric originally containing hair of the alpaca. Now made in rayon-and-wool blends. Plain weave. Used for women's spring coats, suits, sportswear.

alpaca crepe. Two-ply. Gives somewhat the appearance of wool. Term used for a soft, dull combination crepe.

bark crepe. A fabric that produces the effect of rough bark on trees. A crepe with extreme surface interest.

batiste. Soft, thin lightweight fabric. Made of various fibers, including spun rayon. White, colors, or printed. Plain weave. Lingerie, dresses, blouses.

Bedford cord. A corded material that can be made with various fibers, particularly adaptable to rayon. Has tailored appearance. Cords run lengthwise. Novelty weave, a type of raised plain weave. Used for riding habits, coats, sportswear, suits.

bengaline. A ribbed fabric. Ribs run crosswise. A substantial, somewhat dressy fabric resembling poplin, but with a heavier rib. Plain weave. Used for women's formal coats, suits.

bird's-eye. A distinctive weave; small diamond twill pattern featuring a small dot in the center that resembles a bird's eye. Seen in bird's-eye piqué and diapers.

broadcloth. A fine, closely woven fabric originally made in cotton for shirtings and dress goods, and in wool for dress goods, suitings, and coatings. Now also made in rayon in shirting and dress weights. Also in wool blends in suitings, coatings, and wool-like dress weights. Plain weave. In all-rayon, used for sportswear, shirts, pajamas.

brocade. Originally, heavy silk with elaborate pattern. Now made with various fibers. Brocade has slightly raised designs or an embossed appearance as contrasted with damask, which has a very flat pattern. A contrast of surfaces in the weave may produce design, or different colors may be used. Novelty weave, Jacquard. Example: satin or twill figures on plain, twill, or satin grounds. Used for draperies and upholstery; in lighter weights, for formal evening wear.

brocatelle. A fabric similar to brocade but having designs in high relief. Weave is usually a filling satin or a twill figure on plain or satin ground. Used for draperies, upholstery.

canton crepe. A crepe with modified rippled texture. Heavier than crepe de chine.

casement cloth. A term covering many curtain fabrics of various fibers. Variety of weaves are used.

cavalry twill. A sturdy, substantial fabric with a pronounced diagonal raised cord. Twill weave. Sportswear, uniforms, riding habits, ski wear.

challis. Originally a silk-and-worsted fabric. A light, soft, pliable fabric. Usually printed in small floral designs, but may also be plain color. Plain weave. Used for dresses, negligees, ties, shirts, pajamas.

chambray. A plain-weave fabric generally characterized by a colored warp and a white filling, giving a mixture effect. Used for sportswear, women's and children's summer wear, men's shirts, pajamas.

chenille. A tufted fluffy yarn that looks like a caterpillar. Also a fabric made from such a yarn. Used for rugs, mats, spreads, knitting yarn, robes.

chiffon. (1) Descriptive term indicating light weight, as chiffon velvet, chiffon taffeta. (2) Thin gauzelike fabric with soft or sometimes stiff finish. Plain weave. Evening dresses, formal blouses, trimmings.

corduroy. A fabric having ridges or cords in the pile. Formerly made in cotton only, now in combinations. Variation of plain weave. For men's and women's sportswear, children's wear, infants' wraps, slip covers, draperies.

covert. Originally a medium-weight suiting of woolen or worsted yarns. Now developed in spun rayon or blends with wool. In dress as well as suiting weights. It has a speckled effect in color. Twill weave, sometimes satin. Used for sportswear, riding habits, suits, coats, raincoats.

crash. Term applied to fabrics having coarse uneven yarns and rough texture. Plain or twill weave, or twill variations. Used for sportswear, men's, women's, and children's summer suits and coats, draperies.

crepe. A fabric made of highly twisted yarn extremely versatile in texture, ranging from a fine, flat crepe to pebbly and mossy effects and, in extreme cases, to barklike, roughish textures. Rayon and acetate are used extensively in crepes. Fabrics of this family have a wide range of suitability in women's wear. Usually plain weave.

crepe de chine. Crepy fabric that in texture falls between canton and flat crepe. Mainly for lingerie; formerly for dresses.

crepe georgette. A lightweight semisheer crepe.

crepe marocain. Heavier dress-weight crepe. An exaggerated canton crepe in texture.

crepon. Originally wool crepe. Has a wavy texture with waves running lengthwise. Mostly used for prints.

damask. Flatter than brocade and reversible. Jacquard weave. Satin or twill filling figures woven on plain, twill, or satin ground formed by warp. For upholstery and hangings. Lighter weights for formal evening wear and wraps; also table linens, bedspreads, face towels.

doeskin. Twilled fabric napped on one side. Twill or satin weave. Used for sportswear, coats, suits.

duvetyn. Originally a soft woolen fabric with fine downy back. Twill or satin weave. Used for coats, suits, dresses.

éponge. Soft, loose, spongy fabric similar to terry cloth. Novelty weave. Used for sportswear, summer suits, coats.

etched-out fabrics. Also called *burnt-out.* A fabric containing two different yarns in which pattern effects have been produced by acid. The acid is used to treat one of the yarns so as to remove certain portions of it, creating a patterned effect. Any of the three basic weaves or their variations. Used for dresses, curtains.

faille. A flat-ribbed fabric having body and drape. Ribs are wider and flatter than in grosgrain. Tailors well and wears well if not too loose in weave. Variation of plain weave. Used for women's spring coats, suits, dresses.

felt. An unwoven fabric that can now be made by using wool and a percentage of rayon or other fibers.

flannel. Soft lightweight fabric with slightly napped surface. Originally made in wool; now made extensively in spun rayon or in wool blends. Plain or twill weave. Used in medium weight for dresses and sportswear; in light weight for shirts and sports blouses, children's wear; in heavier weight for suitings and coatings.

flat crepe. Smoothest of crepe family. Inaccurately called French crepe.

foulard. Soft, light fabric, originally silk or wool, now in rayon or acetate. Usually printed. Twill weave. For dresses, neckties.

frieze. Originally a heavy woolen overcoating with nap on the face. Can be made in spun rayon and wool in similar texture. Double-cloth weave with twill construction. Used for overcoats.

frise. Pile fabric of uncut loops. Variation of plain weave. For upholstery.

fur fabrics. Large class of pile fabrics of various fibers, imitating furs by dyeing and special finishing. Fabric can be either woven or knitted. Any variation of basic weaves. Used for popular-priced winter coats and trimmings.

gabardine. A firm, durable fabric with a steep diagonal. Modern gabardines are made in spun rayon, wool, cotton, or blends in both dress and suiting weights. Twill weave. Used for men's, women's, and children's wear, sportswear, suits, uniforms, riding habits, fabric shoes, raincoats.

gauze. A light, sheer fabric having an open, lacy effect. Leno weave.

gros de Londres. Cross-ribbed dress fabric with heavy and fine ribs alternating, or ribs of different colors. Plain weave or plain variations. Used for dresses, evening wear.

grosgrain. Firm, stiff, closely woven ribbed fabric. Much grosgrain ribbon is made of rayon. Ribs heavier and closer than in poplin, rounder than in faille. Plain weave or plain variation. Used for neckties, ribbons, trimmings, millinery.

hopsacking. A rough-textured fabric with open weave. Resembles sacking, as name implies. Plain weave. Used for men's slacks and shirts, women's sportswear, draperies.

jersey. Plain knitted or ribbed. Originally wool, now featured extensively in rayon and acetate in plain and novelty effects. May also be had in wool blends. Used for women's dress fabrics, sportswear, underwear.

lamé. Any fabric using metal threads in warp or filling or for decoration. Any weave. Used for formal evening wear.

linen-textured rayon. A large and important category of rayon fabrics having the distinctive textures of linens. These range from sheer handkerchief-linen texture to heavier, rougher butcher-linen texture. Usually plain weave. Used in lighter weight for handkerchiefs, women's and children's dresses, tablecloths, towels, sheets, pillowcases; heavier weights for summer coats, suits, sportswear.

madras. Soft fabric for shirts. May be white or yarn-dyed. Variation of plain or twill weave. Fancy effects in weaving with corded stripes or small figures. True madras has woven figures. For shirts, sportswear.

marquisette. Loose, open, sheer fabric of leno construction in which warp yarns are in pairs, whipping around one another between picks of filling yarns. Each thread is locked. Novelty leno weave. Used for curtains, evening wear.

matelassé. Cloth having a raised pattern as if quilted or wadded. Rayon matelassé crepe looks somewhat blistered. A novelty double weave showing a quilted effect: plain, twill, or satin. Used for women's dresses, evening wear.

milanese. A type of warp-knit fabric, originally silk, used in gloves and women's underwear. Milanese has a distinctive diagonal cross effect.

mock romaine crepe. Similar to romaine crepe in texture and appearance. Different filling construction.

mogador. Originally a tie silk. Resembles fine faille. Plain weave. Used for ties, sportswear.

moiré. A watered or waved effect, usually on taffeta or faille, produced by a special finish. Steaming or wetting will destroy the pattern except on acetate. Plain weave. Used for women's dressy coats, suits, dresses, evening wear, bathrobes, dressing gowns, draperies, bedspreads.

mossy crepe. Also called *sand crepe*. Texture gives fine moss effect.

mousseline. Taken from "mousseline de soie," meaning "silk muslin." Firmer than chiffon, stiffer than voile. A sheer, crisp, formal fabric. Plain weave Used for evening wear, collars, cuffs, trimmings.

net. Originally all nets and laces were made with a needle or with bobbins. In modern nets, the same effect is produced by machinery. There are a variety of meshes. Used for curtains, trimmings, evening gowns, veiling; heavier nets for tablecloths, bedspreads, curtains.

ninon. A sheer, crisp fabric, heavier than chiffon. Plain weave. Used for evening wear and curtains.

organza. Thin, transparent, stiff, wiry fabric. Crushes but is easily pressed. Plain weave. For evening dresses, trimmings, neckwear.

ottoman. Heavy cross-corded fabric having larger and rounder ribs than faille and bengaline. The heavy ribs may alternate with thinner ribs. Variation of plain weave. Used for evening wraps, formal coats, suits.

oxford shirting or suiting. Basket-weave fabrics, which may be made in plaid or two-color effects. Heavy qualities suitable for summer suits, skirts, jackets; lighter weight for sportswear, shirts.

pin check. Fine check made with different-colored yarns. Usually woven. Smaller than shepherd's check.

piqué. Originally a cotton fabric with raised stripes or welts running lengthwise or on diagonal. Knit construction may give similar effect, not so crisp. Variation of plain weave. Used for sportswear, children's wear, summer evening wear.

plush. Cut-pile fabric with a pile of greater depth than velvet. Variation of plain weave. Used for coats, trimmings, upholstery.

poplin. Originally made in silk. A cross-ribbed fabric between taffeta and bengaline in weight and appearance. The effect is created by a coarser yarn in the filling than in the warp. Plain weave. Used for women's wear, shirts, pajamas.

ratiné. A fabric made of nubby or knotty yarns. Frequently rough and spongy in texture. Plain weave or variation of basic weaves. Used for sportswear, dresses, draperies.

rep. A fabric with narrow ribs running lengthwise. Variation of plain weave. Used for women's wear, neckties, draperies, upholstery.

romaine crepe. A heavy sheer combination crepe similar to alpaca crepe but slightly flatter.

satin. A fabric with a lustrous surface in satin weave. *Crepe satin* is soft and lustrous; used for women's dresses, formal wear, negligees, draperies, and bedspreads. *Panne satin* is a stiff slipper satin; used for formal evening or bridal wear. Panne or crepe satin is used for *lining satin,* usually lighter in weight than dress satin. Panne or crepe satin can be finished as *wash satin* for blouses and lingerie. *Upholstery satin* is heavy, usually with cotton back.

seersucker. A lightweight fabric with crinkled stripes. Does not require ironing after laundering. Originally made in cotton. May be plain, printed, or cross-dyed. Plain weave. Used for women's wear, children's wear, sportswear, and, in heavier weights, for men's summer suits.

serge. A twill fabric with a smooth finish. The twill is very fine and close. Made of spun rayon, wool, cotton, or blends. Twill weave. Used for women's dresses, suits, coats, children's wear, men's suits.

shantung. Originally a silk fabric typified by uneven yarns in the filling, resulting in an interesting slubbed or nubbed texture. Now made in rayon extensively. Plain weave. Used for sportswear, women's summer suits, pajamas, robes.

sharkskin. Originally a two-color worsted suiting in various weaves, with basket-weave effects most common. Plain, twill, and basic weave variations. (1) Sharkskin suiting is now also made in spun rayon and wool blends, for men's and women's suits. (2) Term also used to describe a well-known acetate sports fabric typified by heavy, semicrisp texture. Used for men's and women's sportswear, summer suits.

shepherd's check. Fabrics having small, even checks. Usually twill weave. Used for sportswear, women's suits, dresses.

surah. Soft, flexible, lightweight, lustrous twill-weave fabric. Used for sports dresses, tailored dresses, blouses, mufflers, ties.

taffeta. A plain, closely woven, smooth crisp fabric, now in rayon and acetate. The warp and the filling are of the same or nearly the same yarn size. Plain weave. Used for dresses, children's wear, trimmings, linings, millinery, hangings, draperies, bedspreads, comfortables, lamp shades. *Faille taffeta* has alternating thick and thin crosswise ribs. *Pigment taffeta* is made of dull or pigmented yarns. *Tissue taffeta* is of very light weight.

tartan. Originally, Scotch plaids in woolens or worsteds in the distinctive designs and colors of Highland clans. Used for children's wear in particular; also women's sportswear.

tricot. Correct name for jersey cloth. Most important of warp-knit fabrics. On the right side, it appears like rib knitting; on the wrong side, the ribs run crosswise. Used for underwear, dress fabrics, sportswear, bathing suits, gloves.

tricotine. Originally, worsted dress goods resembling gabardine but woven with a double twill. Twill weave. Used for women's suits, coats.

triple sheer. Term in common usage describing a tightly woven sheer fabric with a fine, flat surface. Almost opaque.

tweed. Originally, all-wool homespun made in Scotland. Now in blends. Roughish fabric with wiry, somewhat hairy texture, casual or sportslike in appearance. In mixtures, nubbed, and slubbed effects. Plain, twill, herringbone twill, or novelty weaves. Coats, suits, dresses.

velour. A woven fabric napped on one side. Originally made in wool. Now also made in blends. Plain or satin weave. Used for women's coats, draperies, upholstery.

velvet. Broad and inclusive term covering almost all warp-pile fabrics except plush, chenille, terry, velveteen, and corduroy. Velvets are woven double, face to face, and cut apart while still on the loom. *Chiffon velvet* is of light weight. *Lyons velvet* is the name given stiff velvets. *Panne velvet* refers to the finish on lightweight velvet; the pile is laid flat in one direction. *Transparent velvet* is a very lightweight velvet. Variation of plain weave. Used for evening wear, formal daytime fashions, negligees, draperies.

velveteen. A fabric with short pile resembling velvet but woven single. Variation of plain weave. Used for women's wear, children's wear, draperies, bedspreads.

voile. A light, transparent fabric similar to mousseline but softer and more clinging. Plain weave. Used for dresses, curtains.

whipcord. A twill fabric with pronounced diagonals. Twill weave. Used for riding habits, uniforms, sportswear.

ARNEL

Method of Manufacture of Arnel Fiber. As early as 1914, prior to the commercial production of cellulose acetate, fibers known chemically as *triacetate cellulose* were produced. They were, however, never fully exploited. Problems involving production, dyes, and finishes were not sufficiently pursued and solved, but were minimized or dropped.

With the advancement of chemistry and the development of advanced textile engineering techniques, the Celanese Corporation of America began commercial production of its triacetate cellulose fiber, Arnel, in 1954. The process of manufacturing Arnel is similar to the method of producing cellulose acetate. The flow chart on page 219 is representative of triacetate cellulose production. There is, however, a difference in preparing the spinning dope prior to extruding the fibers through the spinneret. Instead of acetone, another solvent, that the Celanese Corporation is not willing to disclose, is used. The resultant chemical composition of the fiber is triacetate cellulose. Its properties are different from those of the other cellulosic fibers.

Delustering. In its normal condition, Arnel is highly lustrous. To increase its versatility, it may be delustered by adding a delusterant to the spinning solution in a manner similar to the way acetate is delustered, so that either bright or dull fiber may be produced. The addition of the delusterant has no effect on the properties of the fiber other than to dull it.

Types of Arnel Yarns. Arnel yarns are produced in two forms in a wide variety of deniers. The denier of each fiber in the yarns is dependent on the size of the holes in the spinneret. The ultimate denier of each yarn is dependent on the number of fibers in the yarn.

• *Multifilament Yarns.* Arnel multifilament yarns are made by twisting 15 to 160 filaments around each other. The subsequent denier of the thrown yarns ranges from 50 to 600 denier. The strength, texture, and draping quality of the yarns are dependent on the number of filaments, the denier of these filaments, and the amount of the twist in the yarns. The greater the twist, the stronger the yarn, but the higher the twist, the rougher or harder the yarn will feel. The lower the denier and the greater the number of filaments, the better the fabric will drape. Innumerable variations are possible to obtain the desired effects.

A special type of multifilament thick-and-thin yarn has been developed. This yarn varies in thickness throughout its length to give the impression of a spun slub yarn, but it has the general properties of multifilament yarns.

• *Spun Yarns.* Arnel staple can be produced by cutting the filaments into any standard length desired. The staple ranges in 2.5, 3.0, and 5.0 denier per fiber. The staple can be spun on a system such as used for cotton, woolens, or worsteds to produce yarns that resemble these other textiles. Arnel staple may also be blended with other staples to obtain yarns and fabrics that will have characteristics of all the fibers used.

Finishing Arnel Fabrics. Arnel fabrics can be given a variety of finishes depending on the effects desired. The most common finishes are:

Embossing—for pattern or design
Water repellency—for resistance to water and rain
Spot resistance—for resistance to water and oil stains

Sizing—for stiffness and body
Antistatic—for protection against static and as a dust repellent
Heat setting—for crease and shape retention

Fabrics of Arnel can be given shallow and surface embossing patterns with heated engraved rollers. This technique can be used to obtain moiré and glazed effects. Such embossed patterns are durable to repeated home washings and to tumble dryers. Where pressing is required to remove mussiness, a light steam pressing will remove the wrinkles without reducing the shallow embossed texture.

Silicone resins, properly applied to Arnel fabrics, provide a durable water repellency. Such a finish also provides spot resistance against water-borne substances as well as a reduction in the spreading of oil stains when a cationic softener is used.

Sizing may be given to Arnel fabrics to provide stiffness, firmness, and body. The effectiveness of the sizing varies, depending on the technique used. For example, a silicone resin provides a durable finish that imparts the scroop and rustle desirable in taffeta. Some sizings help fabrics retain a very firm hand after repeated washings, but the cloth wrinkles easily and tears more easily than without such finishes.

Arnel fabrics have a tendency to develop static electricity when they are rubbed, as when worn. This may cause the fabric to crackle and cling undesirably. Also, the static electricity attracts and holds dust particles. Limited durable antistatic finishes have been developed. They are limited in that they greatly reduce the static behavior of the fabric, but are not absolutely antistatic, and the effectiveness of the finish is reduced with washing and dry cleaning.

Arnel is thermoplastic. Consequently, when properly heat-treated, Arnel fabrics may be heat-set so that they will retain their shape, creases, and pleats after repeated washings. Although the type of yarn used and the construction of the fabric have some influence on the effectiveness of the heat-setting finish, Arnel fabrics of either multifilament or spun yarns, whether woven or knitted, generally retain their shape well when properly heat-set.

Judging Arnel Fabrics. A wide variety of fabrics are being made of Arnel. Since these fabrics can be made of multifilament yarns and spun yarns and can be woven or knitted in any of the standard manners, Arnel fabrics tend to look and feel like similar fabrics made of other textiles, such as cotton, wool, silk, rayon, and acetate. Arnel, however, lends its own distinctive properties to the finished fabric. As is true with other fibers, there are similarities between certain properties of Arnel and various other individual fibers. But Arnel has its own combination of distinctive characteristics with its own advantages and disadvantages. The general properties of fabrics made of Arnel are given here.

• *Strength*. Arnel is not a strong fiber. Its strength approximates that of acetate, although technically its strength falls in between that of acetate and wool. Arnel has poor abrasion resistance, like acetate, and a much lower abrasion resistance than wool. Arnel is therefore not suited for garments that are expected to take hard wear.

• *Elasticity*. Arnel can be stretched about the same as acetate but is more resilient. It will not wrinkle easily even at high humidity, and any wrinkles that may develop from packing or wearing will fall out readily when allowed to hang properly for a reasonable period of time.

• *Heat Conductivity*. Like acetate, Arnel does not have a high rate of heat conductivity and is therefore warmer than cotton, linen, or rayon. This may be compensated by using finer yarns and sheerer construction, thus providing Arnel fabrics with year-round versatility.

• *Absorbency*. Arnel is less absorbent than acetate. Since it does not absorb much water, Arnel is well suited for fabrics where some amount of water repellency is desirable. Also, because Arnel gets wet primarily on the surface rather than saturated within the fiber, fabrics made of Arnel dry rapidly when they are wet. On the other hand, the relatively low moisture absorbency of Arnel makes it uncomfortable when worn next to the skin in warm, humid weather. Sheerness of the fabric may counteract this characteristic to some extent.

• *Cleanliness and Washability*. Under the microscope the appearance of Arnel fiber is similar to that of acetate. Being relatively smooth, the fibers tend to shed dirt; and the fabric washes easily. Arnel has good resistance to common household bleaches and has a high degree of shrink resistance. Arnel fabrics when wet are not weakened to the same extent as acetate and therefore can be safely home-washed and tumble-dried. All that is required for washing is reasonable care and the use of ordinary soaps or detergents. Ordinary hot-water temperatures of not more than 160 degrees Fahrenheit may be safely used.

Since Arnel fabric lends itself so readily to home laundering and can be heat-set, garments made of Arnel may be sold as "wash-and-wear." If proper heat-setting treatment has been given to the fabric, the garments will return to their original shape after laundering. They are likely to need little or no ironing if not wrung or crushed but allowed to dry while properly buttoned and carefully hung on a wooden hanger.

Fabrics made of Arnel have superior resistance to damage, such as glazing, when ironed even at high ironing temperatures. No great precaution, therefore, need be taken when ironing is desired. If the construction of the garment does not permit laundering due to padding or interlining, clothing made of Arnel may be safely dry-cleaned.

• *Effect of Light.* Fabrics of Arnel lose some strength when exposed to sunlight but are generally more resistant to light than silk, rayon, acetate, and semidull nylon. This indicates that Arnel fabrics are suited for curtains and can be used for normal outdoor wear.

• *Resistance to Mildew.* Arnel has extremely high resistance to deterioration by mildew. Arnel fabrics do not lose strength or become stained from mildew and are well suited for a variety of purposes where they might be exposed to damp conditions.

• *Resistance to Moths.* Fabrics made of Arnel are resistant to attack from moths and carpet beetles. Mothproofing is not necessary.

• *Reaction to Alkalies.* Arnel has a very high resistance to alkalies. Fabrics of Arnel will be weakened only by very strong solutions at very high temperature. Ordinary household alkalies, such as strong soaps and ammonia, will have no harmful effect.

• *Reaction to Acids.* In general, the effect of acids on Arnel is similar to their effect on acetate. Fabrics of Arnel are more resistant to acids than cotton, linen, silk, or rayon but would be decomposed by concentrated solutions of strong acids.

• *Affinity for Dyes.* Dyes similar to those used for acetate may be used on fabrics of Arnel. But Arnel has a lower absorptive ability than acetate and does not take dyes as readily. Techniques have been developed, however, that result in more uniform color.

If properly treated, dyed fabrics made of Arnel are more resistant to fume or gas fading and crocking than acetate fabrics. In general, dyes that have good washfastness on acetate have an even higher fastness on Arnel. Lightfastness, perspiration fastness, and resistance to wet bleeding are similar to acetate. To obtain good fastness in black, Arnel is also produced in solution-dyed black filament and staple form. Such fibers have a very high degree of fastness to all conditions.

• *Resistance to Perspiration.* Fabrics of Arnel have good resistance to perspiration. Such fabrics are not easily deteriorated or discolored by perspiration if properly finished.

Arnel Fiber Blends. To obtain special styling and performance characteristics, blending of Arnel staple fiber with other fibers is sometimes advantageous. Processing and finishing characteristics, as well as the contribution to fabric performance, have a bearing on the selection of fibers and the percentages used in blends with Arnel.

• *Arnel and Cotton.* Arnel provides easy care and shape retention when these fabrics are laundered. Arnel and cotton blended fabrics resist wrinkling and need little or no ironing. Cotton provides strength, abrasion resistance, and durability. Such fabrics are given greater absorbency by the cotton and are therefore less clammy and more comfortable in warm, humid weather.

This type of blend increases the styling properties and permits interesting cross-dyeing possibilities. Arnel and cotton blends have a cottonlike hand and appearance. To retain the intrinsic desirable properties of Arnel, such blends should not contain more than 30 per cent cotton. Some blends contain 50 per cent or more of cotton, permitting higher yarn counts; that is, finer yarns, which may be desirable where styling is the prime consideration. This greater amount of cotton will, however, decrease the desirable characteristics of Arnel.

• *Arnel and Wool.* A wide variation of blend proportions is possible and feasible with Arnel and wool blends. The Arnel provides wrinkle resistance and shape retention. The wool provides a fair amount of abrasion resistance, drape, resilience, and absorbency. Such blends will not be as warm as all-wool fabrics, which may be of advantage for use in mild weather.

• *Arnel and Rayon.* Blends of up to 30 per cent rayon and the remainder Arnel are satisfactory. Rayon provides absorbency and contributes to such styling as textural effects and cross dyeing. Arnel provides wrinkle resistance, shape retention, and easy care in handling and washing. However, such blends cannot take hard wear.

▶ TEST YOURSELF ON THIS CHAPTER

1. Compare the qualities of rayon, acetate, Arnel, and those of natural fibers.
2. What are multifilament yarns? What are spun yarns?
3. What is the source of rayon? How is the material made into a fiber?
4. What are the general characteristics of spun rayon fabrics?
5. What differences are there in the production of viscose and cuprammonium rayons? What are the differences in their characteristics or properties?
6. Name five rayon trade names and indicate any differences in properties.
7. What are the trade names for solution-dyed rayons and acetates? How do they compare in colorfastness with yarn-dyed and piece-dyed rayons and acetates?
8. How are acetate yarns made? What are three trade names for acetate yarns?
9. How is Arnel made? What types of Arnel yarns are available?
10. What fibers are blended with acetate? with Arnel? Why?

14 · NYLON | The Synthetic Polyamide Fiber

The word *nylon* is a generic term that designates a group of related chemical compounds. Nylon is not a trade name or a trade-mark. It is referred to here as a textile, just as are cotton, linen, wool, silk, rayon, and acetate.

History of Nylon. Responsibility for the discovery or invention of nylon belongs to E. I. du Pont de Nemours & Company. More specifically, the credit belongs to Dr. Wallace H. Carothers and his staff of organic chemists of that company's chemical department. Realizing that there was a need for a more active program of research to provide new developments that would insure the future growth of the company, the Du Pont Company began a long-range program of chemical exploration in 1928. Deviating from the applied research previously conducted, this fundamental research aimed primarily to develop basic knowledge of chemical materials and processes. Dr. Carothers was interested in obtaining a better understanding of polymerization. He wanted to know how and why certain molecules join to form "giant" molecules, such as those that occur in cotton, silk, and rubber. After many months of research, one of Dr. Carothers' assistants discovered that one polymer, which looked like clear, heavy molasses when molten, could be drawn out into a long fiber. When it cooled, the fiber could be drawn out farther to several times its original length. This strand was strong, lustrous, and silky. The question naturally arose as to whether this would make a good textile fiber.

At this point, the experiments became practical. The Carothers group was working with a type of compound called *polyesters*. A great many were synthesized. Each was deficient in one or more vital textile properties. Attempting to find a better fiber, they mixed polyesters and polyamides, which are related to polyesters. They were not successful and therefore decided to discontinue the mixtures and concentrate on the polyamides. One of the chemists filled a container, fitted with the tip of a hypodermic needle, with a hot viscous polyamide solution. He squirted a stream of it into the air, and the stream cooled into a fine filament. After the lustrous fiber was drawn and tested, it was found to be strong and pliable and had such promise that a large group of chemists and engineers were employed to make it a commercial success. During the next several years, research with a series of polyamides continued. In February, 1935, one of these was made from hexamethylene diamine and adipic acid. This polymer was called "66" because both of its component chemical compounds contain six carbon atoms per molecule. This "66" polymer proved to be best and is still the choice among hundreds of other polyamides that have been produced.

The name *nylon* was given to this material. (The name has no meaning. It was chosen because it was "short, catchy, and hard to mispronounce.") The discovery was made public in 1938. Since nylon is proteinlike in composition, the fiber was said to be similar in certain of its properties to silk, wool, and hair. Furthermore, this new fiber had additional wonderful properties of its own. On May 15, 1940, nylon hosiery went on sale throughout the country. After that, nylon began to be used for a wide variety of garments. Today, nylon is manufactured by the Du Pont Company and other firms licensed by that company to produce it in various forms in their own plants.

Method of Manufacture of Nylon Fiber.

Nylon is actually a group of related chemical compounds. It is composed of hydrogen, nitrogen, oxygen, and carbon in controlled proportions and structural arrangements. Variations can result in types of nylon plastics, such as combs, brushes, and gears. We are here concerned with the production of nylon yarn.

• *The Nylon Process.* By a series of chemical steps, two chemicals called *hexamethylene diamine* and *adipic acid* are made. These are combined to form nylon salt. Then, since the nylon salt is to be shipped to the spinning mill, it is dissolved in water for easy handling. At the spinning mill, it is heated in large evaporators until a concentrated solution is obtained. The concentrated nylon salt solution is then transferred to an autoclave, which is like a huge pressure cooker. The heat combines the molecules of the two chemicals into giant chainlike ones, called *linear superpolymers.* This process gives nylon a molecular structure somewhat like wool and silk and is also the source of nylon's strength and elasticity. The linear superpolymer is then allowed to flow out of a slot in the autoclave onto a slowly revolving casting wheel. As the ribbons of molten nylon resin are deposited on the wheel, they are sprayed with cold water, which hardens them to milky white, opaque ribbons. The ribbons are removed from the casting wheel to a chipper, which transforms them into flakes.

• *Spinning the Yarn.* Nylon yarn can be made in several ways. The most important of these methods is the *melt process.* Nylon flakes from several autoclaves are blended and poured into the hopper of the spinning machine to insure uniformity in the final nylon yarn. Through a valve in the bottom of

Courtesy E. I. du Pont de Nemours & Co., Inc.

In these autoclaves, polymerization takes place, joining small molecules to make large ones, and creating nylon polymer.

the hopper, the nylon flakes fall onto a hot grid, which melts them. The molten nylon is pumped through a sand filter to the spinneret, a disk about the size of a silver dollar. The spinneret has one or more holes, depending on the pur-

Nylon polymer, pressed out on this huge casting wheel, is sprayed with water and solidifies into a strip resembling ivory.

Courtesy E. I. du Pont de Nemours & Co., Inc.

From tiny holes in this spinneret, fine filaments of nylon are pressed out and later wound together to form nylon yarn.

Courtesy E. I. du Pont de Nemours & Co., Inc.

pose for which the yarn is to be made. As the filaments come out of the spinneret and hit the air, they solidify. After they cool, the filaments converge, pass through a conditioner where they are moistened sufficiently to make them adhere together, and are given a few turns per inch to form a single thread and facilitate further handling.

• *Drawing the Fiber.* Up to this point, the chemical structure of the filaments is about the same as the flakes from which they were made. The filaments are opaque, have poor pliability, and are not very strong because of the random arrangement of the linear superpolymer molecules. This can be changed, however, by stretching, or cold-drawing, the filaments from two to seven times their original length. The amount of stretching is dependent on the denier, elasticity, and strength desired. As the filaments are stretched, they become more and more transparent. The polyamide molecules straighten out, become parallelized, and are brought very close together. Up to a point, the nylon becomes stronger, more elastic, more flexible and pliable.

This elongation by cold-drawing, which is permanent, is accomplished by unwinding the yarn from one spool and winding it onto another spool that is rotating much faster. The speed of the second spool determines the amount of cold-drawing; that is, if the nylon filament is to be stretched four times its original length, it is unwound from one spool and wound on another at a speed that will subject it to a four-fold stretch during the operation.

Delustering Nylon. Nylon may be delustered by a process similar to delustering rayon and acetate. The delusterants are titanium oxide, barium sulphate, zinc oxide, or zinc sulphate. When any of these chemical compounds are mixed with the polyamide solution, they will cause the nylon to be somewhat delustered. Then it is possible to obtain either a bright lustrous nylon that can be used for satin; a semidull, or dully nylon, for curtains.

Types of Nylon Yarn. The diameter of the individual nylon filaments is determined by the rate of delivery from the pump to the spinneret, by the number of holes in the spinneret, and by the rate at which the yarn is drawn away from the spinneret. The size or denier of the yarn before drawing is determined by the diameter and number of filaments in the yarn. The denier of the yarn after drawing is determined by its original denier and the amount of cold-drawing. If it is drawn three times its original length, the stretched yarn will be one-third of its original denier. The individual filaments produced range from 0.1 to 15 denier.

• *Monofilament Yarns.* A 12-denier single-filament yarn is being manufactured. The monofilament yarns are being used by the hosiery industry and for industrial filters. These yarns are very fine and have little or no twist. Consequently, they are relatively weak nylon yarns. Heavier denier, strong monofilament yarns are also produced for various purposes.

• *Multifilament Yarns.* Multifilament yarns are made in both standard and high-tenacity forms. The number of filaments in each yarn varies according to the purpose of the yarn. The yarns range in denier from 20 to 210. Multifilament yarns are stronger than monofilament yarns because of the numerous filaments. The strength can be further increased by the amount of twist per inch given to the yarns.

• *Spun Yarns.* Nylon filaments may be cut about 1 to 5 inches in staple length. The individual filaments range in denier from 1.5 to 15. The staple is usually crimped and spun on a cotton system. These yarns are fuzzy and soft. They have a lower tensile strength but a greater abrasion resistance. They are not as elastic as the filament yarns and take longer to dry.

• *Stretch Yarns.* Nylon filaments can be processed to have a crimp or coiled characteristic. This gives yarns made of such nylon filaments the ability to be greatly stretched, like a spring, and come back to shape when the tension is released. These yarns are produced under several trade names, of which one of the better-known is Helanca. (See page 62.)

• *Textured Yarns.* Nylon filaments can also be processed to have a looped characteristic. Thrown yarns of these filaments have a texture and hand similar to yarns made of a staple fiber, such as cotton, but retain all the other characteristics of filament yarns. One of the best-known of these textured yarns is Taslan, discussed on page 65.

Trade Names of Nylon Yarns. To identify the products of the several companies under license by Du Pont, the manufacturers have given trade names to their nylon yarns, which may be found in advertisements and on labels or tags attached to garments and fabrics.

Trade Name	Description	Manufacturer
Caprolan	Heavy nylon yarn for industrial fabrics	Allied Chemical Dye Corp.
Nylenka	Nylon staple fiber	American Enka Corp.
Chemstrand nylon	Nylon staple and filament	The Chemstrand Corp.
Du Pont nylon	Nylon filament, staple, and crimped staple	E. I. du Pont de Nemours & Co.
IRC nylon	Nylon staple	Industrial Rayon Corp

Finishing Nylon Fabrics. Nylon fabrics can be given various finishes.

Heat-setting—for permanent shape
Embossing—for pattern or design
Moiréing—for effect
Nylonizing—for increased absorbency
Water repellency—for protection against water

An outstanding feature of nylon is that it is thermoplastic; consequently, a nylon fabric or garment can be heat-set by subjecting it to a high degree of heat while being held in a particular shape. After being heat-set, the fabric or garment will always retain its shape, creases, or pleats, and require little or no ironing. Washing, dry cleaning, or wear will not cause loss of shape. Properly done, heat-setting prevents nylon fabrics from shrinking.

Since nylon is thermoplastic, the application of a hot embossing roller will cause the nylon to melt in conformity with the embossing pattern. This results in a permanent finish that cannot be removed by wearing, washing, or dry cleaning. The same principle applies to nylon moiré. As with thermoplastic acetate, nylon moiré is permanent. Nylon is not very absorbent. For shirts and lingerie, this is a disadvantage. To overcome this, nylon fabrics may be nylonized, a process that appreciably increases the absorbency of nylon. Nylon fabrics may be treated with a water-repellent finish, which makes them ideal for rainwear and for shower curtains.

Judging Nylon Fabrics. Nylon fabrics are produced similar to cotton batiste and plissé, to the texture of linen, to jersey for sweaters, and to silk, rayon, or acetate shantung and velvet. The properties of these fabrics depend on whether the fabric is made of multifilament or spun yarn, how it is woven or knitted, and whether it has a close or an open construction.

• *Strength.* Next to Fiberglas, nylon is the strongest of all textile fibers, although one of the lightest. Its strength will not deteriorate with age. These advantages make nylon desirable for sheer hosiery, curtains, blouses, and dress fabrics. Nylon not only has great tensile strength with light weight, but it is also tough and pliable. Nylon has the highest resistance to abrasion of any fiber. It can take a tremendous amount of rubbing, scraping, bending, and twisting

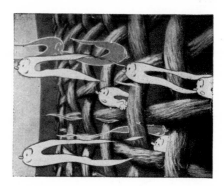

Garments made of open-weave fabrics give a "window screen" effect. That is, they are cool because heat and perspiration are able to escape easily.

without breaking down. Spun nylon yarn has even a higher abrasion resistance than filament nylon, which makes it desirable for socks and upholstery.

• *Elasticity.* Nylon is one of the most elastic fibers that exist today. It has a natural tendency to return to its original shape. Nylon has excellent resilience. Creases from knotting and crushing hang out. Pile fabrics, such as velvets, keep a neat uncrushed appearance. Like any other textile, nylon has its own limit of elasticity. If stretched too much, it will not completely recover its shape. In addition, the type of yarn and the construction of the fabric may contribute to the behavior of the garment. For example, spun nylon is not as elastic as filament nylon. Knitted spun nylon fabrics, such as those used in sweaters, will sag more easily than knitted filament nylon fabrics, such as those used in tricot.

• *Heat Conductivity.* Nylon fabrics may or may not conduct heat well. The warmth or coolness of a nylon garment depends on the weave of the fabric and on the type of yarn used. The smoothness, roundness, and fineness of nylon filaments permit the manufacture of very smooth low-denier yarns, which can be packed very closely when weaving the fabric. If nylon fabric is woven compactly, it will not be porous. The tight construction will not permit air to circulate through the fabric, and the heat and moisture of the body will not readily pass through it, but will build up between the fabric and the body, and

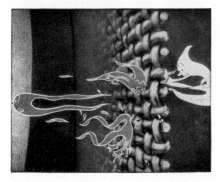

A tightly woven material is warm, since heat and moisture are pent up. You would not want such a fabric for summer clothing.

Courtesy Du Pont Magazine

In spun fabrics, short crimped nylon fibers are twisted together into fuzzy yarns. The millions of insulating air spaces trap water, so drying is slower.

Water droplets slide off smooth nylon multifilaments easily. This, plus the fact that nylon itself absorbs little water, means that fabrics dry quickly.

the wearer will feel very warm. Such fabrics are good for winter apparel, such as windbreakers, but are not suitable for summer garments.

On the other hand, these fine nylon filament yarns may be woven into extremely thin, lightweight, sheer fabrics. These materials are very porous and permit the circulation of air. Consequently, they are cool and can be used for summer blouses and curtains.

Spun nylon yarn will produce warm fabrics. These yarns are composed of thousands of short crimped fibers twisted together, which provide millions of tiny dead-air spaces that act as insulators. This insulation makes spun nylon fabrics warm and therefore useful for sweaters and winter socks.

• *Absorbency.* Nylon does not absorb much moisture. Fabrics made of nylon filament yarns will not readily get wet through the material. Most of the water remains on the surface and runs off the smooth fabric, which therefore dries quickly. Such fabrics are useful for raincoats and shower curtains. Spun nylon fabrics, however, will not dry quickly. Droplets of water tend to cling to the sides of the thousands of staple fibers, clogging the air spaces and relatively increasing the drying time for spun nylon fabrics. Nylon's low absorbency has a disadvantage in that the fabric feels clammy and uncomfortable in warm, humid weather.

• *Cleanliness and Washability.* Dirt particles do not cling to nylon because of its smooth surface. It can be easily washed with warm soapy water. Spots often come clean merely by using a damp cloth. Nylon, however, should be bleached with great care, otherwise it will deteriorate. Nylon also may be readily dry-cleaned. Spun nylon has a tendency to pill, or form balls, on the surface of the fabric. Nylon filament fabrics dry very quickly. They need little or no ironing because the garments are usually heat-set to retain their shape, pleats, or creases. Like acetate, nylon will melt if the iron is too hot.

• *Effect of Light.* Bright nylon is more resistant to the effects of sunlight than most other fibers. Dull nylon will deteriorate a little more quickly than bright nylon; however, even dull nylon has good resistance to light.

• *Resistance to Mildew.* Mildew has absolutely no effect on nylon. Mildew may form on nylon, but it will not weaken the fabric.

• *Resistance to Moths.* Moths and other insects will not attack nylon because it has no attraction for them.

• *Reaction to Alkalies.* Nylon is substantially inert to alkalies.

• *Reaction to Acids.* Nylon is decomposed by cold concentrated solutions of such mineral acids as hydrochloric, sulphuric, and nitric acids. A boiling dilute 5 per cent solution of hydrochloric acid will destroy nylon.

• *Affinity for Dyes.* Nylon has good affinity for most of the dyes used for silk, wool, and acetate. The colors have good resistance to fading.

• *Resistance to Perspiration.* Nylon fabrics are resistant to perspiration. The color, however, may be affected.

Nylon Fiber Blends.

The consumer uses many textile products that do not possess all the properties he would like them to have. He would, for example, like overcoats with sufficient warmth but less weight; cool, light summer clothes that would not lose their fresh, clean appearance on hot sticky days; fabrics that would wash readily, dry quickly, and not lose their shape. Textile designers and engineers are producing new fabrics to meet such needs. These combine or blend two or more fibers to give the desired properties to the fabrics.

• *Nylon and Cotton.* When properly combined with cotton, nylon adds strength, which allows the development of unusually fine textures not possible to obtain from cotton alone. Nylon provides smoothness, silkiness, and dirt rejection. It also reduces the weight of the fabric and increases its wrinkle resistance. The cotton gives softness and moisture absorption. This combination permits the weaving of fabrics that are soft, supple, and extremely serviceable If the combination is not properly balanced, the cotton may shrink, causing the fabric to pucker. Also, the nylon fibers may cut the cotton fibers.

• *Nylon and Wool.* The proper combination of nylon and wool will produce a lighter weight fabric with greater durability. Such a fabric will retain the hand, drape, and warmth of wool as well as the elasticity, resilience, and shape retention of nylon. Such fabrics are always labeled as to the percentages of nylon and wool that they contain. The properties of the fabric will be in direct proportion to the amount used of each of the two fibers. A blend of 10 to 15 per cent nylon and the remainder wool is considered satisfactory.

• *Nylon and Silk.* In this combination, the silk improves the hand and provides moisture absorption. The nylon improves the stability or shape retention, and the elasticity and strength.

• *Nylon and Rayon.* In this blend, the nylon gives wrinkle resistance and strength. The rayon gives suppleness, drape, and moisture absorption. Such a combination makes possible a fine-quality fabric of extremely light weight. As with cotton, if the combination is not properly balanced, the rayon may shrink, causing the fabric to pucker. Also, an improper blend of nylon and rayon may result in the nylon fibers cutting the rayon fibers.

• *Nylon and Acetate.* The acetate in such a blend provides a luxurious hand. The nylon gives light weight and strength. This combination may have the disadvantages of the possible improper balance mentioned for cotton and rayon. Also, neither nylon nor acetate absorbs much moisture. Such fabrics may feel clammy and uncomfortable in warm and humid atmospheres.

• *Nylon and Arnel.* A blend of 15 per cent nylon and 85 per cent Arnel in gabardines for shirts, slacks, and fabrics for outerwear is a satisfactory combination. The nylon provides strength to give good durability. Fabrics of this blend hold their creases and pleats and shape well. They can be laundered easily and need little or no ironing. Garments made of such a blend are among those classed as wash-and-wear type.

▶ TEST YOURSELF ON THIS CHAPTER

  1. Who was responsible for discovering nylon?
  2. What is nylon? May any company manufacture it?
  3. What types of yarns can be made of nylon? Describe them.
  4. Why are some nylon fabrics warm while others are cold?
  5. Why do some nylon fabrics dry faster than others?
  6. What advantage does heat setting give to nylon garments?
  7. Is nylon damaged by mildew? by moths?
  8. What is the reaction of nylon to alkalies and to acids? to perspiration?
  9. What are the properties of a nylon-cotton fabric? its disadvantages?
 10. What are the outstanding properties of a nylon-wool fabric?

15 · DACRON | The Synthetic Polyester Fiber

The name *Dacron* is a trade-mark owned by E. I. du Pont de Nemours & Company for a particular synthetic polyester fiber. The groundwork for the development of Dacron polyester fiber was laid by Dr. W. H. Carothers in his experiments with giant molecular structures, but he devoted the major portion of his research to polyamides, which resulted in the development of nylon.

History of Dacron. After studying the published works of Dr. Carothers, British research chemists decided to examine the possibilities of polyesters. During the period of 1939–1941, investigations were conducted in the laboratories of the Calico Printers Association, Ltd., by J. R. Whinfield, J. T. Dickson, W. K. Birtwhistle, and C. G. Ritchie. The work resulted in the development of a polyester fiber known in England as *Terylene*. In 1946, the Du Pont Company purchased the exclusive rights to produce this polyester fiber in the United States. Under the temporary name of Fiber V, and in essentially the same chemical form, Du Pont conducted intensive developmental work. By 1951, the company was producing commercially this fiber, which it called *Dacron*.

Method of Manufacture of Dacron Fiber. The process of manufacture of Dacron polyester fiber is similar to that of nylon, but the chemicals used are different. The polymer is produced by the catalyzed ester interchange between the glycol and dimethyl terephthalate. A hard porcelainlike substance is produced that melts at a temperature slightly above 480 degrees Fahrenheit. This viscous melt is extruded through a spinneret and subsequently drawn into filaments of Dacron polyester fiber.

Types and Forms of Dacron Yarn. Dacron polyester fibers are made in four different types: 51, 54, 56, and 64. The major difference between types is their strength-stretch relationship. Type 51 is the strongest with most stretch resistance; that is, the least stretchability. Type 56 is second srongest with less stretch resistance. Type 54 has the least stretch resistance. Recently developed Type 64, although the weakest variety, is still twice as strong as wool and has greater abrasion resistance than wool. It also has greater dyeing versatility than the other three types. These types of Dacron are being produced in the following forms.

• *Continuous-Filament Yarns.* Continuous-filament yarns are made in two forms: monofilament and multifilament. The multifilament yarns are:

    40 denier, 34 filament semidull apparel yarn—Type 56
    70 denier, 34 filament semidull apparel yarn—Type 56
    70 denier, 34 filament bright industrial yarn—Type 51
    210 denier, 34 filament bright industrial yarn—Type 51

Dacron continuous-filament yarns are used for such sheer lightweight fabrics as curtains, tulle, voile, and organdy, which are crisp, highly wrinkle-resistant, and shape-retentive.

• *Spun Yarn.* Spun Dacron yarns of various sizes are made of 3-denier semidull Type 54 staple, $1\frac{1}{2}$ and $2\frac{1}{2}$ inches in length. This staple is spun into yarn on the cotton or wool systems depending on the ultimate yarn desired. The spun yarns are used for summer suitings, which require unusual resiliency and dimensional stability to prevent puckering and change in shape in humid weather. They are also used for heavier weight fabrics for outerwear, and for knitted fabrics because of the excellent shape retention and stretch resistance of Dacron.

Type 64 is produced in 3 denier staple and may be spun into yarn on the worsted or rayon systems. These yarns are used for winter-weight and spring-weight fabrics. Such fabrics include finished worsteds like sharpskins, gabardines, and Bedford cords, as well as such napped unfinished worsteds as flannel and serge. Fabrics of Type 64 have a greater resistance to pilling than fabrics of yarns of other types of Dacron.

• *Tow.* Semidull Type 54 Dacron tow is produced in 3 denier and 6 denier filament forms: Type 64 polyester fiber, in 3 denier tow form.

Finishing Dacron Fabrics. Several finishes can be given to Dacron fabrics to increase their usefulness. Among the most important are:

Heat-setting—for permanent shape   Antistatic finish—for reduction of
Preshrinking—for dimensional stability   static electricity

Fabrics made of continuous-filament Dacron yarn can be heat-set in about the same manner as nylon. Setting at temperatures ranging from 350 to 425 degrees Fahrenheit on a hot roller produces fabrics that are dimensionally stable to repeated washing and ironing. Fabrics made of Dacron spun yarn are effectively stabilized in normal dyeing and finishing operations.

Stabilized fabrics made of either Dacron continuous-filament yarn or spun yarn have excellent wrinkle resistance and recovery from wrinkling. Essentially permanent creases can be pressed into them at the ordinary ironing temperature for rayon (about 275 degrees Fahrenheit) and remain sharp even after the fabric is washed. Such creases, however, can be ironed out if desired. This means that such garments as suits made of Dacron staple will hold their shape and press in abnormally damp weather and even when wet.

Continuous-filament Dacron yarn is capable of 15 to 20 per cent shrinkage in finishing. This means that such fabrics will not shrink to any significant extent thereafter. It is also possible to produce fabrics with very little porosity by this preshrinking procedure. Fabrics made of Dacron yarn are subject to the accumulation of static electricity. Where this would prove objectionable, Dacron fabrics can be treated with antistatic agents.

Judging Dacron Fabrics. Although four types of Dacron polyester fiber are produced for different purposes, the following generalities may be made.

• *Strength.* Dacron is a strong fiber. It is exceeded in strength only by Fiberglas and nylon. This property not only gives it a great advantage where fabrics of durability are required, but also provides one of the important advantages for blending Dacron with other fibers.

• *Elasticity.* Dacron is often characterized as having a high degree of stretch resistance, which means that Dacron fabrics are not likely to stretch out of shape too easily. This property makes Dacron particularly suited for knitted garments; the sagging and stretching that would ordinarily occur are reduced. Dacron has a very high degree of resilience. Not only does a Dacron fabric resist wrinkling when dry, but it also resists wrinkling when wet. For example, a suit of Dacron will keep its pressed appearance after many wearings even in rain or moist, humid weather.

• *Heat Conductivity.* Fabrics of Dacron polyester fiber are better conductors of heat than fabrics made of acrylic fibers (discussed in the next chapter). Dacron fiber is round and, in the staple form, will not bulk up in a yarn as much as the acrylic fibers do. This results in a smoother yarn with less air spaces and less insulation. While a fabric of Dacron would not be as warm as a fabric made of the acrylics, or of silk, wool, or Vicara, it would be warmer than if made of cotton, linen, or rayon. One of the reasons for the apparent greater warmth of Dacron is its low absorbency.

• *Absorbency.* Dacron is one of the least absorbent fibers. Only Saran and Fiberglas are less absorbent. This low absorbency has two important advantages. Dacron fabrics will dry very rapidly, since almost all the moisture will lie on the surface rather than penetrate the yarns. Furthermore, this low absorbency means that Dacron fabrics will not stain easily. Most substances that would stain other fabrics lie on the surface and can be wiped or washed off easily. Fab-

rics of low absorbency have the disadvantage of being clammy and uncomfortable in humid weather. In warm weather, they will not absorb perspiration or atmospheric moisture. As a result, the wearer feels most uncomfortable,
but only when wearing the fabric next to the skin.

• *Cleanliness and Washability.* Since Dacron fabrics have a very low absorbency, stains lie on the surface and can easily be washed or dry-cleaned
away. Strong soaps and bleaches are not needed. Fabrics of Dacron filament yarn
dry very quickly. Those of spun yarn dry comparatively rapidly if wrung out
well. There is essentially no water shrinkage of Dacron fabrics; therefore,
shirts, blouses, and even slacks made entirely of Dacron (including the sewing
thread) may be safely laundered.

When ironing Dacron fabrics, it is best to use a moderately hot iron as for
rayon. Excessive heat will cause Dacron to melt. (Burning tobacco will quickly
melt holes in such fabrics. Certain resins are being used to coat the material,
thus minimizing this danger.) Actually, little ironing is needed even after long
wear or after being completely wet, because garments made of Dacron hold
their shape and creases after being heat-set. Furthermore, the wrinkle resistance
of Dacron is extremely good.

• *Effect of Light.* Dacron has good resistance to degradation by light. Over
a prolonged period of time, however, Dacron definitely does deteriorate.

• *Resistance to Mildew.* Dacron fabrics are absolutely resistant to mildew.
They will not be stained or weakened.

• *Resistance to Moths.* Dacron is unaffected by moths or by carpet beetles.

• *Reaction to Alkalies.* At room temperature, Dacron has good resistance
to weak alkalies and fair resistance to strong alkalies. At boiling temperatures,
it has poor resistance to weak alkalies and dissolves in strong alkalies.

• *Reaction to Acids.* Dacron has excellent-to-good resistance to most acids.
Such strong acids as sulphuric acid will cause decomposition if the temperature
is high enough.

• *Affinity for Dyes.* Dacron can be dyed with specialized techniques to a
complete range of shades. The results have good-to-excellent washfastness and
fair-to-good lightfastness.

• *Resistance to Perspiration.* Dacron is not easily affected by perspiration.

Dacron Fiber Blends. Dacron polyester fiber has been successfully blended
with many other fibers. Various effects and combinations of properties are
derived from these blends depending on the fibers used and on the percentages
in the blends. One of the most important characteristics that Dacron provides
is its high degree of shape retention for garments that may be washed and
subsequently require little or no ironing.

• *Dacron and Cotton.* For satisfactory wash-and-wear purposes, fabrics for rainwear, tailored clothing, dress shirts, and sports shirts should have a blend of at least 65 per cent Dacron with the cotton. Dacron will provide wrinkle resistance and shape retention. Cotton will provide absorbency and consequent comfort. However, unless properly constructed and properly cared for, a fabric of a Dacron and cotton blend may pucker and lose its shape if the cotton should shrink or if cotton thread is used in sewing.

• *Dacron and Wool.* In combination with wool, Dacron provides outstanding wrinkle resistance and crease retention, so that wet or dry the shape retention is improved according to the proportions used. The greater abrasion resistance of Dacron also provides longer wear. The wool contributes good draping quality and elasticity. The wool also reduces the hazard of melted holes due to burning tobacco. A blend of 60 per cent Dacron and 40 per cent wool provides a cloth warm enough for year-round suits.

• *Dacron and Rayon.* In such a blend, Dacron gives greater resiliency, shape retention, and durability. The rayon provides absorbency and variety of color and texture. For satisfactory wash-and-wear service, a blend of at least 55 per cent Dacron with the rayon is desirable.

• *Dacron and Nylon.* Nylon contributes strength and abrasion resistance. Dacron contributes outstanding wrinkle resistance. Such a combination offers stability, easy laundering, quick drying, and resistance to damage from mildew and insects. The fabric will be clammy to the skin, however, in warm, humid weather. Since both fibers are thermoplastic and neither is very absorbent, any combination in the blend will provide good wash-and-wear characteristics. Care should be taken to avoid pilling of fabrics with this type of blend.

• *Dacron and Arnel.* The most important contribution that Dacron makes to such a blend is its strength. Again, both fibers are thermoplastic; and fabrics made of such a blend will have excellent shape retention and provide good wash-and-wear service. The fabric, however, will pill, unless made of a fine-count yarn of this blend.

► TEST YOURSELF ON THIS CHAPTER

1. What is Dacron? May any company produce or imitate it? Why?
2. What types of yarns are made of Dacron? Explain the differences.
3. Discuss the washability and general care of fabrics made of Dacron.
4. How does the strength of Dacron compare to that of other fibers?
5. What is the effect of mildew on Dacron? What is the effect of moths?
6. What reaction has Dacron to alkalies, acids, and perspiration?
7. Discuss the possible value of Dacron fabrics and blends for summer wear.
8. What are the outstanding properties of a Dacron-wool fabric?

16 · ORLON, ACRILAN, DYNEL, CRESLAN, VEREL

The Acrylic Synthetic Fibers

Basically, acrylic is a type of plastic. The acrylic fibers are composed of large polymerized molecules. In textile fiber form, these fibers look and feel much like other fibers, but have additional and valuable properties of their own. While the fibers discussed in this chapter are not all necessarily wholly acrylic, they are sufficiently related chemically to be classified together. Some of their properties are similar, others are different, according to their related chemical compositions and their methods of production.

History of Acrylics. Dr. Carothers' discovery of the fiber-forming properties of linear superpolymers spurred research men everywhere to investigate the fiber-forming possibilities of a host of polymers. The first acrylic fiber, *Orlon,* became a reality when, in 1944, a "semiworks" was built under the auspices of the Research Section of Du Pont's Acetate Division. Until August, 1945, the development of Orlon acrylic fiber was concerned primarily with its possible aid in the war effort, but was not brought to fruition before World War II ended. By early 1946, Orlon looked promising enough for commercialization. Process development continued, and in October, 1948, the Du Pont Company built a plant near Camden, South Carolina, capable of producing 6½ million pounds of yarn a year. Production of Orlon started in May, 1950.

Following the lead of the Du Pont Company, The Chemstrand Corporation developed another acrylic fiber, which they named *Acrilan.* A plant was built in Decatur, Alabama; and operations, with a capacity of 30 million pounds annually, were started late in 1952.

The Carbide and Carbon Chemicals Company started experimenting with superpolymers in 1934. The company contributed much to the present knowledge of these substances, but it was not until 1949 that *Dynel,* a partly acrylic staple fiber, was developed. The first commercial plant started production of 5 million pounds annually in July, 1950. Since then, the company's name has been changed to the Union Carbide Chemicals Company, a division of Union Carbide Corporation; and the production and use of Dynel have expanded.

For many years, the American Cyanamid Company manufactured a chemical known as *acrylonitrile* for use by other companies in the manufacture of such products as acrylic fibers. The company eventually decided to experiment in the production of its own acrylic fiber. After much experimentation, it produced in 1953 a fiber tentatively designated as X-51 at its pilot plant in Stamford, Connecticut. After spending fifteen years on research, the American Cyanamid Company began commercial production in 1958 of its own acrylic fiber, *Creslan,* in a new plant near Pensacola, Florida.

In an effort to diversify its position in textile fibers, Eastman Chemical Products, Inc., a subsidiary of Eastman Kodak Company, also entered the acrylic fiber field. After due experimentation, the company announced the production of its own acrylic fiber, *Verel,* in March, 1956. Commercial production of Verel was begun in 1958 at newly developed facilities of the company's corporate associate, Tennessee Eastman Company, which also manufactures acetate fibers at Kingsport, Tennessee.

ORLON

Method of Manufacture of Orlon Fiber. The manufacture of Orlon resin is the result of a complicated chemical synthesis. Acrylonitrile may be made from acetylene or from ethylene. When the ethylene is treated with hypochlorous acid, a chlorohydrin is formed. The chlorohydrin is reacted with sodium hydroxide to form ethylene oxide. Hydrocyanic acid is added to the ethylene oxide, producing cyanoalcohol, which is dehydrated to yield acrylonitrile. The acrylonitrile is then polymerized into polyacrylonitrile resin, a long-chain linear polymer. The polyacrylonitrile is dissolved in a suitable solvent, such as dimethylformamide, and extruded through a spinneret. After coagulation, the filaments are oriented and stabilized by stretching.

Delustering Orlon. By the addition of a delusterant, such as is used for nylon, Orlon is made semidull. This appears to have no effect on the inherent properties of the fiber.

Types of Orlon Yarn. After orientation and stabilization, the Orlon filaments are cut into staple lengths for spinning into yarn.

• *Spun Yarn.* Orlon staple ranges from 1.5 to 6 denier per filament and is cut into lengths of 1.5 to 4 inches, depending on the type of yarn to be made. The staple is crimped and spun on a cotton or wool system into fuzzy yarns. The more twist in the yarns, the finer, smoother, and harder the yarns will be. The less twist in the yarns, the thicker and softer the yarns will be. Spun yarns of Orlon with a low twist have the hand of cashmere. Soft spun Orlon yarns, however, are fuzzy and have a tendency to pill or form little balls on the surface of the fabric.

• *High-Bulk Yarn.* Orlon crimped staple may be spun into relatively thick, soft, spongy yarns called high-bulk yarns. Such yarns produce warm, lightweight fabrics with a luxurious hand. Sometimes Orlon crimped staple may be blended with other fibers, resulting in greater stretch as well as high bulk in the yarn. For further discussion, see page 64.

Finishing Orlon Fabrics. Several finishes can be given to Orlon fabrics to increase their usefulness. Among the most important are:

Heat-setting—for permanent shape
Water repellency—for protection against water

An outstanding feature of Orlon is that a fabric or garment made of Orlon can be given a permanent shape by being subjected to a high degree of heat. After being heat-set, the fabric will retain its shape, creases, or pleats. Washing, dry cleaning, or wear will not cause loss of shape.

Orlon is not a particularly absorbent textile. To make it even less absorbent, it may be treated with Zelan. This process makes the fabric water-repellent and is therefore desirable for rainwear and children's playclothes.

Judging Orlon Fabrics. The properties of Orlon fabrics depend on the type of yarn that is used as well as how the material is woven or knitted.

• *Strength.* Orlon fiber is of moderate strength. It is, however, the weakest of the acrylic fibers. Compared to the natural fibers it is weaker than all with the exception of wool. Since Orlon fiber is used primarily as a replacement for wool, its greater strength is an advantage. The abrasion resistance of Orlon is good and compares favorably with that of wool.

• *Elasticity.* Like the other acrylics, Orlon has little stretch. It has very good resilience, however, and therefore will not wrinkle easily. Orlon staple fabrics are not as lively in springing out from a creased position as Dacron and wool, but they are nevertheless good in this respect. The low stretchability makes Orlon useful for knitted wear, since it is not likely to stretch unduly.

The high resilience makes Orlon desirable for men's slacks and suits as well as for women's dresses.

• *Heat Conductivity*. Like all acrylics, Orlon does not conduct heat rapidly; therefore, Orlon fabrics can be warm. Orlon is dog-bone in shape, which provides overlapping and bulk (with little weight). As a result, staple Orlon fabrics have approximately 20 per cent greater insulating power per ounce of fiber than wool fabrics. Since an ounce of Orlon fabric is thicker than an ounce of wool fabric, it is possible to obtain an Orlon fabric that, while being as thick and as warm as wool, is about 20 per cent lighter in weight.

• *Absorbency*. Orlon, like the other acrylics, has a low absorbency. Nevertheless, fabrics made of Orlon staple will take on quite a bit of water due to the staple's adsorbency; that is, the tendency for water droplets to cling to the surface of the individual fibers. Since these water droplets get into the air spaces between the fibers and evaporate slowly, Orlon spun yarn fabrics dry slowly although not as slowly as wool fabrics.

This low absorbency gives Orlon the advantage of resisting stains. Many substances that are ordinarily absorbed by other fibers merely remain on the surface of fabrics made of Orlon yarns and can be easily removed by wiping, washing, or dry cleaning.

• *Cleanliness and Washability*. Orlon fabrics do not soil or stain easily. Washing or dry cleaning quickly renews their freshness. A mild soap should, however, be used in laundering since strong soaps will damage Orlon. If desired, any ordinary cleaning fluid and household bleaches may be safely used.

Soft, bulky Orlon yarns will pill. To reduce this tendency, such garments as sweaters should be laundered, while turned inside out, with as little rubbing as possible. After rinsing through mild suds and then lukewarm water, squeeze out the water, turn the garment right side out, spread it on a towel, and gently brush it with a very soft brush while drying. The tendency of Orlon to pill is reduced when it is blended with most other fibers. Fairly tightly spun yarns of Orlon are not likely to pill readily because they are harder, smoother, and not too fuzzy.

Orlon fabrics should be ironed with a moderately warm iron; in fact, they may be ironed while dry. Old creases may be removed, and new ones added. Since fabrics of Orlon may be heat-set, it is often unnecessary to press them, but some ironing to smooth the cloth may be desired.

• *Effect of Light*. Orlon has outstanding resistance to the effect of light. Its extreme resistance to such degradation makes it especially useful for such outdoor purposes as awnings, curtains, draperies, and uniforms.

• *Resistance to Mildew*. Mildew may form on the surface, but it will have no effect on Orlon fabric. It may be easily wiped off.

• *Resistance to Moths.* Orlon is unaffected by moths or their larvae, or by carpet beetles.

• *Reaction to Alkalies.* Orlon has fair-to-good resistance to weak alkalies.

• *Reaction to Acids.* Orlon is exceedingly resistant to strong mineral acids as well as organic acids.

• *Affinity for Dyes.* Formerly, it was difficult to dye Orlon; however, the Orlon now produced has greatly improved dyeability. It can be dyed in a wide range of colors and hues. The colors have satisfactory fastness to washing and light.

• *Resistance to Perspiration.* All indications are that Orlon fabrics are not readily deteriorated by perspiration, but the color may be affected.

Orlon Fiber Blends. Orlon has many desirable properties that may be imparted to fabrics containing fibers other than Orlon, depending on the relative amount of each fiber used.

• *Orlon and Cotton.* In combination with cotton, Orlon adds light weight and body. The cotton contributes strength and absorbency. The fabric is wrinkle-resistant, retains its shape well, and provides easy care. A blend of 80 per cent or more of Orlon with cotton will provide the general characteristics of a wash-and-wear fabric, such as is used for sports shirts.

• *Orlon and Wool.* One of the outstanding characteristics of Orlon is its bulk, so that when the staple is blended with wool, the resulting fabric is light-weight and yet warm. It also has a soft hand. Fabrics of this combination have very good crease retention and wrinkle recovery. These blends are washable. Where there is a good proportion of Orlon, the fabrics seldom need pressing. A good blend for a wash-and-wear tailored garment should have 70 per cent or more Orlon with the wool. Such a blend will also be stronger than an all-wool fabric. Too much Orlon in such a fabric makes the cloth too bulky.

• *Orlon and Silk.* Orlon and silk together provide interesting cross-dye and texture effects. Such blends have outstanding hand and excellent stability. In addition to the good appearance, the combination gives long wear. The Orlon contributes easy-care qualities and shape retention. The silk contributes absorbency and strength. The fabric is very resilient and may be warm, depending on its weight.

• *Orlon and Rayon.* To the versatility of rayon, Orlon adds wrinkle resistance and stability. New and unusual surface and dye effects, including cross dyes, are possible. Orlon provides a dry, warm, and soft hand. A wash-and-wear blend should have at least 70 per cent Orlon with the rayon.

• *Orlon and Acetate.* A combination of Orlon and acetate in a fabric provides a soft, luxurious feel and excellent drapability. It also has excellent shape retention and good resilience. The fabric launders easily (with a mild soap and warm water), dries rapidly, and is easy to iron. The Orlon also provides greater resistance to sunlight. Neither Orlon nor acetate, however, is particularly absorbent, which presents a disadvantage in warm, humid weather. Such blends will be warm and clammy.

• *Orlon and Nylon.* The strength and abrasion resistance of nylon combined with the luxurious hand and covering power of Orlon produce attractive, warm, strong fabrics. Similar qualities of Orlon and nylon, such as wrinkle resistance, crease retention, and easy care, are increased when these fibers are combined. But such fabrics will not be very absorbent.

• *Orlon and Dacron.* Orlon improves the hand of a fabric when combined with Dacron, giving better body comfort and warmth. Dacron contributes even greater wrinkle resistance, especially under humid conditions. A 50/50 blend of Dacron and Orlon will provide good wash-and-wear characteristics. Such a fabric will wear well because of the strength of Dacron and the good abrasion resistance of Orlon; however, it is likely to pill if care is not exercised.

ACRILAN

Method of Manufacture of Acrilan Fiber.   The processing of Acrilan is similar to that of Orlon. Natural gas and air are combined to form ammonia. Ammonia and natural gas are combined to produce hydrocyanic acid. Natural gas, at elevated temperatures, produces acetylene which, when combined with hydrocyanic acid, produces acrylonitrile. Then the acrylonitrile is polymerized. This polyacrylonitrile in powder form is dissolved by a suitable solvent and passed through spinnerets into a coagulating bath to produce continuous filaments called *tow.* The fibers are then washed, stretched, and crimped. Finally, the crimped filaments are cut into staple, dried, opened, and baled. The fiber is a light cream color and is semidull.

Types of Acrilan Yarn.   Acrilan fiber is made in 3- and 5-denier diameters. Since all the fibers are cut into staple, the only form of Acrilan yarn is the spun yarn. Using a method similar to that used for rayon staple, Acrilan fiber may be spun into yarn on the cotton, woolen, or worsted system depending on the desired purpose.

Finishing Acrilan Fabrics.   Acrilan may be finished similarly to Orlon. The outstanding feature is heat setting, which will permit semipermanent creases. Care must be taken in the process because dry heat in excess of 300 degrees Fahrenheit for more than a few minutes will yellow the fiber. With proper precautions, Acrilan fabrics will be bulky and silky.

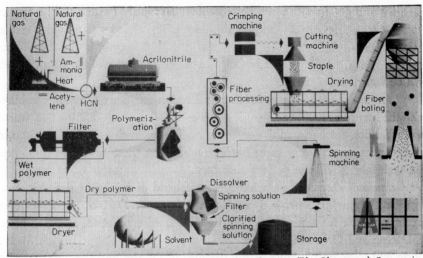

Diagrammatic flow chart of Acrilan production.

Judging Acrilan Fabrics. Acrilan fabrics are made only of spun yarn. The properties of the fabrics are partially dependent on the manner in which the yarn is spun as well as on the construction of the cloth.

• *Strength.* Acrilan is of moderate strength. It is slightly stronger than Orlon but weaker than the other acrylic fibers. Compared to those natural fibers with which it is sometimes blended, Acrilan is weaker than cotton but stronger than wool. It is also stronger than rayon and acetate.

• *Elasticity.* Acrilan has little stretchability. This low elastic characteristic makes it particularly suitable for knitted wear and for garments where retention of shape is desired. Acrilan has very good resilience. It will not wrinkle easily and therefore is good for dresses, suits, and slacks.

• *Heat Conductivity.* Acrilan is a bulky, soft, warm fiber similar in insulating value to the other acrylic fibers. It is almost as warm as wool but lighter in weight. Thus Acrilan provides warmth with light weight. This combination makes Acrilan particularly suitable for blankets as well as for winter wear.

• *Absorbency.* Like the other acrylic fibers, Acrilan has little absorbency. Nevertheless, Acrilan yarns, like Orlon yarns, have quite a bit of adsorbency and dry slowly because the water that gets trapped between the fibers evaporates slowly. This low absorbency gives Acrilan the advantage of resisting stains. Watery or oily substances, which stain other textiles, are not readily absorbed into Acrilan fabrics. They lie on the surface and can be easily removed by wiping, washing, or dry cleaning.

• *Cleanliness and Washability.* It is relatively easy to keep Acrilan fabrics clean. They may be readily dry-cleaned. Laundering is also no problem, although it is preferable to use a mild soap or detergent. Since Acrilan fabrics may be heat-set, it is often unnecessary to iron them, although some pressing with a moderately warm iron to smooth the cloth may be desired. Too hot an iron or heat for too long a period will cause yellowing.

• *Effect of Light.* Acrilan has good resistance to the effect of sunlight although it is not so resistant as Orlon. Compared to other fibers, it is one of the most light-resistant textiles, and this indicates its value for outdoor uses.

• *Resistance to Mildew.* Like the other acrylic fibers, Acrilan is wholly resistant to mildew. Any mildew that forms on the surface can be easily removed, and there will be no damage to the fabric.

• *Resistance to Moths.* Acrilan is unaffected by moths. Together with its warmth and loft, Acrilan is, in this respect, well suited for both garments and rugs. This provides a particularly good advantage over wool.

• *Reaction to Alkalies.* Acrilan has good resistance to weak alkalies. Its resistance decreases as the strength of the alkali, the temperature, and the length of immersion increase.

• *Reaction to Acids.* Acrilan has good resistance to strong mineral acids as well as to organic acids.

• *Affinity for Dyes.* Acrilan may be dyed with acetate dyes, but lightfastness is poor. Wool dyes give greater fastness and a wide range of colors.

• *Resistance to Perspiration.* Acrilan is also resistant to perspiration.

Acrilan Fiber Blends. Acrilan is readily adaptable to blending with other fibers. The chief blends are with cotton, wool, rayon, and acetate.

• *Acrilan and Cotton.* In combination with cotton, Acrilan adds warmth, light weight, and wrinkle resistance. The cotton provides strength. The fabric can be laundered and pressed easily.

• *Acrilan and Wool.* The primary value of blending Acrilan and wool is to provide the same warmth as an all-wool fabric but with less weight. The combination also provides a resilient, wrinkle-resistant fabric that nevertheless tends to retain creases and pleats. Acrilan will also add strength but too much of this fiber in the blend will make the fabric too bulky.

• *Acrilan and Rayon.* Various surface and color effects are possible by blending Acrilan and rayon. The Acrilan provides greater resilience and shape retention. Such a fabric will also be warmer than an all-rayon fabric.

• *Acrilan and Acetate.* A combination of Acrilan and acetate produces a soft, warm fabric with good draping qualities, good shape retention, and resilience. The fabric can be easily laundered or dry-cleaned.

Acrilan acrylic fiber being measured for blending with other fibers, such as cotton, wool, rayon, or acetate

Courtesy The Chemstrand Corporation

• *Acrilan and Nylon.* The strength of nylon and the warmth of Acrilan together can produce a blend that would also be resilient and stable.

DYNEL

Method of Manufacture of Dynel Fiber. The production of Dynel is only partially similar to that of such acrylic fibers as Orlon and Acrilan. This is because Dynel is actually only 40 per cent acrylic while the other 60 per cent is vinyl chloride. The question might be raised as to whether Dynel should not be classified more rightly as a vinyl chloride than as an acrylic. The answer is that the properties and end uses of Dynel compete more nearly with those of the wholly acrylic fibers.

Dynel is the result of copolymerization of acrylonitrile (a clear liquid used to produce other acrylic fibers) and vinyl chloride (a gas used to produce vinyl plastics). When acrylonitrile and vinyl chloride are combined under heat and pressure, they copolymerize and form a white powdery resin. This resin is dissolved in acetone (the basic ingredient of nail-polish removers) producing a viscous solution similar in appearance to that of acetate. It is then passed through spinnerets into a water bath from which it emerges as a tow or group of continuous filaments. The tow is dried, stretched, annealed, and cut into desired staple lengths. The fiber is then crimped and baled for shipment to the spinner where it is twisted and spun into yarn.

Types of Dynel Yarn. Dynel fiber is semidull. It is made in 2, 3, 6, 12, and 24 denier diameters. Since all the fibers are cut into staple from 1¼ to 5 inches

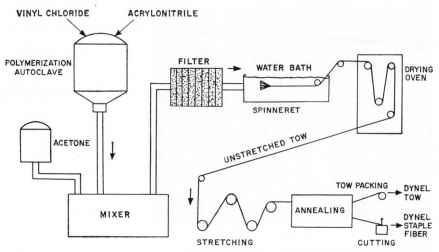

Courtesy Union Carbide Chemicals Co.

Flow chart showing the manufacturing process of Dynel acrylic fiber.

in length, the only form of Dynel yarn is spun yarn. Using a method similar to that used for Acrilan staple, Dynel fiber may be spun into yarn on the cotton, woolen, or worsted system depending on the desired purpose.

Finishing Dynel Fabrics. Dynel may be finished somewhat like the other acrylic fibers. The outstanding feature is heat setting, which molds a fabric or garment into permanent shape and also permits permanent creases and pleats. These shapes are resistant to change due to wetting and are relatively permanent until the shaping temperature is again equaled or excelled.

Sequence of the production of Dynel acrylic fiber from the vinyl chloride and acry-lonitrile copolymer resin to tow, to crimped staple, to spun yarn.

Courtesy Union Carbide Chemicals Co.

Dynel emerges from each spinning bath as groups of endless fibers called tow.

Courtesy Carbide & Carbon Chemicals Co.

Judging Dynel Fabrics.

Dynel fabrics are made only of spun yarn. The manner in which the yarn is spun and the construction of the cloth, as well as the intrinsic properties of the Dynel fiber, are important in judging the fabric.

• *Strength.* Dynel is the strongest of the acrylic fibers. Although it is weaker than cotton, linen, or silk, it is two to three times as strong as wool. It is also stronger than rayon, acetate, and Arnel but weaker than nylon. Dynel also has good abrasion resistance which assures long wear. This property makes Dynel very desirable for blending with other fibers that are not as strong.

• *Elasticity.* Like the other acrylic fibers, Dynel has very little stretchability. It is, however, highly resilient, thus assuring lasting loft (springiness) and softness. This resilience and loft make possible fabrics with an extremely pleasant permanent nap that will not pill. Dynel is therefore a desirable fiber for

Dynel tow is cut to length, then crimped and sent by conveyor to the balers.

Courtesy Carbide & Carbon Chemicals Co.

blankets and such fabrics as flannel. Due to the high degree of resilience of Dynel, fabrics made of this fiber "bounce back" into shape. They do not wrinkle easily, and any wrinkles that may form fall out readily. Dynel fabrics hold their shape well even in damp weather.

• *Heat Conductivity.* Dynel is a soft, bulky, warm fiber similar in insulating value to other acrylic fibers. It is about as warm and heavy as wool.

• *Absorbency.* Dynel is about the least absorbent of the acrylic fibers; in fact, of all textile fibers. The only fibers less absorbent are Dacron, Saran, and Fiberglas. This has certain disadvantages, such as making a garment uncomfortable in warm, humid weather. But it has the advantage of resistance to staining. Such stains as catsup, coffee, mustard, or ink come out in washing, leaving no trace.

• *Cleanliness and Washability.* Dynel can be washed or dry-cleaned easily. It loses very little strength while wet and is not damaged by soaps, detergents, or bleaches. Dynel fabrics resist shrinking and retain their shape in washing and dry cleaning. The water temperature should, however, be below 160 degrees Fahrenheit; otherwise the fabric will become harsh. Dynel is one of the fastest drying fibers. Even heavily napped and knitted fabrics dry relatively quickly. Dynel fabrics need little ironing. When ironing is desired, the iron should be warm or set at the "rayon setting" because Dynel has a low melting point; however, it is flame-resistant.

• *Effect of Light.* Although Dynel is not as resistant as Orlon to the effect of sunlight, it has good resistance to deterioration from light. Dynel has about the same resistance as cotton to the effect of light. Over an extended period of time it darkens and weakens. It is satisfactory for use as curtains and draperies.

• *Resistance to Mildew.* Like the other acrylic fibers, Dynel is wholly resistant to mildew.

• *Resistance to Moths.* Dynel is not damaged by moths or carpet beetles. Together with its warmth, this provides a particularly good advantage over wool. Dynel may therefore be safely used for rugs as well as clothing.

• *Reaction to Alkalies.* Dynel has high resistance to strong alkalies. Common household cleaning alkalies, such as soap, ammonia, lye, and detergents, have no effect on Dynel. This resistance to such corrosive chemicals makes Dynel useful in industrial plants for clothes, gloves, filters, and the like.

• *Reaction to Acids.* Dynel is extremely resistant to acids. In some industrial operations, Dynel work clothing is regularly washed in sulphuric and other strong acids to remove chemical contaminants.

• *Affinity for Dyes.* Dynel can be dyed in a full range of colors from lights through darks with excellent fastness to fumes, crocking, washing, and good fastness to light. Almost the entire range of acetate dyestuffs, many of the direct dyes, and certain vat dyes can be used. As a result, dyestuffs can be selected to match nearly any color and withstand nearly every type of service required of the finished fabric.

Solution dyeing is sometimes used in the production of Dynel. This technique is employed to produce such colors as black, brown, and gray for Dynel fibers that are to be used to make furlike fabrics. These dyes have excellent fastness to all conditions.

• *Resistance to Perspiration.* Dynel is absolutely resistant to deterioration from perspiration.

Dynel Fiber Blends. Dynel has been found to be an excellent blending fiber. It works well with other staple fibers and contributes worthwhile properties to fabrics.

• *Dynel and Cotton.* In a blend of Dynel and cotton, Dynel contributes softness, warmth, and resistance to shrinkage. Cotton contributes strength. Together, the blend provides a durable, comfortable, launderable fabric. A satisfactory blend should have 25 to 50 per cent Dynel with the rest cotton.

• *Dynel and Wool.* A combination of Dynel and wool provides a warm, resilient, wrinkle-resistant fabric. The Dynel contributes shape retention and greater strength. The bulking power of Dynel also means that more warmth is possible with less weight. The wool also reduces the tendency of Dynel to glaze and harden from a hot pressing iron or other application of heat. A satisfactory blend should have about 35 per cent Dynel with the rest wool.

• *Dynel and Rayon.* To a rayon blend, Dynel contributes warmth, light

This luxurious robe is made of a blend of Dynel and Orlon to produce a furlike fabric resembling mink.

Courtesy Union Carbide Chemicals Co.

weight, resilience, and shape retention. Rayon provides the needed absorbency for greater comfort. There should be a proportion of 25 to 35 per cent Dynel with the rest rayon for satisfactory results.

• *Dynel and Acetate.* In combination, Dynel and acetate produce fabrics that are richly textured, warm, and resilient. They retain their shape and creases, and they drape well. Such a fabric, however, will have low absorbency. For satisfactory results, a combination of 25 to 35 per cent Dynel with the rest acetate is desirable.

• *Dynel and Nylon.* In a combination of Dynel and nylon, Dynel provides warmth, and nylon provides strength, abrasion resistance, and elasticity. Such a blend produces a resilient, wrinkle-resistant, shape-retentive fabric that launders easily and dries relatively fast.

• *Dynel and Orlon.* One of the most outstanding of the successful Dynel blends is the furlike fabric of Dynel and Orlon made for women's coats. The original version of this blend was Borgana, a blend of Dynel and Orlon in the pile on a knit backing of 100 per cent Dynel. Both fibers provided resistance to stretching and shrinking. Orlon contributed the softness, and Dynel was responsible for the luster and body.

As a result of the success of Borgana, other similar fabrics were produced. Some used the same fiber combination. One used pile of Dynel and Orlon on a cotton back, and there were other combinations. The better known of these fabrics are O'llegro, Andante, Mutation, Glanara, Bakella, Dynasty, and Cloud No. 9. Their popularity has sprung from their ability to fill a longfelt need in the moderate-to-better-priced coat field; that is, to provide warm, durable garments resembling expensive fur coats but at prices more people can afford.

CRESLAN

Method of Manufacture of Creslan Fiber.

Creslan acrylic fiber is produced from a copolymer containing a high percentage of acrylonitrile. After polymerization, acrylonitrile copolymer is dissolved in a solvent, filtered and deaerated to form a spinning solution. A delustering agent is added, and the spinning solution is extruded through a spinneret into an aqueous bath, from which it emerges as a tow, or group of continuous filaments of 11 to 18 denier per filament. The tow is washed to remove the solvent and stretched to impart fiber properties. It is also crimped and treated with an antistatic to aid textile processing. Creslan may be packaged in cartons for shipment as tow, or cut, opened, and baled for shipment as staple of various lengths depending on the processing needs.

Types of Creslan Yarn. Modification of the method of manufacture of Creslan fiber permits the production of both low-shrinkage and high-shrinkage varieties. Consequently, two types of yarns may be produced.

• *Spun Yarns.* Low-shrinkage Creslan fiber may be used to spin into yarns on the cotton or wool systems. The denier and lengths of staple are dependent on the yarn desired. This indicates a wide versatility for Creslan acrylic yarns.

• *Bulk Yarns.* Low-shrinkage and high-shrinkage Creslan fibers may be blended and then spun into yarn. Subsequent immersion of such a yarn in boiling water results in hardly any shrinkage in the low-shrinkage fibers but a great deal in the high-shrinkage fibers. This results in a lightweight, spongy, bulky yarn.

Finishing Creslan Fabrics. Fabrics of Creslan may generally be given the same kinds of finishes given to fabrics of other acrylic fibers. Like the other acrylic fibers, Creslan is thermoplastic. Fabrics and garments of Creslan fiber can be permanently heat-set. This is a major finishing treatment given to such products. They can be given pleats, creases, or any shape, heated under carefully controlled conditions, and thereafter retain the desired shape through repeated wearing, washing, and dry cleaning.

Judging Creslan Fabrics. The properties of fabrics of Creslan will depend on the properties of the fiber itself, the type of spun yarn used, and the construction of the fabric. The following facts concerning the properties of Creslan fiber should be kept in mind.

• *Strength.* Creslan is of moderate strength among the acrylic fibers, being a little weaker than Dynel and Verel but stronger than Orlon and Acrilan. Compared to all fibers, generally, Creslan is of moderate strength. Its resilience adds good abrasion resistance to its strength. Fabrics of Creslan, therefore, give good wear.

• *Elasticity.* Creslan has very little stretchability; however, as just stated, it has excellent resilience. Fabrics of Creslan will not stretch or sag much, and they will not wrinkle easily. Wrinkles that may form will tend to fall out readily.

• *Heat Conductivity.* Like the other acrylic fibers, Creslan does not conduct heat rapidly. The crimped characteristic of the fiber gives it good bulking power, particularly since the fiber's resilience gives it excellent loft. Consequently, yarns of Creslan have high insulative properties but are lightweight. Fabrics of Creslan can provide adequate warmth for such outerwear as jackets and coats.

• *Absorbency.* Creslan is second to Verel in absorbency among the acrylic fibers. Compared to all other fibers, it is slightly less absorbent than nylon. This low absorbency gives fabrics of Creslan the property of resisting stains. Such fabrics dry fairly rapidly when wet.

• *Cleanliness and Washability.* Fabrics made of Creslan can be easily laundered with any mild soap in warm water. Strong soaps containing much alkali will cause yellowing, particularly if the water is very hot. Household bleaches may be safely used.

Creslan fabrics may be safely dry-cleaned. They have good dimensional stability. If properly constructed and finished, they will not shrink and will retain pleats and shape after washing or dry cleaning. If ironing is desired, Creslan fabrics may be pressed while damp with a warm iron as used for nylon.

• *Effect of Light.* Creslan has fairly good resistance to degradation by sunlight. In general, it is more resistant than the natural fibers to the weakening effect of sunlight.

• *Resistance to Mildew.* Creslan is absolutely resistant to deterioration by mildew.

• *Resistance to Moths.* Creslan is unaffected by moths and their larvae or by carpet beetles.

• *Reaction to Alkalies.* Creslan has fair resistance to alkalies. Exposure to alkalies at high temperatures will cause yellowing. Higher concentrations and higher temperatures will cause more severe damage.

• *Reaction to Acids.* In general, Creslan has excellent resistance to acids. There is a tendency to bleach when the acid concentration is high.

• *Affinity for Dyes.* According to laboratory tests, Creslan takes acetate, acid, direct, basic, vat, and soluble vat dyes rather well. Colorfastness to light, washing, crocking, and perspiration is generally good.

• *Resistance to Perspiration.* All indications are that fabrics of Creslan are not readily deteriorated by perspiration.

Creslan Fiber Blends. In 1958, the manufacturer had made fabrics only of 100 per cent Creslan fiber. But it is expected that one of the greatest uses of the fiber will be in blends with such other fibers as cotton, wool, rayon, and acetate. It is too early to state with certainty the possible results of such blends, but it is likely that they will be similar to the blending of the other acrylic fibers with all other fibers.

VEREL

Method of Manufacture of Verel Fiber. The Tennessee Eastman Company, manufacturers of Verel, are reluctant to disclose its method of manufacture. The company identifies Verel, however, as a modified acrylic fiber, which indicates that it is probably made along the general procedure of producing other acrylic fibers, with certain modifications. Verel is extruded from the spinneret in continuous semidull filament strands in the form of tow. These strands of fiber are of 2 and 3 denier each. The tow is then cut into staple of 1.5, 2, and 2.5 inches in length.

Types of Verel Yarn. Since Verel is produced only in staple form, it can be made only into spun yarns.

• *Spun Yarns.* Verel can be spun into yarn on the cotton or wool system to produce several types of spun yarns. On the cotton system, a range of yarn counts is possible within the spin limits presented below.

Denier per Filament	Filament Length	Spin Count
2	1.5	40s
3	1.5	27s
3	2	30s
3	2.5	34s
2 (50%) } blended 3 (50%)	1.5 } blended 1.5	31s

Blends of Verel and other staple fibers can produce a variety of spun yarns. In the case of wool blends, almost any count can be spun of good quality. In a 50/50 blend with combed Pima cotton, yarns containing 2 denier per filament, 1.5-inch staple Verel, have been spun to 68s. Also, in a 50/50 blend of 1.5 denier per filament, 2-inch staple of Verel and viscose rayon, yarns have been spun to 34s.

Finishing Verel Fabrics. Fabrics of Verel may be given finishes similar to those of other acrylic fibers. They may be dyed and may be napped to be given a very soft, luxurious, warm hand. Verel fabrics may be heat-set to retain pleats, creases, and shape in garments.

An added interesting feature of Verel is that it comes in three types of shrinkage: Regular, a stabilized, low-shrink yarn; Type I, a medium-shrink yarn; and Type II, a high-shrink yarn. When these yarns are woven into fabrics and the fabrics are properly processed, shrinkage will develop in the fabric to produce permanently textured and three-dimensional effects.

Some fabrics must be given flame-resistant finishes. Verel, however, is flame-resistant fiber and need not be given such a finish. Where extreme flame resistance is needed, specially developed Type F R Verel is available.

Judging Verel Fabrics. All fabrics made of Verel are constructed from spun yarns. The spun yarn used to produce the fabric has a contributory effect on the characteristics of the fabric as well as on its construction. Even the type of Verel will have an effect on the characteristics of the fabric. The following properties, however, can be generally expected from fabrics of Verel.

• *Strength.* Like the other acrylic fibers, Verel is of moderate strength. Among the acrylics, it is second in strength to Dynel and stronger than Orlon, Acrilan, and Creslan. Comparing Verel to the natural fibers, it is about twice as strong as wool but is weaker than cotton, linen, or silk. Verel is stronger than rayon, acetate, and Arnel but is weaker than nylon. Fabrics of Verel have fairly good abrasion resistance.

• *Elasticity.* The elasticity of Verel is comparable to other acrylic fibers. It has very little stretchability. There tends to be a moderate amount of recovery when it has been stretched. Verel has good resilience. Wrinkles tend to fall out relatively easily. Any wrinkles that may persist will iron out readily at the "low" or "rayon setting."

• *Heat Conductivity.* Like the other acrylic fibers, Verel does not conduct heat rapidly. In addition to its low heat conduction due to its chemical composition, Verel fibers have the added characteristic of having a cross-section dog-bone shape similar to that of Orlon fiber. As with Orlon fibers, this gives Verel fibers an overlapping quality that produces high bulk with relatively little fiber, and consequently makes fabrics lightweight. Also, the spun characteristic of Verel yarns provides air pockets among the staple which contribute insulation to the fabric.

• *Absorbency.* Although Verel is less absorbent than any of the natural fibers as well as rayon, acetate, Arnel, or nylon, it has some absorbency. In fact, it is the most absorbent of the acrylic fibers. This means that Verel will not only absorb more moisture than the other acrylic fibers but will have a slightly more comfortable feeling in humid weather. Fabrics of Verel will dry more slowly than fabrics of the other acrylic fibers.

• *Cleanliness and Washability.* Fabrics of Verel may be washed or dry-cleaned by the conventional methods without difficulty. Verel has an excellent white color and should not be bleached because such treatment causes the fiber to discolor. Regular Verel fiber has very little shrinkage even at high water temperatures. Garments tend to retain their size and shape. But Verel has a tendency to pill, and the fabric should not be unduly rubbed. Soft brushing will reduce any pilling.

Verel is a thermoplastic fiber. Fabrics of Verel tend to retain their shape. Pleats and creases tend to stay in the fabrics after washing, and little ironing is needed. If ironing is done at a low setting, fabrics of Verel will iron easily. If the iron is too hot, such fabrics will stiffen and glaze.

• *Effect of Light*. Verel is highly resistant to degradation from sunlight. This makes Verel well-suited for drapery and similar home-furnishing uses.

• *Resistance to Mildew*. Verel is wholly resistant to mildew and can be safely used in damp climates.

• *Resistance to Moths*. Verel is unaffected by moths or carpet beetles. This characteristic, along with its warmth and resilience, makes it suitable not only for clothing but also for rugs.

• *Reaction to Alkalies*. Verel has good resistance to alkalies; however, excessive exposure to alkalies will cause discoloration. It is therefore best not to use strong soaps or other household cleaning agents.

• *Reaction to Acids*. Verel has excellent resistance to acids.

• *Affinity for Dyes*. Three classes of dyes—basic, acetate, and neutral-dyeing premetalized dyes—are considered the most effective for dyeing Verel in a wide range of colors from bright pastels to blacks and navies. Basic dyes are generally used when brighter shades are required, as for specialty fabrics. Acetate dyes may be used for brighter shades, in some cases, than can be obtained with premetalized dyes; but colorfastness is generally somewhat less. Neutral-dyeing premetalized dyes provide the best all-round lightfastness and wash-fastness.

The affinity of Verel to this variety of dyestuffs permits a multitude of dyeing effects including cross-dyeing when Verel is blended or combined with other fibers.

• *Resistance to Perspiration*. All indications are that fabrics of Verel are not readily deteriorated by perspiration. The color may, however, be affected.

Verel Fiber Blends. Verel has properties that make it very suitable for blending with other fibers. Some very desirable results can be accomplished.

• *Verel and Cotton*. One of the important factors in determining the percentages of fibers in a blend of Verel and cotton is the cost. Cotton is relatively inexpensive and, therefore, the greater the amount of Verel in the blend, the more expensive the fabric. Fabrics containing up to 25 per cent Verel are within reasonable price range.

To this type of blend, Verel contributes a soft, pliable hand with good drapability. Verel also provides dimensional stability, so that the fabric will not wrinkle easily, will resist shrinkage, and will retain its shape. Cotton contributes greater absorbency and additional strength. Fabrics of a Verel and cotton blend are used for underwear, children's sleepers, sports shirts, and outer garments.

• *Verel and Wool.* A blend of Verel and wool produces a warm fabric but light in weight due to the lightness and bulkiness of Verel fiber. Verel also provides greater strength, good shape retention, and wrinkle resistance. The thermoplastic characteristic of Verel also tends to hold creases and pleats in fabrics of such blends. Wool provides body and elasticity. Verel and wool blends are particularly well-suited for flannels.

• *Verel and Rayon.* Verel has been satisfactorily blended with viscose rayon. Verel provides wrinkle resistance and shape retention. Rayon provides absorbency, coolness, and comfort.

• *Verel and Acetate.* Since both acetate and Verel are thermoplastic, such a blend can produce fabrics and garments with good wash-and-wear characteristics. In addition to the wrinkle-resistant and shape-retentive characteristics of both fibers, acetate can reduce the bulk of the fabric while Verel can add strength. One disadvantage of such a blend is the relatively low absorbency of both fibers, which would cause the fabric to be somewhat uncomfortable next to the skin in humid weather.

▶ TEST YOURSELF ON THIS CHAPTER

1. What is an acrylic fiber? How does it differ in composition from other synthetic fibers?
2. Give the trade names for the five acrylic fibers. Which companies produce each one?
3. Compare the strength of acrylic fibers with each other and with other fibers.
4. Compare the elasticity of the acrylic fibers with each other and with other fibers.
5. Discuss the washability and general care of fabrics made of acrylic fibers.
6. What general types of yarns can be made from each of the acrylic fibers?
7. Discuss the reactions of each of the acrylic fibers to acids, alkalies, and perspiration.
8. Discuss the affinity for dyes and the colorfastness of each of the acrylic fibers.
9. What are the general properties of acrylic fibers that tend to improve blends?
10. What effect has mildew on each of the acrylic fibers? moths? other insects?

17 · ZEFRAN | The Nitrile-Acrylic Alloy Fiber

Zefran is the trade-mark of a synthetic textile fiber created by The Dow Chemical Company. It is related to the polyacrylonitriles. Its manufacturer, however, emphasizes the distinction between Zefran and acrylonitrile copolymer fibers, which we refer to as acrylic fibers, by indicating that Zefran is an alloy or chemical blend of polymers, one of which is acrylonitrile. This requires the classification of Zefran as a nitrile-acrylic alloy fiber.

History of Zefran. The development of Zefran was begun in 1949. Research in the laboratories of The Dow Chemical Company was concerned with polymers and particularly with polyacrylonitriles. One of the problems associated with polyacrylonitriles had been their low affinity for dyes and the limited fastness of the colors. After several years of intensive research, a chemical alloy with acrylonitrile was produced having properties similar to those of acrylic fibers plus superior dyeing properties. This fiber could be dyed with a wide variety of dyes including those used for natural fibers as well as those used for man-made and synthetic fibers. This not only meant greater affinity for dyes but also greater possibilities for blending this new fiber with a wide array of other fibers without being hampered by dyeing problems frequently encountered with blending. Satisfied that they had a desirable product which was commercially feasible, The Dow Chemical Company established the trade-mark of that fiber as Zefran and began its commercial production in 1958 at Warwick, Virginia.

Method of Manufacture of Zefran Fiber. Precise information concerning the nature of the blend that produces Zefran, or the method of its production, cannot be given, since the manufacturer is reluctant to divulge information concerning the manufacturing processes or the raw materials used. All that can be stated is that Zefran is a nitrile-acrylic alloy produced somewhat along the general procedure used in the manufacture of acrylic fibers, with certain modifications. It is extruded from the spinneret in bright and semidull tow forms and cut into staple lengths of 1½ to 4½ inches.

272

Types of Zefran Yarns. Since Zefran is produced only in staple form, the types of yarns that can be produced are somewhat limited. The form of the yarn is dependent on whether or not the fiber has been crimped.

• *Spun Yarns.* Zefran staple can be spun into yarn on the cotton or wool systems. It can also be blended with cotton, rayon, or wool, and spun into yarn. The yarns produced can vary in fuzziness or smoothness.

• *Bulk Yarns.* When Zefran staple is crimped, this characteristic becomes permanent. The crimped Zefran may be spun into yarns of high bulk and covering power having low weight. This means that fabrics of Zefran can be thick and resilient, having more warmth or insulating value than comparable fabrics of cotton, rayon, or wool.

Finishing Zefran Fabrics. Various finishes have been and are being developed for fabrics of Zefran. Such fabrics may be either dyed or printed in a wide variety of colors. They may be napped to be given a soft, warm hand and may be heat-set to retain pleats, creases, and shape in fabric or garments.

Research is being conducted to develop other types of Zefran nitrile-acrylic alloy fiber with different amounts of residual shrinkage. The purpose is to create types of Zefran yarns that will shrink when fabrics constructed of them are subjected to heat or hot water. This would cause the yarns to pucker and give a three-dimensional effect to such fabrics.

Judging Zefran Fabrics. Commercial production of Zefran began in 1958. There will be further developmental work. Fabrics of Zefran have been tested to a limited extent. At this writing (1958), consumers have not had enough opportunity to completely evaluate them. The following general characteristics of Zefran may, however, be kept in mind.

• *Strength.* Zefran is a rather strong fiber. It is stronger than any of the acrylic fibers with which it may be reasonably compared. When compared with the natural fibers, Zefran is weaker than cotton, linen, or silk, but stronger than all man-made or synthetic fibers with the exception of Fiberglas, nylon, or Dacron. In addition to its relatively good strength, fabrics of Zefran have very good abrasion resistance and are likely to be very durable.

• *Elasticity.* Zefran has greater elongation and recovery than the acrylic, polyester (Dacron), or dinitrile (Darvan) fibers but not as great as wool, nylon, or Vicara. It also has an extremely high rate of wrinkle recovery, greater than that of Dacron and the acrylic fibers discussed in Chapter 16. It is this characteristic of high wrinkle recovery that makes Zefran highly desirable for blends.

• *Heat Conductivity.* Indications are that Zefran does not have a high rate of heat conductivity. The cross-section shape of the fiber is somewhat round, and therefore lacks the natural bulking characteristic of an acrylic fiber like Orlon. But Zefran fibers can be permanently crimped to provide sufficient bulk in yarn form, producing the desirable insulative effect. In fact, fabrics of Zefran can be produced that will be warmer than comparable fabrics of wool. These fabrics will also be lighter in weight than wool, though not quite so lightweight as fabrics of some of the acrylic fibers.

• *Absorbency.* Zefran nitrile-acrylic alloy fiber is more absorbent than its related polyacrylonitrile (acrylic) fibers with the exception of Verel. Zefran, however, is much less absorbent than any of the natural fibers or some of the man-made or synthetic fibers. This means that, while fabrics of Zefran will dry more slowly than fabrics of most of the acrylic fibers, they will dry faster than cotton, wool, or rayon.

The greater absorbency of Zefran compared with the acrylic fibers is due to its alloy composition. Since Zefran is not wholly acrylic, its other component provides some additional absorbency. This greater absorbency not only provides greater comfort in humid weather but also reduces the tendency to develop static electricity in the fabric.

• *Cleanliness and Washability.* Although fabrics of Zefran are made of spun yarn and have varying degrees of fuzz to catch and hold dirt, Zefran has the advantages of cleanliness and washability. It develops less static electricity than most acrylic fibers or Dacron and consequently does not attract or hold dust particles easily on its surface. Also, fabrics of Zefran have excellent wrinkle recovery, good shrink resistance, and excellent shape retention. Creases placed in fabrics of Zefran stay in extremely well after repeated washing and require no ironing. This makes Zefran highly suitable for wash-and-wear garments. For best results, the garment should be entirely of Zefran. If ironing is desired, fabrics of Zefran may be safely ironed at temperatures higher than for the acrylic fibers. Zefran has a sticking temperature of 490 degrees Fahrenheit.

When washing fabrics of Zefran, it is best to use a mild soap. Hot water may be safely used. If desired, ordinary household bleaches may be used. Fabrics of Zefran may also be safely dry-cleaned.

• *Effect of Light.* Zefran is highly resistant to degradation from exposure to sunlight. Along with other desirable properties, this indicates that Zefran is very suitable for drapery and upholstery fabrics.

• *Resistance to Mildew.* Zefran is wholly resistant to mildew and is therefore undamaged even when hung or stored under damp conditions.

• *Resistance to Moths.* Fabrics of Zefran are unaffected by moths or other insects. Like the acrylic fibers, this offers a decided advantage over wool.

• *Reaction to Alkalies.* Zefran is resistant to weak alkalies. Although it will turn yellow when subjected to strong hot alkalies, it may be safely subjected to mercerizing conditions when blended with cotton.

• *Reaction to Acids.* Zefran has excellent resistance to acids of up to 40 per cent concentration.

• *Affinity for Dyes.* Because of the greater absorbency of Zefran nitrile-acrylic alloy fiber than most of the acrylic fibers, it takes dyes much better. Satisfactory dyes are available for essentially all colors and end uses. Vat dyes generally provide good-to-excellent lightfastness and excellent washfastness. Acid, basic, sulphur, direct, and acetate dyes may be used, but their colorfastness is not generally as good. Such dyes, however, may be necessary when Zefran is blended with fibers that require specific dyes to obtain certain colors.

• *Resistance to Perspiration.* There is no indication that perspiration will deteriorate Zefran, but the color may be affected.

Zefran Fiber Blends.

Zefran has been blended to a limited extent with cotton, rayon, and wool. Development of blends continues. The following results have been achieved.

• *Zefran and Cotton.* A blend of Zefran and cotton provides a comfortable, durable fabric that will wash easily, dry fairly rapidly, and need little or no ironing. The Zefran provides shrink resistance, resilience, and shape retention. Cotton increases the absorbency and lowers the cost of the fabric.

• *Zefran and Wool.* A blend of 50 per cent Zefran and 50 per cent wool has twice the wrinkle recovery of an all-wool fabric and almost as much wrinkle recovery as an all-Zefran fabric. Due to the Zefran, garments of such a blend show excellent dimensional stability after repeated home washings. They show no appreciable shrinkage and need little ironing. They are warm, comfortable to wear, and do not pill. Zefran also provides greater strength, and the combination provides good abrasion resistance, making a durable fabric.

• *Zefran and Rayon.* A major contribution of Zefran in a blend of Zefran and rayon is wrinkle recovery and dimensional stability. A blend of 50 per cent Zefran with 50 per cent rayon will have three times the wrinkle recovery of an all-rayon fabric and actually be more resilient than an all-wool fabric. Zefran will also provide greater strength. Rayon will provide greater absorbency and contribute to the comfort of such a fabric. Such a blend may be classified among the wash-and-wear fabrics.

▶ TEST YOURSELF ON THIS CHAPTER

1. What is Zefran? What company makes it?
2. What do you consider to be the major good features of Zefran?
3. What do you consider to be the limitations of Zefran?
4. Discuss the washing, dry cleaning, and ironing of Zefran fabrics.
5. What types of blends containing Zefran are good? Why?
6. Compare the affinity for dyes of Zefran with that of other fibers.
7. For what uses is Zefran best suited? Why?

18 · DARVAN | The Dinitrile Fiber

A *dinitrile fiber* is a synthetic textile fiber. It is a polymer containing an entirely new and interesting chemical compound substance called *vinylidene dinitrile* as its basic constituent. Darvan is the first and presently the only fiber of this type. There are indications that the discovery of vinylidene dinitrile and the subsequent creation of Darvan may lead to a whole new family of fibers, just as the creation of Orlon acrylic fiber was followed by the development of other acrylic fibers.

History of Darvan. In search of a new synthetic fiber for tire cords during World War II, scientists at the B. F. Goodrich Research Center accomplished a major scientific achievement in 1947 by synthesizing a new monomer called vinylidene dinitrile. Continued experimentation with vinylidene dinitrile revealed that it would polymerize readily. Further research showed that it would copolymerize with other monomers like acrylonitrile to produce interesting and unusual properties in the resultant copolymer. Various combinations of copolymers became possible. The researchers eventually produced a copolymer of vinylidene dinitrile and vinyl acetate in fiber form that had commercial textile value because of many desirable features. B. F. Goodrich Chemical Company, a division of B. F. Goodrich Company, thereupon received a patent for its process and established the trade name of Darlan for its dinitrile fiber in 1956 and began pilot-stage production at Avon Lake, Ohio. Subsequently, the company changed the trade-mark of its fiber to Darvan and began commercial production in 1958.

Method of Manufacture of Darvan Fiber. The raw materials for the manufacture of Darvan dinitrile fiber are natural gas and ammonia. From these two common substances, acetate anhydride and hydrogen cyanide are obtained. These two chemical compounds react to form a chemically complicated substance, acetoxydicyanoethane, which when properly heated breaks down to vinylidene dinitrile and acetic acid. The new monomer, vinylidene dinitrile, is then copolymerized with vinyl acetate. The copolymer is dissolved in a suitable solvent, and as the solution is extruded through a spinneret, the solvent is re-

276

moved to produce a tow of continuous strands of bright, semidull, or dull fibers. The tow is oriented by stretching and stabilizing. The fibers of 1½ to 6 denier are then cut into staple generally 1½ to 4½ inches in length.

Types of Darvan Yarns. Since Darvan is produced only in staple form, the types of yarns that can be produced are somewhat limited.

• *Spun Yarns.* Darvan staple can be spun into yarn on the cotton or wool systems. Darvan can be blended with cotton or wool to produce cotton, woolen, or worsted type blended yarns. The yarns are somewhat fuzzy and have a pleasant soft hand.

• *Bulk Yarns.* The cross-section shape of Darvan fiber is somewhat long and flat. In addition to this natural characteristic, Darvan staple can be crimp-set under steam pressure to develop a permanent crimp. Combination of these two factors permits the production of lofty high-bulk yarns. These yarns are extremely soft and are thick, warm, and lightweight.

Finishing Darvan Fabrics. One of the major finishes given to fabrics of Darvan is heat setting. Since Darvan is thermoplastic, fabrics and garments of Darvan may be given permanent pleats and creases. Heat-set fabrics of Darvan have excellent shape retention.

Fabrics of Darvan may be napped for greater warmth and softness. They may also be dyed but with some difficulty at present. Developmental work in the area of finishes on fabrics of Darvan continues.

Judging Darvan Fabrics. Darvan is still (1958) in the pilot stage of production, and additional developmental work has been indicated by its manufacturer. Furthermore, fabrics of Darvan have not had adequate trial by consumers to provide complete evaluation. The following general characteristics of Darvan may, however, be kept in mind.

• *Strength.* Darvan is not a particularly strong fiber. In fact, it is weaker than all fibers except wool, acetate, and Arnel. Its abrasion resistance appears to be a little better. Indications are that Darvan is more abrasion-resistant than rayon but less than the acrylic fibers. Fabrics of Darvan are likely to be more durable than rayon fabrics, slightly less durable than any fabrics of the acrylic fibers, and far less durable than nylon fabrics.

• *Elasticity.* Darvan has greater elongation and recovery than the acrylic or polyester (Dacron) fibers but not as great as wool, nylon, Zefran, or Vicara. It has an extremely high rate of wrinkle recovery, surpassing that of Dacron and the acrylic fibers. This indicates that it is one of the most shape-retentive of fibers.

• *Heat Conductivity.* Indications are that Darvan has a low rate of heat conductivity. This and the high bulking power of Darvan, due to the fiber's cross-section shape, make Darvan well-suited for very warm fabrics with light weight.

• *Absorbency.* Darvan is not a particularly absorbent fiber, although a little more absorbent than all the acrylic fibers except Verel. It is less absorbent than Zefran. This indicates that fabrics of Darvan are likely to be a little more comfortable than fabrics of less absorbent fibers. At the same time, Darvan is still somewhat water-repellent and will dry fairly rapidly.

• *Cleanliness and Washability.* Since Darvan is made into spun yarns that produce fabrics with various amounts of surface fuzz, it is likely to catch dirt easily. Unless the yarns are tightly spun, the dirt may impregnate the fabric. Indications are, however, that fabrics of Darvan dry-clean and wash readily. Household bleaches may be safely used. Hydrogen peroxide should not be used.

As Darvan is extremely shape-retentive, fabrics of Darvan have little stretch and very good wrinkle resistance and excellent wrinkle recovery. Garments of Darvan will not shrink when washed at ordinary temperatures and will return to their shape when dry. Darvan is a thermoplastic fiber. Fabrics of Darvan can be given permanent creases and pleats that will be retained after washing and therefore can be placed in the wash-and-wear category. When ironing or pressing is desired, the temperature of the iron should be about the same as for ironing rayon. Darvan melts at 340 to 350 degrees Fahrenheit, and if the iron is too hot the fabric will glaze and stiffen.

• *Effect of Light.* Darvan is highly resistant to degradation from exposure to sunlight. This indicates that Darvan is an excellent fiber for drapery fabrics.

• *Resistance to Mildew.* Darvan is wholly resistant to mildew and may be safely used or stored under damp conditions.

• *Resistance to Moths.* Fabrics of Darvan are unaffected by moth and carpet-beetle larvae.

• *Reaction to Alkalies.* Darvan has only fair resistance to alkalies. When washing fabrics of Darvan, it is best to use a mild soap or detergent.

• *Reaction to Acids.* Darvan has good resistance to acids.

• *Affinity for Dyes.* Darvan is a difficult fiber to dye, but it can be stock-dyed, yarn-dyed, or piece-dyed. It has limited affinity for vat and selected acid dyes. With proper techniques, acetate dyes may be used to obtain light, pastel, and some medium and dark shades. Basic dyes obtain some medium shades, and azoic dyes obtain some dark shades. There is difficulty in obtaining uniform color in the dark shades, which indicates that these dyes are not very fast to light or atmospheric fumes.

• *Resistance to Perspiration.* Indications are that Darvan has satisfactory resistance to deterioration from perspiration, but the dyed color may be affected.

Darvan Fiber Blends. Darvan has been blended to a limited extent with cotton and with wool. Development of blends with these fibers continues. The following general results have been achieved.

• *Darvan and Cotton.* In a blend of Darvan and cotton, the cotton contributes strength and absorbency. Darvan provides a soft hand, wrinkle resistance, and shape retention. Tests of this blend show that in certain constructions pilling is much less severe than with similar fabrics of other blends. Although fabrics of this blend feel soft and delicate, durability is proving completely satisfactory in wear and commercial launderings. It is also expected that fabrics of Darvan and cotton will come within the general wash-and-wear category.

• *Darvan and Wool.* Both woolen and worsted type fabrics have been made of Darvan and wool blends. Darvan contributes a soft hand, good wrinkle resistance, and excellent crease retention. Wool also contributes resilience as well as absorbency, body, and good drapability. Both fibers provide warmth. Fabrics of such blends appear to have good durability and almost complete lack of pilling.

▶ **TEST YOURSELF ON THIS CHAPTER**

1. What is Darvan? What company makes it? May another company make a fiber like it? Explain.
2. What are the chief advantages of Darvan?
3. What are the disadvantages of Darvan?
4. What kinds of yarns can be made of Darvan?
5. Discuss the general care of fabrics made of Darvan with regard to washing, dry cleaning, and ironing.
6. What types of blends have been made with Darvan? What are the characteristics of these blends?
7. Discuss the affinity for dyes of Darvan. What are the indications as to their fastness?

19 · VICARA | A Protein Fiber

Considerable research has been done to develop a man-made fiber from the proteins of milk, peanuts, soybeans, and corn. The most recent fiber to be produced commercially is *Vicara,* a corn protein fiber. Although its production has been recently discontinued, it is discussed here to provide an understanding of the general nature of protein fibers, the methods of production, properties, and uses.

History of Vicara. In 1935, L. C. Smallen of the Corn Products Refining Company was granted a patent for the manufacture of man-made protein fiber from the vegetable protein *zein,* which is contained in corn gluten. Subsequent research was conducted in the public interest by the Northern Regional Laboratory of the United States Department of Agriculture and the Harris Research Laboratories in Washington, D. C., to prove that a commercial textile fiber could be produced from zein. Industrial research and development were carried on over a period of years by the Virginia Carolina Chemical Corporation. This finally resulted, in 1948, in the commercial production by this company of a zein fiber, which it named Vicara, at the former Aralac plant in Taftville, Connecticut. The displacing of Aralac, a protein fiber made of the casein of skim milk, made Vicara the only man-made protein fiber being manufactured in the United States in 1949.

Method of Manufacture of Vicara Fiber. In preparing a spinning solution, the basic ingredient is the corn protein, zein. The dry powdered zein is wetted with water to produce a smooth suspension. It is then chemically treated, and a thick viscous spinning solution results. When this solution is properly aged, it is forced under pressure through a large spinneret, which may have as many as 270,000 holes, thus producing a large mass of filaments called tow. To coagulate the protein from the mildly alkaline spinning solution, a dilute acid precipitating bath is used. The streams of protein spinning solution enter this bath, coagulation takes place, and the filaments are gathered to make the tow, which is then wound on a large wheel while it is thoroughly washed with water to free it from acids and salts.

At this stage, the tow is still unsatisfactory for textile uses and must be given aftertreatments to produce the best possible fiber for a particular use. The

Courtesy Virginia Carolina Chemical Corp.

Equipment for testing Vicara tow.

first of these is a precuring treatment with a mild solution of formaldehyde to regulate the softness or stiffness, flexibility, and strength. For example, a low cure results in greatly elongated filaments of small diameter that will be soft, flexible, and susceptible to a large amount of shrinkage in water. A high cure results in filaments that cannot be stretched much and will be heavier in diameter, coarser, stiffer, but stronger. After precuring, the tow is usually stretched from 200 to 250 per cent in length, held under tension, and postcured. The tow is then cut into staple lengths of 0.5 to 6 inches, packed in 300- and 500-pound bales, and shipped to the spinning mills.

Types of Vicara Yarn. Vicara fiber is made in 2, 3, 4, 5, and 7 denier diameters. Since all the fibers are cut into staple, the only form of Vicara yarn is the spun yarn. Using methods similar to those used for other staple, Vicara may be spun into yarn on the cotton, woolen, or worsted system. Vicara is often used with other fibers to produce blended yarns as well as for 100 per cent Vicara yarns.

Finishing of Vicara Fabrics. Since Vicara is often used for blending and takes a variety of finishes well, fabrics containing Vicara are generally finished according to the needs of the particular blend or of the dominant fiber. Fabrics containing Vicara are being finished by standard methods. Resin finishes are applied with excellent results, but fabrics containing Vicara usually require less resin to obtain the desired result.

Judging Vicara in Fabrics. As indicated in the manufacture of Vicara, there are slight variations in the properties of the fiber, depending on the desired results. The following general statements may be made:

• *Strength.* Vicara is approximately as strong as wool. While this means that Vicara is not a particularly strong fiber, its resilience and elasticity give it good abrasion resistance so that satisfactory wear can be obtained from Vicara fabrics. Also like wool, Vicara loses much strength while wet, in fact, up to 50 per cent of its strength. Care must therefore be taken not to put undue strain, such as pulling or wringing, on wet fabrics containing Vicara.

• *Elasticity.* One of the outstanding properties of Vicara is its elasticity. Vicara will stretch 30 to 35 per cent when wet and 30 to 40 per cent when dry without breaking. Its elastic recovery is very good. After being stretched up to 5 per cent of its length, its recovery is practically 100 per cent. This elasticity rivals that of nylon. Although the elastic recovery of nylon is 100 per cent after being stretched 8 per cent, its elongation does not quite equal that of Vicara. Vicara also has very good resilience. It resists wrinkling to a marked degree. These properties result in making Vicara a soft and flexible fiber. Yet, fabrics of Vicara will have good dimensional stability. As a result, Vicara is very suitable for knitted goods because they will tend to retain their original shape.

• *Heat Conductivity.* The heat conductivity of Vicara is low. In other words, Vicara is a warm fiber. Laboratory tests have indicated that its insulating value is similar to that of animal fibers in fabrics of like construction.

• *Absorbency.* Vicara is inherently water-repellent. This water repellency is permanent; but at temperatures above 110 degrees Fahrenheit, it is temporarily lost. This means that, while Vicara is not absorbent at less than room temperatures, it is absorbent above room temperatures. In fact, at the higher temperatures, the absorbency of Vicara approaches that of wool. This combination of water repellency and absorbency gives Vicara some outstanding advantages. It is suitable for outdoor wear during inclement weather. At the same time, it is comfortable to wear, since it will absorb perspiration and will not feel clammy in humid weather.

• *Cleanliness and Washability.* The water repellency of Vicara does not interfere with its washing or cleaning since the repellency is not apparent at temperatures above 110 degrees Fahrenheit. Vicara is not damaged by dry cleaning. In fact, it dry-cleans similarly to wool. If a bleach is desired, it may be safely used. This is particularly advantageous when the fabric is a blend of Vicara and some such fiber as cotton. Washing will not cause Vicara to shrink, even though the water is boiling. Nor will Vicara felt or pill. Since Vicara weakens considerably and can elongate or stretch greatly when wet, Vicara fabrics should not be wrung or twisted. They should be squeezed and allowed to dry while lying flat. Unlike other protein fibers, such as wool, Vicara does not have a disagreeable odor when wet. It has a faint, pleasant odor that disappears completely when the fabric is dry. Vicara may be pressed or ironed at a temperature similar to that of wool. It loses some strength at temperatures above 350 degrees Fahrenheit and will decompose at 470 to 475 degrees Fahrenheit.

• *Effect of Light.* Vicara is subject to slow deterioration by sunlight in a manner similar to animal fibers. The natural golden color of the fiber is not permanent to light. It will not deteriorate merely because of age.

• *Resistance to Mildew.* Vicara has good resistance to mildew.

• *Resistance to Moths.* Moth larvae and carpet beetles will not eat Vicara.

• *Reaction to Alkalies.* Unlike animal and other protein fibers, Vicara is not drastically affected by alkalies. When blended with cotton, it may be safely mercerized. Ordinary household cleaning substances containing alkali will not harm Vicara.

• *Reaction to Acids.* Vicara also has good resistance to acids. This means that carbonizing will not damage Vicara.

• *Affinity for Dyes.* The resistance of Vicara to acids and alkalies permits it to be safely dyed by either acid or alkali dyes. Vicara may be dyed by a variety of dyes and methods used on other fibers. Where pastel shades are desired, the natural golden color must first be removed by a bleach.

• *Resistance to Perspiration.* Vicara has good resistance to perspiration. The color may be affected, but the perspiration will not weaken the fabric.

Vicara Fiber Blends.   Vicara is "the fiber that improves the blend." While Vicara may be used by itself in the manufacture of fabrics, it is recommended as a blend with other fibers. This permits the complementary blending of the properties of Vicara and of other fibers. The care of the blended fabric is dictated by the properties of the fiber with which Vicara is blended.

• *Vicara and Cotton.* To a blend with cotton, Vicara brings drape, elasticity, resilience, softness, and warmth. Cotton provides the strength. Such a blend gives a fabric absorbency and a comfortable feel.

• *Vicara and Wool.* Vicara looks and feels more like wool than any other man-made fiber. Its elasticity, resilience, absorbency, and warmth are similar to wool. The chief advantages of such a blend is that the fabric will be less expensive, will not pill, felt, or shrink as much, and will feel softer.

• *Vicara and Rayon.* Vicara contributes elasticity and resilience to a blend with rayon. The fabric will drape well and feel soft. It will be warmer and more mildew-resistant than an all-rayon fabric. A greater variety of dye effects is also possible. Such a fabric is not particularly strong, since neither Vicara nor rayon is very strong compared to other man-made and synthetic fibers. The resilience and elasticity of Vicara, however, reduce such a fabric's tendency to fray and thereby increase the durability of the blend.

• *Vicara and Nylon.* In a blend with nylon, Vicara provides absorbency, softness, and drape. The nylon provides strength, abrasion resistance, and shape retention.

▶ TEST YOURSELF ON THIS CHAPTER

1. What is Vicara? May any company produce or imitate it? Explain.
2. Vicara is like what natural fiber? In what ways are they similar?
3. What kind of yarn is made of Vicara?
4. Discuss the washability and general care of fabrics made of Vicara.
5. How do the elasticity and resilience of Vicara compare to those of other fibers?
6. Compare the strength of Vicara to that of other fibers.
7. What effect do alkalies and acids have on Vicara?
8. What effect has Vicara in a blend with wool?
9. What are the properties of a Vicara-nylon blend in a fabric?
10. How well does Vicara absorb dyes? Does perspiration affect these dyes?

20 · SARAN

The Synthetic Vinylidene Chloride Fiber

The word *Saran* is a generic term that refers to a particular type of plastic fiber. The term is also used as a trade name. This fiber is a linear copolymer of vinylidene chloride and vinyl chloride.

History of Saran. The chemical compound, vinylidene chloride, was discovered in 1840. It is a clear, colorless liquid that boils at 32 degrees centigrade. Although chemists since 1920 had observed that it could easily polymerize, it was not until 1936 that further research was conducted. At that time, The Dow Chemical Company began a research program, probably spurred by the successful results of other companies' research with polymers, which ultimately resulted in 1940 in the commercialization of Saran.

Method of Manufacture of Saran Fiber. The raw materials used to produce vinylidene chloride are ethylene, which is derived by cracking natural petroleum, and chlorine, which is electrolyzed from sea water. Ethylene is treated with chlorine to produce trichlorethane, which in turn is treated with lime to produce unpolymerized vinylidene chloride. The vinylidene chloride is then copolymerized with a small quantity of vinyl chloride to produce a powdered resin. The resin is melted and extruded through a spinneret into a water-cooling bath. While still being cooled, it is drawn out or stretched 400 per cent to increase its strength, similar to the way in which nylon is processed.

Types of Saran Yarns. Saran is made in monofilament, multifilament, and staple form.

• *Monofilament Yarns.* These yarns are made in a wide variety of diameters. Some companies express the thickness of the yarns in denier, others in terms of a decimal part of the inch. In denier, monofilament Saran yarn is produced in 70 and 124 denier; in inches, in a range of .005 to .05 inch in diameter. It is used for a wide variety of purposes, such as window screens, handbags, millinery fabrics, and trimmings. Saran is also produced in rattanlike monofilament strips. This form is readily adapted to fabrics used for seat covers in automobiles, buses, and railroad cars, as well as for outdoor furniture.

• *Multifilament Yarns.* The production of Saran multifilament yarns is more limited. They are used for brocades and other fabrics. The amount of twist given to each of the following yarns varies depending on the desired ultimate result.

750 denier, of 50 filaments
1200 denier, of 100 filaments
3000 denier, of 300 filaments

• *Staple.* Saran staple fiber comes in lengths of 2 to 40 inches in three forms: straight, crimped, and curled. The straight staple fiber is made in 10, 22, 30, 45, 60, and 70 denier and is used for a wide variety of purposes, including outerwear, linings, and filter cloths. The crimped staple fiber comes in 10 denier diameter. The curled staple comes in 22, 45, and 70 denier and is used primarily for blending with wool in the manufacture of carpets.

Delustering of Saran Yarn.

The natural color of Saran is pale gold or straw. It may be delustered to a translucent or to an opaque appearance by the addition of a delusterant such as titanium dioxide.

Trade Names of Saran Yarns.

Several companies produce Saran yarns. The basic quality of the yarns is the same, since they are all made of the same substances in the same way. The important differences among the yarns are dependent on whether they are monofilament, multifilament, or staple, and on the denier of the fibers and the amount of twist in the yarns.

Lus-Trus Saran, produced by Lus-Trus Extruded Plastics, Inc.
National Saran, produced by The National Plastic Products Company
Saran, produced by the Saran Yarns Company

Velon, produced by Firestone Plastics Company, Inc., is another trade name for Saran. Velon is also made in plastic sheet form for plastic tablecloths and similar protective coverings. Saran Wrap is another trade name for a very thin, clear sheet form used for wrapping foods and other items. It is produced by The Dow Chemical Company.

Except for the plastic sheets, these companies produce only the yarns. The ultimate fabrics are woven by other companies. The quality of Saran fabric depends further on the construction as well as on the type of yarn used.

Judging Saran Fabrics.

Saran has some valuable properties as a textile. It also has some definite limitations.

• *Strength.* The strength of Saran fiber varies with its diameter. Generally, the finer filaments are stronger than the coarser ones. Saran is considerably weaker than Orlon, which is also recommended as an outdoor fabric. Saran is stronger than wool, rayon, or acetate.

• *Elasticity.* The elasticity of Saran is an advantage that contributes to its use for seat covers and as upholstery for outdoor furniture.

• *Heat Conductivity.* Saran fabrics are not good conductors of heat, but are easily affected by it. Saran shrinks and loses strength at about 168 degrees Fahrenheit and melts between 240 and 280 degrees Fahrenheit. This places a serious limitation on Saran fabrics. They cannot be easily ironed. Cigarette sparks are dangerous, since they will melt holes in the Saran fabric.

• *Absorbency.* Saran is one of the least absorbent of all textiles, having virtually no absorbency. Saran cannot be used for such garments as underwear, shirts, blouses, and dresses, since they would not absorb perspiration or atmospheric moisture and therefore would be uncomfortable. On the other hand, Saran fabrics, being virtually waterproof, are suitable for outerwear, such as raincoats, and for outdoor furniture. Tablecloths are another use for Saran.

• *Cleanliness and Washability.* Saran fabrics may be easily cleaned by merely wiping them with a damp cloth. If desired, laundering or dry cleaning is safe. It must be remembered that Saran fabrics should be kept away from heat because of the tendency to melt.

• *Effect of Light.* Subjection to sunlight over a long period of time will tend to darken Saran fabrics slightly, but there is no appreciable loss of strength. This shows Saran's value as an outdoor fabric.

• *Resistance to Mildew.* Saran fabrics are wholly resistant to deterioration from mildew.

• *Resistance to Moths.* Saran is unaffected by moths or other insects.

• *Reaction to Alkalies.* Saran has good resistance to alkalies; however, it is weakened by a solution of ammonium hydroxide.

• *Reaction to Acids.* Saran has good-to-excellent resistance to acids. This resistance to acids as well as alkalies makes Saran very suitable for industrial filter cloths.

• *Affinity for Dyes.* Saran cannot be dyed by the usual methods because it is nonabsorbent. However, by adding the desired color to the solution before the Saran filaments are spun through the spinnerets, it is possible to obtain an extensive variety of colors. These colors, being inside the fibers, are very fast. They will not wash or fade out.

▶ TEST YOURSELF ON THIS CHAPTER

1. What is Saran?
2. What are the leading trade names for Saran yarn?
3. What kind of yarns can be made of Saran? What are the advantages of each of these yarns?
4. For what purposes is Saran most suited? Why?
5. What are the chief advantages and limitations of Saran?

21 · FIBERGLAS | The Glass Fiber

Fiberglas is the trade name for a textile fiber made of glass. Although ordinary glass is hard and unbendable, the fine, transparent Fiberglas textile fibers are pliable and look and feel like silk.

History of Glass Fiber. The idea of making yarns and fabrics from glass is hundreds of years old. During the Renaissance, artisans were drawing out a "spun glass" of fine glass strands or rods for decorative purposes on goblets and vases. In 1893, Edward Drummond Libbey exhibited a glass dress, lamp shades, and other articles of woven glass at the World's Columbian Exposition in Chicago. The fabric was made of bundles of glass fibers woven together with silk threads. The experiment was spectacular but of no practical value, since the fabric was too stiff to be creased, folded, or draped.

Some progress was made during the early 1900's when several patents were issued in Germany and in England on various processes for drawing glass fibers. These fibers were relatively coarse, and the cost was high. During World War I, however, Germany suffered a shortage of asbestos and developed a somewhat primitive method of producing filaments of glass fibers from heat-softened glass rods. These fibers were used for insulating purposes.

It was not until 1931 that experiments were started in the United States to produce glass fibers that were finer, more pliable, and lower in cost. At that time, the Owens-Illinois Glass Company and the Corning Glass Works started to develop a method of drawing out glass from the molten state through fine orifices into pliable filament form. For several years, work progressed in the development of filament and staple yarns. By 1938, sufficient progress was made to indicate a promising future for glass fiber for practical textile purposes. The two companies merged to form the Owens-Corning Fiberglas Corporation. Their textile product is known as *Fiberglas*.

Method of Manufacture of Fiberglas Fiber. There are two methods of producing Fiberglas yarns. Both begin with accurate batch formulation of selected silica sand, limestone, soda ash, and borax (or other ingredients depending on the ultimate purpose of the fiber) in an electric furnace. From the precisely controlled furnace, the molten glass at a temperature of about 2,500 degrees Fahrenheit flows to marble-forming machines that turn out small glass marbles about five-eighths of an inch in diameter. These marbles permit visual inspection of the glass for the purpose of eliminating impurities that would interfere with subsequent operations or lower the desired uniform quality of the fibers. The marbles are then remelted in small electric furnaces. (Later improvements indicate that textile fibers also may be drawn from the original melt, eliminating this marble operation.) From this point on, the two textile operations differ.

• *Continuous-Filament Process.* This process produces continuous filaments of indefinite length having exceptional brilliance. Molten glass flows downward through temperature-resistant metal-alloy bushings (spinnerets) that have more than two hundred small openings. The strand of multiple filaments is carried to a high-speed winder. Since the winder revolves at a much faster rate (more than two miles a minute) than the stream flow from the melting chamber, the tension attenuates the glass while it is still molten, and thus draws out the fibers in parallel filaments to a fraction of the diameter of the openings. After winding, the filaments are twisted and plied to form yarns by methods

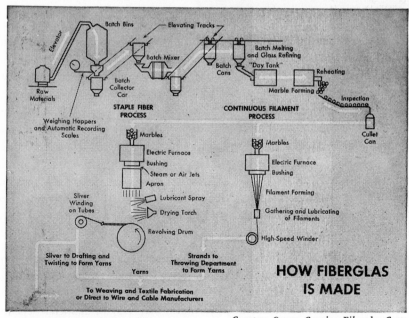

Courtesy Owens-Corning Fiberglas Corp.

A step in the forming of the filament in the continuous-filament process of making Fiberglas is shown in the photograph on another page.

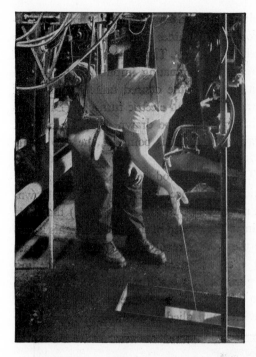

Glass marbles are remelted in electrical furnaces and drawn down through more than one hundred tiny holes, or orifices. Individual glass filaments solidify and are gathered into a single thread on a high-speed winding mechanism, revolving at the rate of more than a mile a minute. Shown here is a group of Fiberglas continuous filaments being pulled down from the melting tank by a winder on the floor below.

Courtesy Owens-Corning Fiberglas Corp.

similar to those used for making other continuous-filament yarns. These yarns are used for such fabrics as curtains and draperies.

• *Staple-Fiber Process.* The staple-fiber process produces fibers that have long-staple characteristics. As the molten glass flows through small holes in the temperature-resistant brushing, jets of compressed air literally jerk the thin stream of molten glass into fine fibers varying in length from 8 to 15 inches. The fibers fall through a spray of lubricant and a drying flame onto a revolving drum on which they form a thin web. This web of staple fibers is gathered from the drum into a sliver. The sliver is then made into yarn by methods similar to those used to make cotton or wool yarn. The yarn thus produced is used primarily for tapes and fabrics for industrial purposes where insulation is needed.

Types of Fiberglas Yarns. Fiberglas yarns are made in two types: continuous-filament and staple yarns. The continuous-filament yarns are produced in a wide variety of diameters with a wide variety of strands, depending on the ultimate use of the yarn. The spun yarn also may vary in diameter depending on its ultimate use.

Finishing Fiberglas Fabrics. A basic finishing operation for all Fiberglas fabrics is to subject the cloth to high temperatures. This releases the stresses that may be present in the yarns as a result of twisting and weaving. This treatment provides the fabrics with such desirable qualities as wrinkle resistance, greater durability, and good hand. They may then be treated in a number of ways. Color may be applied with the aid of a binder to hold the dye to the surface of the cloth. The fabric may be coated with a protective agent to improve its abrasion resistance. For marquisettes, the finish is regulated to produce a crisp yet flexible fabric.

A patented process called *Coronizing* is also available. This process combines a heat-setting treatment with the application of finishing resins. The heat setting relaxes the fibers, permanently crimps the yarns, and sets the weave, giving the fabric a soft hand, good drape, and wrinkleproof qualities. The finishing resins provide abrasion resistance, launderability, and water repellency. Better color retention and the use of pastel shades is possible with the aid of this process.

Judging Fiberglas Fabrics. Most Fiberglas fabrics for consumer purposes have been made of filament yarns. These fabrics are extremely smooth, almost slippery, lustrous, and heavy compared to other textiles. In 1958, Owens-Corning spun a yarn called *Aerocor* that looks and almost feels like wool or mohair. A new process of expanding individual strands or groups of glass fibers permits the weaving of Aerocor like wool or linen into openwork casements. In flat weaves it looks like linen. Color also has been improved. The dye is embedded more deeply.

• *Strength*. Fiberglas is the strongest of all textile fibers. Only high-tenacity nylon used for industrial purposes rivals the strength of Fiberglas. However, since glass cuts glass, as the yarns slide and rub over each other and are flexed, the filaments roughen and break, and the fabric becomes hairy. Coronizing will reduce this tendency considerably.

• *Elasticity*. Fiberglas is virtually inelastic. Being the least elastic of all textiles has obvious disadvantages for clothing; but when used for draperies and curtains, such fabrics will not stretch or sag out of shape. This lack of elasticity has no effect on the flexibility and wrinkle resistance of Fiberglas fabrics. With the aid of certain finishes, Fiberglas fabrics have excellent draping and wrinkle-resistant qualities.

• *Heat Conductivity*. As with ordinary glass, Fiberglas yarns are good conductors of heat. Yet, when Fiberglas is in staple form, the thousands of fibers form cells of trapped air. These dead air spaces act as excellent insulation and make Fiberglas staple batting very effective as an interlining in jackets and coats. (The same principle is applied to insulate refrigerators and stoves.)

• *Absorbency*. Fiberglas is not absorbent. This property represents both advantages and disadvantages. Being nonabsorbent, Fiberglas fabrics are water-repellent and, in general, unaffected by water. The disadvantage of no absorbency makes Fiberglas unsuitable for clothing to be worn next to the skin, because perspiration and humidity would make the fabric uncomfortable.

• *Cleanliness and Washability.* The smoothness of Fiberglas fabric makes it a clean fabric. Dirt and dust do not cling as readily to such fabrics as to rough materials. The cleaning of Fiberglas fabrics is simple and quick. They may be wiped clean with a damp cloth. If complete immersion in water is desired, the temperature of the water and the soap or detergent used is immaterial, since these factors will not affect Fiberglas fabrics. No strenuous agitation of the fabrics is necessary because the dirt comes off easily. The cloth will dry just as fast as the water will evaporate off the surface. If the fabrics are hung properly while wet, ironing is unnecessary.

• *Effect of Heat.* Fiberglas will not burn. It begins to lose strength at 600 degrees Fahrenheit and will begin to soften at about 1,500 degrees Fahrenheit.

• *Effect of Light.* Sunlight has no effect on Fiberglas fabrics. This makes them useful for outdoor purposes, such as awnings, as well as for such decorative fabrics as curtains and draperies.

• *Resistance to Mildew.* Fiberglas is unaffected by mildew, but the binder or resin used to finish or size such a fabric may be attacked by mildew.

• *Resistance to Moths.* Moths and other insects do not attack Fiberglas.

• *Reaction to Alkalies.* Fiberglas will be damaged by hot solutions of weak alkalies and cold solutions of strong alkalies.

• *Reaction to Acids.* Fiberglas is damaged only by hydrofluoric and hot phosphoric acids.

• *Affinity for Dyes.* Since Fiberglas is not absorbent, it cannot take dyes by ordinary methods. Special methods are used to bind the color to the surface of the fabric. Another procedure, adding color to the molten glass before fibers are formed, provides a limited number of colors.

• *Resistance to Perspiration.* Fiberglas is unaffected by perspiration.

▶ TEST YOURSELF ON THIS CHAPTER

I. How are Fiberglas yarns made?
2. Discuss the strength and abrasion-resistant qualities of Fiberglas.
3. What desirable qualities does Coronizing give to Fiberglas fabrics?
4. Discuss the general care required for fabrics made of Fiberglas.
5. How do the elasticity and resilience of Fiberglas compare to those of other fibers?
6. What effect has sunlight on Fiberglas? heat?
7. What effect have alkalies on Fiberglas? acids? perspiration? mildew?
8. What are some of the uses of Fiberglas filaments and of staple fibers?

22 · *KNITTING* | Hosiery—Its Major Product

Fabric may be constructed by processes other than weaving; that is, by knitting, felting, braiding, and netting. Of these four, knitting comes second in importance to weaving. Although the knitting construction is not so widely used for general fabrics as weaving, it possesses qualities that make it preferable for such important clothing as hosiery, sweaters, and underwear.

Hand knitting was probably an early invention of man, but the art seems to have been perfected in western Europe in the fifteenth century. The word *cnyttan* was first mentioned in English literature in 1492. Hand knitting spread rapidly throughout Europe within a few generations. Primitive needles of bone or wood were first used, producing a coarse mesh. The Spaniards began to use steel needles, which produced a closer mesh and a more evenly knit fabric. In 1589, the Reverend William Lee, an Englishman, invented the first knitting machine, which knit 8 loops to 1 inch of width. As this construction was too coarse a mesh, he improved the machine so that it was possible to knit 20 loops to 1 inch. Today, the average is 28 loops; and the modern knitting machine still operates on the same general principles established by William Lee.

Knitted Construction Compared with Weaving. Knitted fabric is constructed with a single yarn that is formed into interlocking loops by the use of wires or needles. The loops may be either loosely or closely constructed according to the purpose of the fabric. Crocheting is knitting in its simplest form. A chain of loops is produced from a single thread by means of a hook. The interlocking loops of the knitted construction permit the fabric to stretch in any direction, even if low-grade yarn having little elasticity or yarn that lacks natural elasticity is used.

Woven fabrics are constructed by the interlacing of two or more yarns, which does not allow the fabric to stretch to any marked degree. If a certain amount of stretching is necessary, woven fabric must be cut on the bias; that is, in a diagonal direction. Even then the fabric can be stretched only in the direction of the diagonal cutting. The advantage of stretchability that knitted fabric possesses is an important consideration where fit and comfort are concerned. Knitted fabrics also give warmth because of the insulative air pockets contained in this type of construction. Knitted fabrics are very absorbent and light in weight, and do not wrinkle easily. It is not always necessary to iron them after washing. These qualities make the knitted construction desirable for underwear and especially for sportswear.

Certain kinds of knitted fabric have one serious disadvantage: if one of the loops breaks, a hole is made, which starts a run. This disadvantage can be eliminated by variation in the stitch, which protects the fabric from raveling if any single stitch is broken.

• *Evaluating Construction of Knitted Fabric.* It will be recalled that thread count (the number of threads per square inch) is used to evaluate the construction of woven fabrics. The construction of knitted fabrics is evaluated by the number of stitches or loops that can be counted in any square inch. When the interlocking loops run lengthwise, each row is called a *wale*. A wale corresponds to the direction of the warp in woven fabrics. When the loops run across the fabric, each row is called a *course*. A course corresponds to the filling or weft. Thus, a knitted fabric having 40 loops or stitches in 1 inch of width, and 50 loops in 1 inch of length, is said to have 40 wales and 50 courses.

Classification of Knitted Fabrics.

Knitted fabrics are divided into two general types: (1) those produced by weft knitting, where one continuous yarn forms courses across the fabric; (2) those produced by warp knitting, where a series of yarns forms wales in the lengthwise direction of the fabric.

• *Weft Knitting.* There are three fundamental stitches in weft knitting: (1) plain knit stitch, (2) purl stitch, (3) rib stitch. Novelty stitches, such as the tuck, the cardigan, and the rack, are merely variations of these three. Weft knitting is the hand method of knitting.

The *plain knit stitch* can be produced flat knit or in tubular form according to the machine used, and therefore is sometimes known as the *flat knit* or *jersey stitch*. It is formed by the interlooping of one or more weft threads, and can be identified by *wales on the right side* of the fabric, or by *courses on the underside*. As the fabric will stretch more in width than in length, the plain knit stitch is used for underwear, sweaters, gloves, and especially hosiery.

The *purl stitch* shows *courses on both sides* of the fabric, and both sides are similar. This stitch produces greater lengthwise stretch. It is used for scarves and for various kinds of sweater suits.

The *rib stitch* is a combination of the plain and the purl stitches. It is a slower stitch to produce and requires more yarn. It is characterized by lengthwise rows and is identified by *wales on both sides* of the fabric. The construction makes the fabric more elastic and therefore appropriate for apparel where snugness of fit is essential. The rib stitch is used for knitting the wristbands of sleeves and the waistlines of knitted garments, and for bathing suits, men's undershirts, and men's and children's socks.

• *Warp Knitting.* Warp-knit fabrics are of only one type, the flat knit, which produces a flat piece of cloth. They are made on a machine called a chain loom. In warp knitting, a series of yarns is placed side by side on separate needles. Wales are produced in the lengthwise direction of the fabric, forming vertical rows of loops. The most commonly used warp-knit fabrics are *tricot* and *milanese;* these are found in underwear, fabric gloves, scarves, and materials for foundation garments. Warp-knit fabrics are less elastic than weft-knit, but they are stronger, firmer, and more resistant to snag. They do not run or ravel when a single stitch is broken.

HOSIERY—A MAJOR PRODUCT OF KNITTING

Before the sixteenth century, the Anglo-Saxon word *hosa* designated a woven cloth garment that covered the lower portion of the body as well as the legs. As knitting was popularized and practiced to a great extent throughout England and Scotland, it soon became customary to knit the leg coverings separately by hand. In the course of time, these garments became known as stockings. Wool was used for such hand knitting. When William Lee invented the knitting machine, the English queen encouraged him to adapt it to the knitting of silk stockings rather than wool ones, as she feared that such a machine would take away the livelihood of the wool hand-knitters. But credit for the later development of machine-knit silk stockings must be given to France, as Lee was invited to that country to set up his machines there when the queen of England failed to grant him a patent. Misfortune still followed Lee, and he died in France before the full value of his knitting machine became apparent.

Hosiery is an important knitted product, and its cost is often a large item in the clothing budget of the consumer. The construction of hosiery should be of interest because it has a bearing on the serviceability of the article. In most cases, the better-constructed hosiery is well worth its extra cost, provided it is given proper care in wearing as well as in laundering.

Yarns Used for Hosiery. Before nylon was developed in 1940, silk had always been the most popular fiber for hosiery because of its strength, elasticity, and pleasing, soft, luxurious texture.

As silk strands are not of even diameter throughout their length, the use of one continuous yarn (which is typical of the knitted construction) had a tendency to develop noticeable rings at points where the diameter of the strand changes, though ever so slightly. A more even texture was obtained by knitting silk hosiery on a machine with a three-carrier attachment, so that three separate yarns are used instead of one continuous yarn. In this way, each yarn appears on every third row, and any irregularities of size are scattered over a large area and are not readily discernible. Silk stockings knit by this method are called *three-carrier construction* or *ringless* hose.

• *Cotton* is suitable for hosiery as it is soft and absorbent and dries quickly. It has less tendency to run when a thread is broken.

• *Wool* is adaptable to hosiery chiefly for warmth. The high absorbency of wool is another good feature. Of course, the grade of the wool yarns used has an important bearing on the quality and price of woolen hose.

• *Rayon* was the first of the man-made or synthetic fibers to be used for hosiery. But it does not possess the elasticity nor strength necessary to produce good-looking, fine hosiery for women.

• *Nylon* has proved to be the outstanding fiber for hosiery. Nylon filament yarn is stronger and more elastic than silk, and it became the first yarn that was acceptable for fine hosiery in place of silk. Nylon has a greater resistance to abrasion and outlasts silk in the heels and toes of stockings. It lacks the absorbent quality of silk, however. Once a thread is broken, a nylon stocking runs fast, and it snags easily.

Nylon yarn can be spun into fine deniers, so that a large variety of styles, types, and weights of women's nylon hosiery can be made. At first, the full-fashioned construction was used, but the use of the circular-knit construction on high-count needle machines has increased because nylon can be preset by heat. A preboarding operation stabilizes the nylon stocking fabric against distortion of stitch by subjecting it to conditions higher in temperature than those that will be subsequently encountered.

The nylon staple can be spun into wool-like yarns, which are usually knitted into men's hosiery. Spun nylon hosiery is soft and warm, and the yarn is even more abrasion-resistant than nylon filament yarn; therefore, spun nylon hosiery is very durable and will wear for a very long time, in fact, outwearing all other hosiery. Spun nylon hosiery launders easily and does not shrink. The one big disadvantage of this type of hosiery is its tendency to cause the feet to perspire.

• *Spun Orlon, spun Dacron,* and *Vicara* yarns are also made into men's hosiery. None of these fibers has the abrasion resistance and wearing qualities of spun nylon. Both Orlon and Dacron have low absorbency and a cashmerelike feel but will not produce durable hosiery.

Types of Hosiery Construction.   There are four types of hosiery construction: (1) full-fashioned; (2) circular, or seamless; (3) fashioned seamless; (4) cut and tailored.

• *Full-fashioned Hosiery.* Full-fashioned hosiery receives its name from the narrowing process performed during the knitting operation to shape the hose to fit the leg. The fabric is knitted flat on two separate machines called the *legger* and the *footer.*

The legger knits the leg of the stocking as well as the heel. It drops loops at appropriate points between the knee and the ankle, thus tapering the width of the stocking. Stitches are also dropped to shape the instep and the heel. The leg is then transferred to the footer, and the foot is knit to the leg. Both operations have been combined on one machine, called a *single unit.*

When the selvages are joined together, the stocking is fully shaped. The joining produces a noticeable seam on the back of full-fashioned hosiery. Small dots, called *fashion marks,* appear on both sides of the seam indicating where the

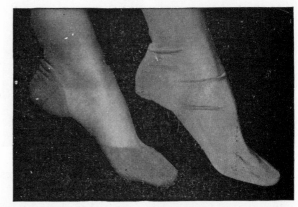

Compare the foot of a full-fashioned stocking (at left) with the foot of a circular-knit stocking (at right).

Courtesy U.S. Department of Agriculture

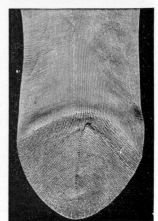

Compare the detailed construction of the well-shaped toe of a full-fashioned stocking (at left) with the toe of a circular-knit stocking (at right).

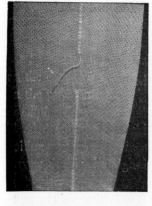

Detailed construction of the leg of a full-fash-ioned stocking, shaped in the knitting, is shown at the left. The mock seam and simulated fashion marks of one type of circular-knit stocking are shown at the right.

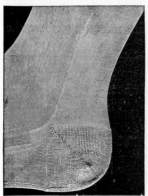

The well-shaped con-struction of a full-fash-ioned heel can be seen at the left. At the right is the heel of a circular-knit stocking.

stitches were decreased during the narrowing process. Lines or wales radiate from these fashion marks.

Because full-fashioned hosiery is shaped in the knitting operation, its fit is assured, and its shape is retained after wearing and washing. On all parts of full-fashioned stockings, there are the same number of loops to the inch.

• *Circular-knit, or Seamless, Hosiery.* Circular hose is knit from hem to toe on a circular machine and is therefore seamless. There are the same number of stitches in the width of circular-knit hosiery from top to toe, making the hose of even width throughout its length. Certain areas must, therefore, stretch to fit the leg and foot and will eventually show signs of strain. After wear and laundering, circular-knit hose returns to its original tubular shape.

Circular-knit hosiery can be made to simulate full-fashioned hosiery by using the more expensive yarns that ordinarily go into the manufacture of better-quality hose and by using mock seams with tuck stitches to resemble fashion marks. The tuck stitches can be recognized as such by noting whether or not

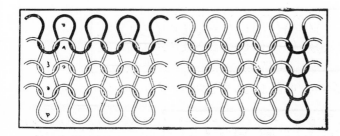

At left: *Illustrating a wale.*

At right: *A course in a plain circular knit fabric.*

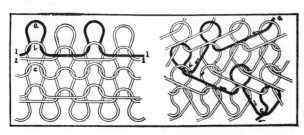

At left: *A "run resist" circular knit fabric.*

At right: *A simple warp (one bar) tricot fabric.*

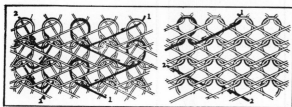

At left: *A double-warp (two bar) tricot fabric.*

At right: *A milanese fabric.*

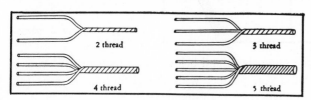

Illustrating the construction of a hosiery yarn.

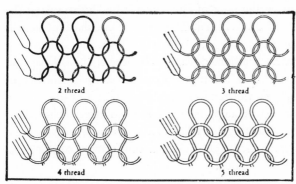

Illustrating how the total size of a hosiery yarn affects the sheerness of the stocking.

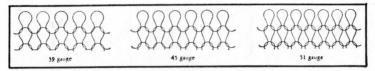

Illustrating relative fineness of 39 gauge, 45 gauge, and 51 gauge.

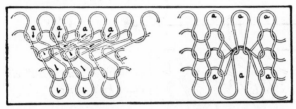

At left: *Fashion marks in full-fashioned stockings.*

At right: *Tuck stitch, used to imitate fashion marks in seamless hosiery.*

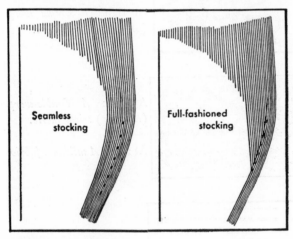

Seamless stocking

Full-fashioned stocking

Illustrating the method of narrowing in seamless and full-fashioned stockings.

Courtesy American Bemberg Corporation

the number of wales is the same above and below the fashion marks. Also, in circular-knit hose, the wales run parallel with the fashion marks; in full-fashioned hose, the wales radiate from the fashion marks.

The application of a seam on the back of circular-knit hosiery simulates the true seam of the full-fashioned construction. This type of circular-knit hose is also known as *mock-seam hosiery*.

• *Fashioned Seamless Hosiery.* Fashioned seamless hosiery is knit on a special flat machine. The hose is started at the toe, where only a small number of needles is used. As the stocking is widened from ankle to calf and finally to hem, one needle at a time is added to obtain the full-fashioned effect. The added stitches form a V at the back of the leg, which identifies fashioned seamless hose. The fashioned seamless construction makes a comfortable stocking because the seam in the foot is eliminated.

• *Cut and Tailored Hosiery.* Cut and tailored hosiery is an inexpensive type of hose. In this construction, circular hose is cut up the back of the leg, and the hose is seamed to fit. This method makes it possible to cut stockings from plain or lace fabrics and to seam them after conforming the fabric to the shape of the leg.

Women's Nylon Hosiery.

Nylon is the most popular textile for hosiery among women. Nevertheless, many women find fault with the durability of their nylon hosiery. For greater service, the following factors should be considered when purchasing nylon hosiery.

• *Types of Stocking Fabric.* The manner in which hosiery is knit has a great deal to do with its durability, appearance, and fit. There are two main types of knit: plain and mesh. The *plain knit,* of which most hosiery is made, has several advantages. It stretches in both directions, has a smooth clear texture, and provides unequaled sheerness. The outstanding disadvantage of the plain knit is that a break in any loop can cause a run.

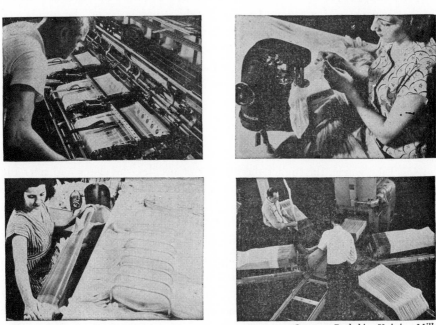

Courtesy Berkshire Knitting Mills

The first four of the eight steps in making nylon stockings are shown here. (1) *knitting,* (2) *seaming,* (3) *inspection,* and (4) *preboarding for shaping. Testing and dyeing follow; then the stockings are boarded again for final shaping and are paired for packaging.*

The *mesh knit* can be produced in a variety of patterns. Usually, the fabric is of a "run-resistant" construction. The yarn can snag but will develop only a hole in the fabric rather than a run because the loops are interlocked. Since most mesh-knit fabrics are less stretchable than plain-knit, special attention should be given to proper fit to avoid unnecessary strain on any part of the stocking. A half-size larger stocking is recommended to make up for this lack of stretch. Mesh-knit hosiery is not as smooth or as sheer and flattering to the leg as plain-knit, but it tends to be more serviceable.

• *Hosiery Sheerness.* The sheerness of nylon hosiery is dependent on the fineness (denier) of the yarn used and the closeness (gauge, for full-fashioned, and needles, for seamless hosiery) of the stitches or loops. The term *denier* indicates the weight of the nylon yarn. The higher the denier, the heavier or thicker the yarn; the lower the denier, the finer the yarn. Nylon deniers most commonly range from 12, which is the finest yarn used, through 15, 20, 30, 40, 50, 60, and 70.

The term *gauge* refers to the closeness or fineness of the loops across the width of the full-fashioned stocking. Technically, the gauge indicates the number of stitches or loops per $1\frac{1}{2}$ inches across a knitted row and may range from a low of 39 through 42, 45, 48, 51, 54, 57, 60, and 66. Each needle makes a loop; the more needles used, the more loops, and the finer the gauge. Since a high gauge uses more and finer stitches, it uses more nylon yarn and gives greater strength to the stocking. The higher the gauge, the finer the stitch, the greater the wearing quality and snag resistance.

In seamless hosiery, the closeness of the loops is measured in terms of *needles* on the circular stocking knitting machine. The needle count ranges from 260 to 432. Like gauge, the higher the number of needles, the closer and finer the knit. Sometimes, a seamless stocking is also referred to by its equivalent gauge count—that is, 432 needle count is as closely knit as 54 gauge, and 400 needle count is similar to 51 gauge.

Gauge affects the appearance and durability of hosiery, but it is the combination of denier and gauge that determines the sheerness of the hose. For example, 45 gauge, 15 denier hosiery is sheerer than 51 gauge, 15 denier hosiery, but the 45 gauge stocking will probably not wear as well because it is not so closely knitted. Likewise, 54 gauge, 15 denier hosiery should wear even better because of the greater number of stitches to each $1\frac{1}{2}$ inches of the stocking. When comparing hosiery deniers and gauges, similar quantities must be used. Each stocking is a combination of the quality of knitting, the quality of the yarn, the denier of the yarn, the gauge, and the construction features. The following facts are helpful when purchasing hosiery.

15 denier, 51 gauge—filmy and supersheer, for evening wear
20 denier, 51 gauge—sheer weight, desirable for evening wear
30 denier, 51 gauge—average weight, for afternoon or business
40 denier, 45 gauge—duty weight, often preferred for daytime wear at home
60 to 70 denier, 45 gauge—service weight, best for outdoors and for extra long wear

• *Construction of Hosiery.* For hosiery to wear well, it must be properly constructed. The fact that strong nylon yarn is used, or that a high gauge is employed in knitting the stocking, does not automatically insure long-wearing hosiery. The *seams* in full-fashioned hosiery should be straight, sturdy, narrow, and trim, with no raw fabric edges showing. Nylon thread should be used because it assures long-wearing and fast-drying fine seams. When correctly sewed, the heel reinforcing, welt, and fashion marks will match on both sides of the seam. The *welt,* or hem, should be 3 to 4 inches long to permit firm anchoring of the garter. The welt should be sufficiently wide and elastic to fit the thigh without binding. It should measure 7 or 8 inches when flat and should stretch to about 12 or 13 inches to be comfortable on the average leg.

There should be a well-constructed *shadow welt,* or *afterwelt,* directly below the welt. It gives added strength to the upper part of the hosiery by taking up the garter strain. Just below the welt or the shadow welt, there should be a row of *"run-stop" stitching* around the stocking, which discourages runs, starting in the welt, from running into the body of the stocking. This stitching can be made in several ways, such as by interlocking the loops during the knitting process.

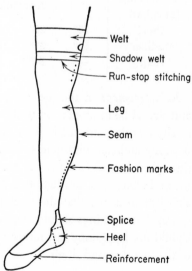

Construction of full-fashioned hosiery.

Welt
Shadow welt
Run-stop stitching
Leg
Seam
Fashion marks
Splice
Heel
Reinforcement

WOMEN'S HOSIERY SIZE CHART

Shoe Width	AAA	AA	A or B	C or D	E or EE
Shoe Size	**Stocking Foot Size**				
2½	8	8	8	8½	8½
3	8½	8½	8½	8½	8½
3½	8½	8½	8½	8½	8½
4	8½	8½	8½	9	9
4½	8½	8½	9	9	9½
5	9	9	9	9	9½
5½	9	9	9½	9½	9½
6	9½	9½	9½	9½	10
6½	9½	9½	9½	10	10
7	9½	9½	10	10	10½
7½	10	10	10	10½	10½
8	10	10	10½	10½	10½
8½	10½	10½	10½	10½	11
9	10½	10½	11	11	11
9½	11	11	11	11	11

LEG-LENGTH CHART

When stocking foot size is	8, 8½, 9	9½	10	10½, 11
and stocking is marked	**Lengths available are**			
"Short"	28"	28"	—	—
"Medium"	30"	31"	31"	32"
"Long"	—	34"	34"	34"

This is a typical leg-length chart. There is some variation in length in inches of hosiery produced by different manufacturers. The salesperson should have accurate information about the brands of hosiery sold in the store.

Reinforcement in the toe, heel, and sole is desirable for greater durability, and should be in proportion to the weight and style of the hosiery. Some styles of sheer hosiery are made with little or no reinforcement. Fortunately, nylon is strong and can withstand unusual rubbing and abrading before it will wear through. The *volume* of the stocking is another important consideration. Since nylon hosiery has unusual two-way stretch, flat measurement alone is not sufficient to assure that the stocking is correctly sized. Good construction requires that stockings should conform to standard leg-form sizes. This volume should not be skimpy but rather should be adequate in both girth and length of the foot, leg, and thigh.

MEN'S AND CHILDREN'S HOSIERY SIZE CHART[1]

Shoe Size	Men's Hosiery	Children's and Infants' Hosiery	Shoe Size	Men's Hosiery	Children's and Infants' Hosiery
1	..	4	7½	10½	6
1½	..	4	8	10½	6½
2	..	4	8½	11	6½
2½	..	4	9	11	7
3	..	4½	9½	11	7
3½	..	4½	10	11½	7
4	..	4½	10½	11½	7½
4½	..	4½	11	12	7½
5	9	5	11½	12	7½
5½	9½	5	12	..	7½
6	9½	5½	12½	..	8
6½	10	5½	13	..	8
7	10	6			

[1] Courtesy National Association of Hosiery Manufacturers.

Regardless of the quality of construction, no hosiery will give proper service unless the wearer selects the correct foot size in accordance with the width and size of her shoe, and the correct leg length.

Men's, Children's, and Infants' Hosiery. Men's, children's, and infants' hosiery, with minor exceptions, is circular-knit and is made of any of the various kinds and combinations of yarns, in many styles and in color effects.

Dyeing of Hosiery. Most stockings are dip-dyed or piece-dyed. This method is satisfactory if proper care is taken to insure evenness of color, for the flesh background quickly reveals inadequately dyed hosiery. By stretching the seamed part of the stocking, the consumer can tell whether the dyeing was well done. Unevenness of color indicates poor or incomplete penetration of the dye. Hosiery is sometimes yarn-dyed. Ingrain stockings are made from yarns that were dyed before knitting. The amount of ingrain hosiery produced today is very small. A richer color results, but the hosiery is not as durable as when piece-dyed.

Care of Hosiery. Hosiery should be washed after each wearing, as perspiration weakens the fiber. Unusual care is necessary in washing, as rough skin or sharp fingernails cause snags, which eventually result in runs. Rings should be removed when hosiery is being handled. Lukewarm water with suds made from mild soap or soap flakes should be used, and the suds squeezed through

CAUSE AND CORRECTION OF HOSIERY RUNS AND BREAKS

Cause of Break	Possible Correction
Too much pull from garters. Lack of elasticity of garter or sharp edge on garter clasp.	Wear longer stockings. Have elastic and garters in good condition.
A skimpy welt or not enough elasticity in welt.	Buy stockings with plenty of stretch in the hem or those with a special stretch-top feature.
Stocking too tight or too long.	Buy stockings with more ample tops and of correct length. Garters should never be put into sheer leg fabric or shadow welt.
Too sheer a stocking for the occasion.	Wear stockings of heavier denier yarn or higher gauge knit.
Improper fastening of garter.	Always fasten garters into hem of stockings. Garters fastened into sheer leg fabric, shadow welt, or on the seams frequently result in tears and runs. Handle hose carefully.
Snags or pulled threads.	Avoid contact with sharp or rough objects, as broken or rough fingernails or toenails, zippers, crinoline skirts, and the like. Buy stockings that fit the leg more snugly. Loose, poorly fitting stockings are more readily snagged.
Strain at knee due to too tight or too short stocking.	Buy longer stockings.
Too small foot size causing excessive wear above heel reinforcement.	Buy larger foot size.
Reinforcement too thin.	Buy hosiery with heavier reinforcements. Use lightly reinforced hosiery or sandal-foot types only for more dressy occasions.
Stocking snagging on rough shoe lining.	Have shoe lining repaired. Wear shoes with snug-fitting heels.
Stocking too short in foot causing runs in toe reinforcing.	Buy larger-sized stockings.
Runs above toe reinforcing when too long stocking is folded under.	Buy smaller-sized stockings.

Cause of Break	Possible Correction
Worn lining in shoe.	Have shoe lining repaired.
Insufficient reinforcement.	Buy hose of heavier denier or more heavily reinforced in toe.
Reinforcement worn through.	Buy stockings more heavily reinforced or of heavier denier for the occasion. Check rough shoe linings.
Friction from bunions, calluses, or similar abrasion.	Take proper care of feet.
Friction from arch supports.	Buy hose with heavier foot reinforcements.

the hose. Stockings should never be wrung or twisted. When drying, they should not be exposed to the direct heat of the sun nor hung near a hot radiator or stove. These precautions apply to all types of hosiery. For wool stockings, the additional precautions for washing any wool fabric should be observed. In addition to careful washing, the following suggestions will also help lengthen the wear of hosiery.

1. Purchase at least two pairs of stockings of the same color, to match pairs when a single stocking has been damaged.

2. Keep stockings in a separate box, when not in use, to prevent contact with anything that may mar their texture.

3. Select the proper size of hose according to well-fitted shoes. The stocking should be at least a half inch longer than the wearer's foot.

▶ TEST YOURSELF ON THIS CHAPTER

1. How does the construction of knitted fabrics differ from woven fabrics?
2. What is the chief advantage gained by the knitted construction?
3. Why is a knitted fabric always a warm fabric?
4. What is a disadvantage of the knitted construction? How can it be eliminated?
5. How would you evaluate the construction of knitted fabrics?
6. What are the types of hosiery construction? What is preferable, and why?
7. How would you judge a pair of women's stockings?
8. What is meant by gauge of hosiery? What is meant by denier?
9. How will the gauge and denier of nylon hosiery influence a consumer's choice?
10. How will the fit of shoes affect the wear of hosiery?
11. Why is it important to examine the reinforcements of hosiery?
12. What are the average lengths of hosiery for women?
13. What considerations should be given to the care of hosiery?
14. Compare cotton, wool, silk, rayon, nylon, Orlon, Dacron, and Vicara for use in men's hosiery.

23 · MINOR TEXTILES

Fibers and Fabric Construction

The textile industry uses other fibers in addition to those already studied. Each has its field of usefulness. Some have qualities that make them suitable for purposes that none of the fibers previously discussed could fulfill economically. Others can be used as acceptable substitutes or even adulterants, as long as the finished goods fulfill the purpose for which they are intended, and the selling price is in line with the value of the product.

Jute. Jute is a natural fiber obtained from a tall plant of the same name. It is grown throughout tropical Asia, chiefly in India, for commercial uses. The plant is easy to cultivate and harvest. The fiber is obtained by retting, similarly to flax. The fine, silklike fiber is easy to spin but is not durable, as it deteriorates rapidly when exposed to moisture. Jute is the cheapest textile fiber and is used in great quantities. Because of its lack of strength, jute is difficult to bleach and can never be made pure white. It can be converted into a wool-like fiber by treatment with a strong caustic soda.

Though jute is often used as an adulterant with other fibers, it can be easily recognized when tested for its marked sensitivity to mineral acids. Concentrated mineral acids readily dissolve jute. Dilute mineral acids rot it quickly. It is especially weak in salt water. Jute is used as a substitute for hemp, as binding threads for carpets and rugs, as rug cushions, as a filler with other fibers, and as a linoleum base. It is made into coarse, cheap fabrics, such as novelty dress goods and heavy cotton bagging.

Kapok. Kapok is a natural fine, white, hairlike fiber obtained from the seed capsules of plants and trees grown in Java, Borneo, Sumatra, and Central America. It is sometimes called "silk cotton" because its luster is almost equal to that of silk. Kapok resembles cotton in general appearance but is always of shorter average staple—less than 1 inch. Under the microscope, kapok can be easily distinguished from cotton, as it appears to be a hollow tube with very thin walls and frequent folds but no twist.

may be built up until a sufficient amount of weight or thickness has accumulated. Timing is important during these processes, so that the web will not be broken or have weak areas. The mass, or batt, may then be cut, and the edges trimmed to the desired width. Finished felt may vary in thickness from a few thousandths of an inch to 3 inches. Any thickness can be obtained by superimposing batts on one another and felting them together. Batts are usually about 40 yards long and 60 to 90 inches wide; their weights vary from 18 to 50 pounds.

The batts are evenly sprinkled with warm water, passed over a steam box to warm the fibers thoroughly, and then pressed between two rollers. The top roller rests on the batt and, with an oscillating motion, exerts the pressure that combined with moisture and heat produces the final felting action.

After the batts have been processed, they are allowed to drain and cool off for about twenty-four hours. The timing for each raw material or blend used in the felt is very important. The felt is then dampened with a suitable lubricant, such as a soap and soda combination, for the fulling process, by which it is subjected to a pounding action with hammers. The fulling time varies from five minutes to half an hour. The longer the felt is fulled, the firmer it will be. But this operation cannot be continued too long, or the quality of the felt would be spoiled. Final operations include washing, stiffening, ironing, brushing to raise a nap, and shearing to produce a smooth even surface. Felt may be made water-repellent and may be flameproofed or mothproofed. It may be dyed against fading, perspiration, cleaning, and washing.

Braiding or Plaiting. Another form of fabric construction is the diagonal or lengthwise interlacing that is most familiar as the method of braiding or plaiting long hair. Braid is formed on a braiding machine by interlacing three or more strands of yarn so that each strand passes over and under one or more of the others.

Braids are divided into two types: (1) flat braids, in the form of strips or narrow flat tapes; (2) round braids, tubular in form, which may be hollow or have a center core of some material. Both types of braiding are produced from any of the textile fibers, as well as from metal threads, tinsel, straw, wire, or leather. This principle of fabric construction is used for making shaped articles, such as straw hats and small rugs; narrow fabrics, such as ribbons and braids for millinery and accessory dress materials; cords and tapes, such as fishlines, shoelaces, wicks, parachute and glider cords, and elastic of various types; and cord coverings for tires, tubing, hose, wires, and cables.

Netting. Netting is an open-mesh form of fabric construction that is held together by knots at each point where the yarns cross one another. The mesh varies in size and type, and ranges from the very open fish net to the finest and most delicate lace designs. The open-mesh construction is characteristic of both nets and laces. The true lace construction is always made with a design. *Bobbinet,* which is a machine-made net, does not have a design, and is therefore not a true lace.

Laces were first made only by hand, and hand laces have always been highly prized as trimming for apparel and as decorative pieces for the home. Unusually beautiful and intricately designed laces are retained in families as heirlooms and are displayed in museums as representative of the handicraft of nations of the world. Real laces, such as needlepoint, bobbin, pillow, darned, and crocheted, are now duplicated so expertly by machine that the average consumer is not able to determine whether a lace is machine-made or handmade. Linen yarns are generally used for expensive laces; but cotton, silk, rayon, and other yarns are used for various qualities and types. Lace may be made by knotting or by looping, braiding, stitching, or twisting.

▶ TEST YOURSELF ON THIS CHAPTER

 1. For what purposes are the minor natural fibers generally used?
 2. Name five minor fibers, and give one use for each.
 3. How are metal threads and tinsel made? For what purposes are they used?
 4. Describe the qualities of asbestos and its uses.
 5. What by-product of the steel industry is used as insulative material? Name four of its qualities.
 6. Why is jute never available in a pure-white color?
 7. Why is kapok always felted, never woven?
 8. How does kapok differ from cotton?
 9. Compare ramie with linen.
10. Why is hemp especially suitable for sailcloth?
11. Describe the felting process.
12. For what purposes is the braided construction used?
13. Why are at least three strands required in braiding?
14. Why is braiding confined to the production of shaped articles?
15. How does felt differ from other fabric construction?
16. Why is wool preferred in making felt fabric?
17. Why are fur fibers used in the production of expensive felt hats?
18. How is felt used for industrial purposes?
19. How does net differ from woven fabric?

24 · TEXTILE FLOOR COVERINGS

Floor coverings have been made from textile fibers for more than 5,000 years. Throughout civilization, rugs and carpets have formed a part of the history and culture of races and nations. Early kings and conquerors included valuable rugs among their treasures and trophies, and many of these famous pieces have retained values that in some cases are inestimable. Priceless handmade carpets and rugs woven hundreds of years ago in the Far East are exhibited today in museums as representative of the patient labor and creative art of weavers whose skills have been passed on through many generations.

Well-chosen rugs or carpets serve as a colorful foundation for the decorative plan and color scheme of all rooms in the modern home. As floor coverings are among the most expensive items in a house-furnishings budget, careful consideration must be given to fiber, color, decorative character and design, size, and construction to obtain the best value for any price level.

Floor coverings are made from various kinds of fibers—cotton, silk, wool, rayon, acetate, nylon, Acrilan, Dynel, Verel, blends of these fibers, and from mohair, jute, hemp, or grass straw. The wool fiber has been the most popular natural fiber for rugs, because wool has offered the advantages of extreme softness, resiliency, absorbency to shock and noise, and, particularly, resistance to long wear when the right fibers and construction have been used. Wool rugs, however, can be attacked by moths and other insects. Rugs of man-made or synthetic fibers are not damaged by these insects. Nylon, Acrilan, Dynel, and Verel are all soft, resilient, and shock absorbing. Nylon is extremely durable, and the acrylic fibers wear rather well but there is some tendency to pill. These synthetic fibers are not particularly absorbent. Rugs made of these fibers therefore resist staining. Spilled substances, such as ink, soda, mustard, and the like, can be wiped up readily without leaving a stain. One great disadvantage of rugs constructed of nylon and acrylic fibers is that, since these fibers are thermoplastic, a burning cigarette or any other very hot object will melt a hole at the point of contact. Of all fibers used for rugs, rayon is the least durable and least resilient; but it is also the least expensive.

Ultimately, the choice of a rug will depend on its attractiveness, its construction, its serviceability, and its cost. The consumer must weigh the relative merits of these factors in making his choice.

Rug Construction. The terms *rug* and *carpet* are used synonymously, but the form or the size in which these coverings are manufactured differs. Rugs may vary in shape as well as in width and length. In general, certain size standards are maintained that in the larger rugs have been adapted to standard sizes of rooms. The term *broadloom* does not refer to quality but describes a type of carpet woven all in one piece on a loom wide enough to produce the width desired.

Construction factors explain differences in quality and price: for example, the type, quality, and quantity of fiber used, the length of staple, the amount of twist, and the number of ply in the yarns. Each factor has a definite bearing on the final price of the finished product.

Terms Used in Carpet Industry. Judging a rug for quality of construction requires some understanding of certain terms used in the carpet industry.

Tufts are the cut loops of surface yarns held in the small squares that are discernible on the reverse side of the rug. *Pitch* expresses the number of warp threads crosswise of the loom to each 27 inches of width. *Wires* refer to the number of tufts to the inch in the warp or lengthwise direction.

The construction of the rug is indicated by the closeness of the tufts in each direction—that is, by the pitch and wires. The number can usually be determined by counting the rows of fiber on the back of the rug. Compact construction of the tufts, represented by a high number of pitch and wires, indicates a dense pile, showing that a greater quantity of wool has been used, resulting in a more durable product. Density of weave is considered the most important factor in determining the durability of floor coverings.

Additional crosswise yarns are used to bind the pile to the backing of the rug. The number of yarns used is indicated by the term *shot*. In a two-shot construction, one crosswise yarn can be seen between each row of tufts, the other crosswise yarn is behind the row. In the three-shot construction, there are two crosswise yarns between each row of tufts and a third yarn in back. The three-shot construction requires additional yarn and more loom operations. Though more expensive, it is more durable.

Classification by Weave. Rugs and carpets may be classified according to weave, of which there are three general types.

1. Cut pile. Examples are Oriental, chenille, Wilton, Axminster, and velvet.
2. Uncut pile. Examples are tapestry and Brussels.
3. Flat weaves. Represented in novelty and special-purpose rugs made from miscellaneous fibers. Ordinarily can be used on either side.

DOMESTIC RUGS

In the United States, floor coverings are often classified as domestic and imported. The *domestic* group includes all kinds of rugs made in this country regardless of the source of their raw materials. The *imported* group includes Oriental, Chinese, Indian, and other foreign products. Today, these divisions and even specific types of rugs do not tell the consumer all that should be known because both good and poor qualities are found in all weaves.

Chenille. Chenille is the most expensive of the domestic types, and it offers the widest range of possibilities with respect to depth of pile, design, colorings, and width. Chenille may be woven even as wide as 30 feet without a seam, and can be made as a single unit to fit irregularly shaped areas. It can be produced with a pile up to a full inch in height. This height, when supported by a heavy wool cushion back, gives a luxuriously soft and resilient quality and remarkable durability.

The chenille construction requires two separate loom operations. First, woolen or worsted yarns are woven into a blanket containing cotton warp threads.

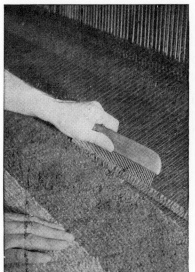

The weft blanket cloth before being cut

The chenille fur or furry caterpillar

The warp of the chenille fur

Courtesy Mohawk Carpet Mills, Inc.

Top left: *Hand tufting in chenille weaving. A steel comb is used to bring the surface yarn in the fur up through strong cotton catcher warp threads, as four motions of a shuttle weave the heavy backing yarn to the base of the fabric.* Top right: *Woolen blanket cloth from which chenille fur, or hairy caterpillar, is made. The cloth is shown partly cut so that the warp of the caterpillar may be seen.*

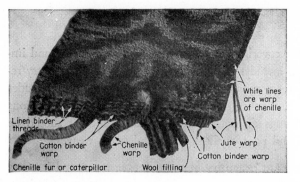

Chenille construction shown in detail.

Actually, this blanket is composed of vertical woolen or worsted yarns bound together by the cotton warp. Another machine cuts the woolen filling halfway, producing furry strips, which are held together by the cotton yarns in the center. This strip, which resembles a caterpillar, is pressed into V-shaped form; and the separate ends are tied together, forming a continuous chain. This chain is subsequently used on the second loom as a filling for the final weaving of the chenille rug. A well-constructed chenille uses a fine quality of wool and a densely packed high pile, which results in the durability characteristic of this weave.

Smyrna rugs resemble chenille, as they are made with a chenille fur. But the fur is twisted into a round yarn instead of the V shape of the chenille. A shot of fiber filling makes the Smyrna rug reversible—the pattern and pile are alike on both sides. It has a shorter pile than the chenille.

Wilton. Wilton is an expensive weave to manufacture, ranking next to chenille. It is always woven on a Jacquard loom and is considered one of the best of all machine-made rugs. In weaving the Wilton, the surface yarn is held in trays called frames. Each frame holds spools wound with yarn of the same color. If there are six full colors in the pattern of a Wilton, there must be six frames. In a six-frame Wilton, only one of the six pile yarns appears on the surface at a time. The other five lie underneath, constituting hidden value in the form of added resiliency and quality. The number of frames in a Wilton

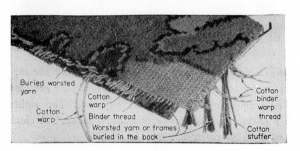

Worsted Wilton construction shown in detail.

Illustrations on these pages courtesy Mohawk Carpet Mills, Inc.

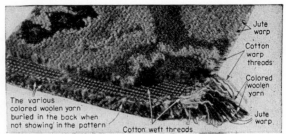

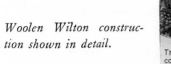

Woolen Wilton construction shown in detail.

varies from two to six, indicating the thickness of its wool cushion and the number of separate colors in its design. A method known as *planting* makes it possible to add, in small areas, more colors than are indicated by the number of frames.

The pile effect of the Wilton is produced by looping the surface yarns over wires that have razor-sharp knives at the ends. When the wires are withdrawn, the knives cut the pile. The Wilton is made with worsted or with woolen yarns. When closely woven, the worsted Wilton offers maximum durability together with fineness of texture and delicacy of design even though it has a short pile. The finest grade of worsted Wilton is woven with six frames, with a three-ply yarn. It has 13 wires to the inch, a three-shot construction, and about 115 tufts to the square inch. Lower grades are woven with a smaller number of frames, have 10 wires to the inch, a two-shot construction, and as few as 60 tufts to the square inch.

The woolen Wilton has a more luxurious feel than the worsted Wilton because of its greater softness and depth of pile. It is made with at least two and a half frames and has 7½ to 9½ wires to the inch and a pitch of 214.

• *Saxony.* Saxony is the name given to a better grade of woolen Wilton made from unusually heavily twisted woolen yarns with large and firm tufts. These yarns produce a luxurious depth of pile with large, loose tufts and a coarse design. The rug is especially durable in spite of its extreme softness.

Brussels. The Brussels was the first type of carpet woven on a Jacquard loom. It is woven like a Wilton except that the wires used to make the surface loops do not have any cutting ends. As the wires are withdrawn, the pile is left as upright loops instead of cut pile. Worsted yarns are used for the pile, producing a very durable product. The best-quality Brussels is usually woven with five frames and has 9 wires to the inch and a pitch of 256.

Axminster. The Axminster rug has been the most popular type of carpet. There is no limit to the number of colors that may be used in its design. The colored yarns are wound on separate loom spools in the weft direction. The spools are fitted in an overhead roller and produce an endless supply of surface

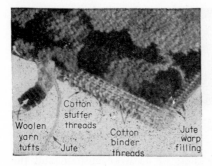

Cotton
stuffer
threads

Woolen
yarn
tufts   Jute   Cotton
binder
threads   Jute
warp
filling

Axminster construction shown in detail.

Courtesy Mohawk Carpet Mills, Inc.

yarn. Weeks are required to set the yarns for an Axminster design; but, once arranged, the 9 by 12 size may be woven in only an hour or two. Only woolen yarn is used for the Axminster, as the weave is not tight enough to permit the use of hard-surfaced worsted yarn. The surface closely resembles hand-knotted carpet, but the Axminster can be easily distinguished from any other type because it can be rolled only in its lengthwise direction. The stiff jute fibers used in the backing form pronounced ridges on the reverse side. The better-quality Axminster has a deep pile, some flexibility in its backing, and as many as 70 tufts to the square inch. The less expensive grades have fewer tufts, a low pile, and a very rigid back.

Velvet. The velvet construction is the simplest pile weave. Its pile is woven over wires having cutting ends that produce the cut tufts as the wires are withdrawn. All the wool lies on the surface of velvet carpet, with no buried yarns in the backing. Only one yarn is used, and it must be uniform and of good quality throughout to absorb the dye evenly when printed. The common method of producing a pattern on velvet rugs is by printing the design after the rug has been constructed. Sometimes, yarns that have been printed before weaving are used. The velvet rug is inexpensive, as it is the fastest type to weave. It is made on an ordinary loom, with worsted or woolen yarns. Twisted yarns are used to produce what is known in the trade as hard-twisted velvets. For firmness, jute yarns, sized with glue, are used as stuffing warp yarns. The

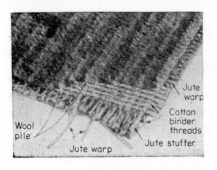

Jute
warp

Cotton
binder
threads

Wool
pile

Jute warp   Jute stuffer

Velvet construction shown in detail.

Courtesy Mohawk Carpet Mills, Inc.

better-quality velvet rug has a deeper pile; its density should range from 56 to 80 tufts to the square inch.

Sheen-Type or American Oriental. The name "American Oriental" is frequently used for the sheen-type or luster-type domestic rugs that are produced by the Wilton, Axminster, or velvet weave. The sheen in the domestic product is obtained by washing or brushing the wool rugs in a chlorine solution, which imparts the characteristic luster of the imported Oriental rug. The patterns are faithful reproductions and in many cases are woven through to the back, as in the genuine Oriental. When made of good-quality yarns, the American Oriental gives satisfactory wear and is very popular.

Tapestry. The construction of the tapestry rug is similar to that of the velvet except that the wires used to form the pile do not have any cutting ends. Thus an uncut pile is left when the wires are withdrawn. Because of its resemblance to the Brussels type, the tapestry rug is sometimes termed *tapestry Brussels*. This is a misnomer. The term attempts to attribute to the tapestry rug the superior construction of the Brussels, which is made on a Jacquard loom with a two- to five-frame construction. The tapestry rug is made on an ordinary loom and requires only one warp yarn. A good grade should have 8 wires and a pitch of 8. The tapestry rug is not intended for heavy or long wear. It does not have the softness of other rugs, nor does it have delicate or distinct designs. It is intended to satisfy the demand for an inexpensive yet sturdy product.

Patent-Back Rugs. In patent-back rugs, each tuft is locked into its place by applying a plastic binder to the back of the rug, or by vulcanizing a solution of rubber cement to the back. Patent-back rugs can be cut in any direction without danger of having frayed edges or raveled yarns; the edges do not require binding. This feature permits the patent-back broadloom to be fitted easily to irregularly shaped areas. Also, holes caused by damage or wear can be cut out and matched pieces put in their places.

Punched Felt Rugs. Punched felt rugs have a heavy burlap base reinforced with jute. Over this base is spread a fine-quality wool, which is punched through to the back. Rubber composition is then spread on the back to lock the fibers. This coating gives the rug a cushioned effect and prevents it from slipping.

Hooked Rugs. Hooked rugs from the Southern and New England states and from Canada are popular as throw rugs for bedrooms and halls. These are handmade of rags and usually reproduce Colonial patterns. They are also produced commercially in room and small sizes in cotton and in wool.

Grass Rugs. A wirelike grass that grows wild in the northeastern section of the United States is used for grass rugs. They are woven with a plain weave that shows on one side. A pattern applied by stencil appears on the other side. Colored warp threads can be used to form geometric designs. Grass rugs are always varnished to preserve their surface.

Sisal Rugs. Sisal fiber imported from Central America and the West Indies can be made into rugs. The chief use of this fiber is for twine and rope, but its durability makes it adaptable for floor coverings. Sisal fiber is obtained from the leaf of a plant. It is twisted into strands and woven similarly to any of the fiber rugs.

IMPORTED RUGS

Oriental. Very few of the Oriental rugs produced before 1795 are on the commercial market today, but many are displayed in museums. These older Orientals are valuable because of their age, beauty, and intricacy of design. Those made in the last eighty years are accepted as "old Orientals," and although scarce, are still obtainable.

Oriental rugs are classified according to the country and the section from which they originated. They are divided into six groups: Persian, Turkish, Caucasian, Turkoman, Indian, and Chinese. These groups can be subclassified according to their weave and also by the method of looping or knot tying that is characteristic of Oriental rug construction. Only two kinds of knots are used for the many kinds of Oriental rugs made throughout Europe and Asia. The Persian or Senna knot is more of a twist or wrapping; the Turkish or Ghiordes knot is a real knot as understood today.

The largest class of Oriental rugs has a pile surface composed of tufts. Each tuft is made separately by means of the knot formed by strands looped around the warp yarns. When the quality of an Oriental rug is being judged, consideration should be given to coloring, design, depth of pile, quality of the yarn, age, condition, and fineness of texture. The number of knots to the square inch may vary from 50 to 500.

The consumer may find it difficult to distinguish between the imported Oriental and the machine-made domestic product. It may be helpful to remember that the reverse side of the Oriental always shows the entire pattern in detail and that the pile is produced by rows of knots, which can be easily seen by separating the pile. The back should also be examined to see whether the entire pattern has the same colors on the reverse side as are on the face of the rug, and to check the number of knots to the square inch.

In the genuine Oriental, the fringe of the rug is never sewed on; it is always an extension of the warp threads. In proportion to size the Oriental is always heavier than the domestic. Experienced rug merchants distinguish the two by examining the dyed portion of the pile nearest the knot. Oriental rugs use natural dyes, which usually fade to a lighter shade of the original color. The domestic rug uses aniline dyes, which fade to different hues.

Chinese. Antique Chinese rugs were made with the Persian or Senna knot, making possible a large number of knots to the inch and a close shearing of the pile. Later, rugs were made with large coarse designs and a deep pile. In more recent years, Chinese rugs have been made in plain colors as well as in the floral and dragon patterns characteristic of Chinese design. The pile is unusually deep, making these rugs remarkably durable.

Indian. Small-sized rugs imported from India are made from felted goat's hair and embroidered by hand with bright wool threads similar to the work found in crewel fabrics. They are known as *Numdah rugs.* They are inexpensive and adaptable for general household use as they can be easily washed. Another rug imported from India, called a *drugget,* is woven with the wool of wire-haired sheep. Jute is used in its backing. It is usually highly colored and should be dry-cleaned instead of washed.

CARE OF RUGS

The appearance and the life of a rug depend on the amount and kind of attention it receives. Dirt and grit must be removed frequently; otherwise, dirt works into the recesses of the pile and into the backing, soon cutting the yarn fibers and finally producing worn areas. A broom, carpet sweeper, or electric cleaner should be used on carpets for a few minutes every day, surely twice a week, cleaning in the direction of the pile, not against it.

When sweeping or brushing a new pile-surfaced rug, loose pieces of the pile, or fuzz, are likely to come off. This is caused by the excess short wool fibers worked in during manufacturing operations. It does not necessarily indicate defects. When ends of tufts appear above the surface of a new rug, clip them level with the surface.

A new wool rug or one recently returned from storage should always be swept and brushed gently because the wool in the rug is in a dry condition, not having had sufficient opportunity to absorb its natural intake of moisture. The constant absorption of moisture from the atmosphere, so important for the healthful condition of a rug, keeps it resilient and resistant to wear. Plenty of water should be kept in a room. It may be in fish bowls or in metal containers on the radiators.

A rug should never be shampooed while it is on the floor. It is impossible to clean the pile thoroughly and to rinse out the soap and dirt completely when the rug remains on the floor. A pile rug made with highly twisted yarns should be dry-cleaned. Washing or shampooing may untwist the yarns. There are some cleaning products that are effective when properly used.

Constant pressure on a rug flattens the tufts or slants them in one direction. The position of the rug should be changed so that the wear may be distributed instead of concentrated in a particular area. This helps to prevent the uneven shading that occurs when sections of a rug show localized wear. An important safeguard in the care of a rug is to place a cushion backing under it to absorb the constant impact. Any stains should be removed promptly. Many spots can be easily removed when fresh. Removal is difficult when a stain has set. The rules for the removal of spots and stains from general textile fabrics apply as well to textile floor coverings. (See Chapter 25.)

Moths and carpet beetles may damage wool rugs. Keeping the rug clean and providing a healthful circulation of air reduces the danger. For this reason, some persons do not put their rugs away during the summer months, letting them remain on the floor for the frequent cleanings so essential for long and serviceable wear. Rugs that are cleaned frequently with a vacuum cleaner are never attacked by moths. If a damaged area is regular in form, this is an indication that the attacking insect is not the moth but the tow bug, which is likely to be found in overstuffed upholstered furniture.

Curling of the corner of a rug can be remedied by applying a hot iron on a damp cloth to both face and back of the corner. The curling is usually caused by constant tripping or by some similar unusual strain.

▶ TEST YOURSELF ON THIS CHAPTER

1. What basic properties of textile fibers are required for floor coverings?
2. What are the two main classifications of floor coverings?
3. What materials are used in making real Oriental rugs?
4. What identifying characteristics distinguish Oriental and Chinese rugs?
5. How does the Brussels carpet differ from broadloom?
6. Describe the Wilton construction. How does a worsted Wilton differ from a woolen Wilton?
7. How can humidity affect floor coverings? How is this indicated to the owner? What remedy is available?
8. Describe the Axminster carpet, showing how to distinguish it from other carpets.
9. What are the advantages of a chenille carpet? the disadvantages?
10. Compare the imported Oriental with the domestic product.
11. Why is the patent-back construction important in carpet production?
12. What are some precautions to take in caring for floor coverings?
13. Under what conditions may a wool rug be left on the floor in summer?

25 · CARE OF
FABRICS

Not only should fabrics be carefully selected, but they should be given proper care throughout their lives. This care includes: (1) frequent brushing and airing of garments, (2) clean storage when not in use, (3) immediate mending when damaged by tearing, (4) stain removal before washing or further use, (5) intelligent choice of cleaning method—washing or dry cleaning, (6) frequent laundering when the fabric is washable, (7) proper laundering method for type of fabric, (8) proper pressing and ironing.

Brushing and Airing. The frequent brushing of garments, especially those having napped surfaces, removes the kind of dirt that starts as dust. The accumulation of dust particles not only soils the fabric, even though the soil is not readily discernible, but eventually causes deterioration.

When a garment is not washable, and does not require frequent dry cleaning, its life can be prolonged and its appearance kept bright and attractive by brushing. To offset the absorption of perspiration in such garments, they should be frequently aired, outdoors if possible. If this is not possible, hang clothes for a time outside the closet in a well-aired room. Frequent brushing with a clothesbrush that has soft but firm bristles is necessary to keep wool garments in good condition. Hang them on wide-shouldered hangers in a closet where clothes are not packed tightly together. Occasional airing is also necessary to prolong the life of wool fiber. Clothes hanging in a closet should always be buttoned, and zippers should be closed.

Clean Storage. Clothing that is not in daily use should be protected from deterioration by storage in dustproof containers in which some kind of moth preventive is used. No useful purpose is served if the garment is stored without careful brushing and airing, for accumulated dirt works damage on such stored articles. For long storage, garments should be washed or dry-cleaned and then properly stored immediately, preferably in sealed containers.

If newly purchased linens are to be stored for a while, they should be washed to remove any possible sizing. There should be no residue of starch in new or used stored linens as it will cause mildew. If white linens are wrapped in blue paper, and the ends of the package are sealed to exclude light and air, the linens will not turn yellow during storage.

Mending. A torn fabric should be mended before further use. Makeshift repair by means of a pin tends to cause a longer tear or fraying, which will be still more difficult to mend. The mended portion will be less noticeable if repaired before the surrounding yarns are further damaged.

Methods of Stain Removal. Successful removal of stains from fabrics depends on the basic principle of not allowing the spot or stain to become set. A stain should be removed at the first possible opportunity because it may be more easily dissolved when fresh. Different fibers require different methods and different stain removers. Use of an incorrect remover may damage or even destroy the fiber content of a fabric. Knowledge of the nature of the stain makes possible the immediate use of the appropriate method and removal agent. Hot water should never be used on an unknown stain. The heat will set the stain, making it more difficult to remove. If the stain is known to be of a nongreasy nature, sponging with cold water may be all that is necessary. On the other hand, a greasy stain requires the use of carbon tetrachloride or some other dry cleaner, such as benzine, gasoline, turpentine, or denatured alcohol. There are four effective methods for removing spots and stains.

• *Dipping.* When the entire fabric can be immersed in the stain remover, the best method is dipping. This is the most convenient method if the spot is large, or if there are many spots on an all-cotton or all-linen fabric.

• *Steaming.* Stains on wool, silk, or any colored fabric may be removed by steaming. The stained area is saturated with steam by spreading the cloth over a bowl partly filled with hot water into which a small amount of the appropriate removal agent has been placed.

• *Drop Method.* Small drops of a removal agent can be applied by means of a medicine dropper, glass rod, or orange stick.

• *Sponging.* Sponging is the most frequently used method of stain removal, but if it is not done with care, it will not be effective. An absorbent cloth or a blotter should be placed underneath the stain to absorb the removal agent as well as the stain. The blotter also prevents further spreading of the wet area. Both the sponging cloth and the absorbent material should be renewed whenever they show the slightest tinge of the stain. The stained portion of the fabric must not be soaked with the cleaning fluid, and the fabric must not be harshly rubbed. Apply small quantities of the fluid with a soft cloth by light strokes in a circular direction from the outer rim of the stain toward its center.

The dipping method may be used for some fabrics.

The drop method requires a medicine dropper, glass rod, or orange stick.

Sponging must be done with care.

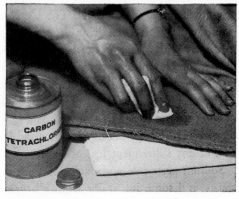

Feather the edges of the stain to prevent formation of a ring, which indicates an improper method of sponging, an excessive amount of cleaning fluid, or lack of sufficiently quick evaporation. Rapid evaporation can be obtained by blowing on the fabric or by placing it in front of an electric fan. A ring can be eliminated by holding the fabric over the spout of a steaming kettle until the area is damp. Then iron immediately.

Stain Removers.   Acids, alkalies, and water are the three types of removal agents. No single chemical can be used to remove all spots from the many different kinds of fibers. For example, acids destroy cotton and linen and cannot be used to remove stains from these fibers. Similarly, alkalies cannot be used on silk and wool. Viscose or cuprammonium rayon can be treated like cotton. Acetate requires special care, as it dissolves in acetone, acetic acid, and chloroform, or when exposed to a hot iron.

Acids and alkalies should be used only as mild solutions. When an acid solution is necessary, any possible damage that might occur to the fabric must be counteracted by applying a weak alkali, such as a solution of bicarbonate of soda or ammonia water to neutralize the acid. The fabric should be thoroughly rinsed in clear water. If an alkali solution is necessary, it should be followed immediately with a mild acid solution, such as lemon juice, vinegar, or a dilute solution of acetic acid, to neutralize the action of the alkali. The fabric should be well rinsed.

Bleaching Agents as Stain Removers.   Various bleaching chemicals are commonly used to remove stains. But such chemicals must be used carefully because they extract color and weaken the cloth. Household bleaches of chlorine solutions (sodium hypochlorite) should be used only on cottons, linens, and rayons—never on silk or wool. If a stain is to be removed with a bleaching chemical, the fabric should be stretched over a bowl of hot water and fastened around the edge of the bowl. The bleaching agent should be dropped on the stained area with a medicine dropper. This application must be followed immediately with a thorough rinsing. The entire procedure must be done quickly so that the bleaching agent will not remain too long on the material and cause undue weakening of the fabric. To prevent weakening, a few drops of oxalic acid or sodium thiosulphate (photographer's hypo) will neutralize the action of any chlorine bleach that may remain in the fabric. If a bleaching agent is used on a colored fabric, the dipping method is advisable to avoid unequal distribution of any subsequent loss of color.

Sodium perborate and oxalic acid are effective in removing iron rust, metal stains, and some ink stains from all types of fabrics. These chemicals are the least harmful of all bleaches, but they must be used quickly to prevent abstraction of the dye. For white woolens, sodium perborate is particularly effective and harmless. For the removal of mildew, ink, iron rust, dye stains, iodine, grass stains, and fruit stains, a solution of one teaspoon of sodium hydrosulphite in a glass of water is one of the most effective bleaches. But the liquid must be used quickly, and the fabric rinsed well. Otherwise, the color will be destroyed, and the fabric weakened.

Hydrogen peroxide may be used on all kinds of fabrics. It is a mild bleach, but it can be made more effective by the addition of a little ammonia. Oxalic acid and sodium hydrosulphite cannot be used on weighted silk. Oxalic acid is poisonous if taken internally. It should be labeled, so that it will not be mistaken for anything else, and placed out of reach.

Solvents. Where a stain is known to be of a greasy nature, the use of a solvent alone is sufficient. Grease stains are easily removed by the following solvents: carbon tetrachloride, benzine, turpentine, Stoddard solvent, gasoline, ether, acetone, alcohol. With the exception of ether, acetone, alcohol, and colored gasoline, these solvents will not change the color of the material. Sponging is generally most effective. The solvent should be applied on the wrong side of the fabric. The absorbent cloth underneath the stain will draw the dissolved grease and solvent from the fabric.

For fresh grease spots or slight oil stains, a sprinkling of talcum, powdered chalk, or magnesium carbonate (magnesite) rubbed into the stained area and left for a while, will absorb the grease. When the absorbent powder is subsequently brushed off, the stain will be entirely removed. Butter stains can be removed in this manner, but they must first be heated to melt the butter before they can be fully absorbed.

Removal of Specific Stains. Many synthetic fibers, such as Orlon, Acrilan, Dynel, Creslan, and Dacron, are not very absorbent. Fabrics of such fibers do not readily stain. Removal of stains generally requires merely wiping with a damp cloth or washing with a mild soap in warm water.

Dry Cleaning. Many consumers make serious mistakes when deciding whether to wash or to dry-clean a fabric. In general, it is best to abide by the advice of the salesperson or by the information sometimes attached by label to a garment or fabric. Though dry cleaning is more expensive than washing, it pays to have a garment dry-cleaned rather than take a chance on washing and ruining the garment. If acetate is dry-cleaned at home, the cleaning fluid must not contain alcohol, chloroform, strong acetic acid, or acetone. Any of these destroy acetate—particularly acetone, which is the solvent used in the acetate process. The commercial dry cleaner identifies acetate by moistening a finger with acetone and rubbing it on some unexposed portion of the fabric. If the threads become hard and feel soaplike, the fabric is acetate.

Kind of Stain	Type of Fabric	Procedure and Removal
Acid	All	Neutralize with ammonia.
Alkali	All	Neutralize with vinegar.
Blood	Cotton, linen	Soak in cold water, then in dilute ammonia. Wash.
Blood	Silk, wool	Sponge with cold water.
Butter	All	Sponge with naphtha or carbon tetrachloride.
Candle wax	All	Scrape away, then sponge with benzine.
Chewing gum	All	Carbon tetrachloride or ether.
Coffee or	Cotton, linen	Sponge with cold water.
chocolate	{ Silk, wool	Glycerin, then hydrogen peroxide.
Fruit	{ Cotton, linen	If fresh, pour boiling water through stain. If stubborn, bleach with Javelle water.
Grass	All	Sponge with alcohol, then with soap and water.
Ice cream	All	Sponge with gasoline or carbon tetrachloride.
Iodine	All	Soak in alcohol, or boil in solution of sodium thiosulphate.
Ink	Cotton, linen	If fresh, soap and water. If dried, use bleach, then oxalic acid, then wash; or put in sweet milk, and let turn sour.
Ink	Silk, wool	Sponge with hydrogen peroxide, then with oxalic acid or skim milk.
Iron rust	Cotton, linen	Oxalic acid, rinse well. Or spread with salt, moisten with lemon juice, and place in sun.
Lipstick	Cotton, linen	Rub with lard until stain is soft. Scrape off grease, and wash in hot suds.
Mildew	Cotton, linen	Sponge with Javelle water.
Milk or cream	All	Sponge with benzine or carbon tetrachloride.
Oil	All	Soap and water or carbon tetrachloride.
Paint	All	Soap and water, sponge with carbon tetrachloride or with turpentine on wrong side of stain.
Perspiration	All	Sponge with peroxide and ammonia.
Rubber	All	Sponge with carbon tetrachloride.
Rust	All	Sponge with lemon, vinegar, or oxalic acid.
Shellac	All	Sponge with denatured alcohol.
Scorch	All	If light, dampen and place in sunlight, or sponge with hydrogen peroxide.
Sugar	All	Sponge with hot water.
Tar	All	Moisten with carbon tetrachloride or with benzine. Scrape off, then sponge residue with same solvent.

Kind of Stain	Type of Fabric	Procedure and Removal
Tea	Cotton, linen	Soak in borax solution, rinse. Or keep stain moist with lemon juice, then expose to sun for day or two.
Varnish	All	Sponge with equal parts of alcohol and benzine.
Vaseline	All	Sponge fresh stains with carbon tetrachloride, or spread talcum. Let stand. Then brush.
Water spot	Silk, wool	Hold in steam until damp. Iron damp.

Laundering Methods. When a fabric is known to be washable, frequent and prompt washing is desirable, particularly of clothing worn next to the skin. If such garments are not washed after each use, they are more difficult to clean, and the body perspiration that they have absorbed causes the fabric to deteriorate while awaiting cleaning. In general, fine underwear and attractive, brightly colored outer garments and household linens should be laundered at home. Knowledge of how to wash fragile and dainty white garments as well as dyed fabrics is essential for good results.

Just knowing that a fabric is washable is not enough information for good results in laundering. The consumer must be acquainted with the proper method for washing each type of garment and fabric. Some fabrics may be subjected to hard laundering, which includes boiling and the use of strong soaps, without too great a strain on their durability. It may be done at home as well as in commercial laundries, where it is customary to use strong substances for bleaching purposes and for sanitary reasons. Before any attempt is made to wash clothes, colored fabrics should be separated from white ones, and heavy work clothes from fine and delicate pieces, as different washing methods are necessary. Bad stains must be removed before the fabrics are immersed in hot water. Slightly soiled clothes that do not require soaking should be washed in water not over 115 degrees Fahrenheit. Extremely hot water tends to set dirt spots and minor spots or stains that may not have needed special treatment. Clothes that are very soiled should be soaked in warm, soapy water for about ten minutes.

A good quality of household soap should be dissolved in a washing machine or in a tub of hot water. Soft water will lather quickly, resulting in a more thorough cleaning. If the water is hard, the soap tends to curd because there is a high concentration of iron, calcium, magnesium, and aluminum salts in hard water. Any of the good commercial water softeners may be used to precipitate these soap-destroying metals in the water. Hard water can be softened by the use of washing soda, or sal soda (hydrated sodium carbonate).

▶ TEST YOURSELF ON THIS CHAPTER

1. In what way does the label on a garment help in caring for the garment?

2. Why should all clothes be placed on hangers when not in use? Why are knitted garments an exception? How should knitted clothes be kept?

3. Why is a firm brush recommended for brushing clothing?

4. Why should garments not be crowded in a clothes closet?

5. Why should white garments be kept separate from colored ones?

6. Give illustrations of what is meant by "needed repairs." Give reasons for attending to these without delay.

7. Why should clothes be given a rest? How does this apply to wool clothes?

8. Why should a stain or spot be removed as soon as it is discovered?

9. For your next buying trip to a retail store, prepare a list of questions that you consider important enough to ask the salesperson to make certain that your selection of the clothing item is a prudent one.

10. Cut six advertisements from a newspaper, and circle all the textile terms that have taken on new meaning for you since studying textiles. Explain how familiarity with these textile terms has proved helpful to you recently.

INDEX